THE CHARLTON
STANDARD CATALOGUE OF

BESWICK ANIMALS

FIFTH EDITION

Diana Callow
John Callow

Marilyn Sweet
Peter Sweet

Publisher
W. K. Cross

The Charlton Press
TORONTO, ONTARIO ❖ PALM HARBOR, FLORIDA

DISCLAIMER

Products listed or shown were manufactured by the John Beswick Studios/Royal Doulton (U.K.) Limited. This book has been produced independently and neither the authors nor the publisher has any connection whatsoever with either Royal Doulton (UK) Limited or the International Collectors Club. Royal Doulton is a registered trade mark and is used in this book with the permission of Royal Doulton (UK) Limited. Any opinions expressed are those of the authors and not necessarily endorsed by Royal Doulton (UK) Limited.

Canadian Cataloguing In Publication Data

The National Library of Canada has catalogued this publication as follows:

The Charlton standard catalogue of Beswick animals

ISSN 1203-8318
ISBN 0-88968-265-8 (5th ed.)

1. Beswick (Firm)–Catalogs. 2. Porcelain animals–Catalogs.
I. Charlton Press. II. Title: Beswick animals.

NK4660.C48 2- 1996– 738.8'2'0294 C96-900264-5

EDITORIAL

Editors	W. K. Cross, Jean Dale
Editorial Assistant	Susan Cross
Graphic Technician	Davina Rowan
Colour Technician	Marina Tsourkis

ACKNOWLEDGMENTS

The Charlton Press wishes to thank those who have helped and assisted with the fifth edition of *The Charlton Standard Catalogue of Beswick Animals.*

SPECIAL THANKS

We would like to thank the staff at Royal Doulton Limited, on both sides of the ocean, for all their help and assistance: **Ian Johnson**, Operations Manager, Giftware and Collectables (UK); **Fiona Hawthorne**, General Manager, Direct and Relationship Marketing (UK); **Maria Murtagh**, Sales and Product Manager (UK); **Tricia A. Gadsden**, Brand Manager - Giftware and Collectables (Can.).

CONTRIBUTORS TO THE FIFTH EDITION

The Publisher would also like to thank the following individuals and companies who graciously supplied pricing, photographs or information, or allowed us access to their collections for photographic purposes:

Morris Abbot, Dereham, Norfolk, England; **D. Adamson**, England; **Dennis Brennan, Brennan's Collectables**, Noosa Heads, Queensland, Australia; **Ed. Cann,** Maple, Ontario; **Mr. K. E. Chard**, Chalfont St. Peter, Bucks., England; **William T. Cross**, William Cross Antiques and Collectibles, Delta, B.C.; **Richard Follett**, Surrey, England; **John Fornaszewski**, Granite City, Illinois; **Mrs. J. Garrard**, Gloucester, England; **Douglas Knibbs**, Verwood, Dorset, England; **John Lowery**, Durham, England; **Joe Schenberg**, St. Louis, Missouri; **Margaret Windmill**, Milton Keynes, Buckinghamshire, England

A SPECIAL NOTE TO COLLECTORS

We welcome and appreciate any comments or suggestions in regard to *The Charlton Standard Catalogue of Beswick Animals.* If any errors or omissions come to your attention, please do not hesitate to write to us, or if you would like to participate in pricing or supply previously unavailable data or information, please contact Jean Dale at (416) 488-1418, or e-mail us at **chpress@charltonpress.com**.

Printed in Canada
in the Province of Ontario

The Charlton Press

Editorial Office
P.O. Box 820, Station Willowdale B
North York, Ontario M2K 2R1
Telephone (416) 488-1418 Fax: (416) 488-4656
Telephone (800) 442-6042 Fax: (800) 442-1542
E-mail: chpress@charltonpress.com www.charltonpress.com

HOW TO USE THIS CATALOGUE

In an effort to bring a little more consistency into our Beswick series of catalogues, which by the way will list only Beswick models, we, with the 5th edition of Beswick Animals, started to make a change in the listings. At the beginning of each chapter you will find the following table 'Model Numbers Transferred To,' this simply means that in our general reorganization the inclusion of those models in an 'Animal' book was considered inappropriate and they have been transferred to *The Charlton Standard Catalogue of Beswick Collectables*. They have not been disregarded.

THE PURPOSE

The fifth edition of this price guide covers the complete range of animals produced at the John Beswick Studios.

As with other catalogues in Charlton's Royal Doulton/ Beswick reference library, this publication has been designed to serve two specifc purposes. First, to furnish the collector with accurate and detailed listings that provide the essential information needed to build a rewarding collection. Second, to provide collectors and dealers with an indication of current market prices for the complete line of Beswick animal figures.

VARIETY CLASSIFICATIONS

In developing the series of Royal Doulton/Beswick catalogues, we found it necessary to divide the model changes into three classifications based on the degree of complexity.

STYLES: When two or more animal figures have the same name - but different physical modelling characteristics - they are listed as **Style One, Style Two** and so after their names. Such figures will also have different model numbers.

VERSIONS: Versions are modifications in a minor style element, such as the Siamese Cat, model 1559. In the first version, the head of the cat shows puffed out cheeks, with the body being fleshy and having a short neck. The second version shows the cat with a sleek tapering face, a long neck and a lean body. Another example of a version change is model 1014 the Welsh Cob (rearing) where the first version has the tail of the horse attached the the ceramic base whilst in the second version the tail of the horse hangs loose.

VARIATIONS: A change in colour is a variation; for example, almost any of the horses or cats with the lists of colourways and finishes are variations.

TABLE OF CONTENTS

PRICING OLD, NEW AND THE INTERNET

The Old

The first edition of Beswick Animals, introduced in 1994, was priced in a manner similar to all the other catalogues we have published over the years.

We had developed four main streams of information upon which we relied for pricing.

(1) Auctions: Auction catalogues and their prices realized provide a wealth of information on what a collector or dealer is willing to pay for an item. We, of course, subscribe to and receive a variety of auction catalogues from all over the world.

(2) **Dealers direct mail catalogues:** There was always a number of active dealers in the direct mail field publishing and distributing detailed price lists. Incorporating these lists in to our analysis was another important factor in arriving at a market price.

(3) Request: Two or three months before a print date pricing requests were mailed to various dealers in different parts of the world requesting their opinion on market prices. These replies were tallied and incorporated into the above data.

(4) Newsletters: We subscribe to every and all newsletter that appears on the subject for which we are producing a price guide. Newsletters give a wealth of information on current happenings in various hobbies, but they also supply goodly quantities of pricing information.

The four streams were compiled into one, extreme high and lows removed, and the results averaged to arrive at a market value. After a while a trend would emerge indicating the direction of the market. We were then ready to build a pricing model that would allow us to arrive at a suggested evaluation.

Over the past three years dramatic changes have taken place in collecting, especially collectables produced in the 20th century which have continuity between similar items. Posters, art pottery, art glass, Beswick Animal figurines, coins and stamps all belong to this category. They all fit the same mould, all have the same properties in common. They all have a high artistic design content, produced in small but reasonable quantities and widely distributed throughout the world. They started life as ornaments or decorations for the home.

The Evolution

The impact the internet would have on collectables was not fully anticipated. All the old avenues such as fairs, shows, dealer stores, retail outlets, direct mail and auction houses would come under severe pressure by the lowering of margins which the internet fostered. This would have a direct impact on pricing

When Beswick Animals, 4th edition, was up for revision in the winter of 2001, the process began of gathering prices to generate the 5th. Our method of collecting pricing information had to change.

Why! Simply because of the tremendous growth of the internet, and looking deeper, the rapid growth of on-line auctions in which 20th century collectables fit so well. Our auction results multiplied more than a thousand fold.

Dealers' websites have all but replaced direct mail. The direct mail house of five years ago is now the virtual store of 2002. Items, prices can all be changed daily, with little effort or cost.

Land based auctions still contribute to pricing for they, through their historical connection with the collectors, gather in the scarce and rare pieces. The value of which is helpful in establishing an overall price trend. Seldom does the rare trend higher, without the basic items being carried along in unison.

Now, following this far, you are starting to wonder what has changed from the old model to the new, it is the internet component comprising two parts: on-line auctions and virtual stores, which were not available previously, but must now be inserted into the equation.

Category	Average items daily Jan. 2001	Jan. 2002	One day in March 2002
Beswick	625	825	1,050
Bunnykins	350	475	650
Coins	6,000	7,200	8,300
Disney	37,500	51,500	65,800
Harry Potter	2,300	12,000	9,600
Lalique	650	400	700
Moorcroft	250	300	290
Royal Doulton	3,500	3,700	4,600
Royal Worcester	600	800	1,000
Stamps	12,700	13,700	17,600
Star Wars	19,000	23,500	25,100

The above table produces what a few years ago would be considered mind-boggling numbers. Take for example **Beswick**, on a yearly basis, in January 2001, nearly 228,000 items were offered for sale. By January 2002 the units offered were projected at over 301,000, by March 2002, the rate was running at almost 383,000. It is impossible to ignore such numbers.

The New

(1) Auctions:

A. Land-based auctions. As before, we continually monitor auction results capturing the pricing data.

B. Virtual auctions. With the new on-line auctions, both dealers and collectors participate. Prices become a true indication at that moment of the value of the item.

(2) Virtual stores: Dealers virtual stores have replaced our previous direct mail component and dealer requests, for now their offerings are available 24-hours a day and are possibly changed on a daily basis.

(3) Newsletters: Newsletters still contribute in their previous way and must not be overlooked.

The price gathering process has changed dramatically. The analizing of the data remains the same.

INTRODUCTION

An article entitled "Equestrian Figures for Collectors —Growth of the House of Beswick," in the *Pottery Gazette and Glass Trade Review* of September 1961, ended with this paragraph: "Among the potters of the present day yet to reach the one hundred-year mark, and whose products are already highly prized, none is more likely to be of future interest to collectors and antique dealers than the House of Beswick." How prophetic this has proved to be. In 1985 the Beswick Collector's Circle was formed as interest in the products of the Beswick factory was aroused. The circle has flourished as more and more people worldwide have joined the search to add to their collections and to seek information in order to enjoy their finds to the full. This book represents the most comprehensive attempt to date to form as complete a guide as possible to the Beswick animal collection.

In 1994 the John Beswick factory celebrated its centenary—a hundred years of producing an unbelievably wide variety of pottery items, from mundane household earthenware right through to the intricate ornamental ware and pure ornaments of all shapes and sizes.

Initially the factory produced plain and decorated ware. An advertisement from about 1900 lists "jugs, tea ware, dinner ware, toilet ware, flower pots, pedestals, novelties, vases, figures, bread trays, cheese dishes, etc., etc." The figures included the traditional Old Staffordshire dogs, but hares and hounds, horses, generals, a cow and calf, milkmaids, gardeners and Puss in Boots are also mentioned. Unfortunately many of these pieces were not marked Beswick.

From the start the Beswick factory was very much a family-run firm. James Wright Beswick, the founder, and his sons, John and Gilbert, and John's son, John Ewart, were all very committed to the factory's success. In 1934 ,when John Ewart Beswick became chairman and managing director and his uncle, Gilbert Beswick, was sales manager, several new pieces were introduced to the range, and recorded in the "shape book."

Arthur Gredington in his studio

This was the start of shape numbers being impressed into the base whenever possible and also the more widespread use of a Beswick backstamp.

Five years later Arthur Gredington took up his appointment as the first full-time modeller. His influence was enormous, for he had a great talent for modelling not only accurate and realistic animals of all kinds , but also ones of the comical variety, for example the very appealing "Grebie," number 1006. Consequently his name appears more than that of any other person in this book.

James Hayward also made an outstanding contribution to the high quality associated with the Beswick name. As decorating manager from 1934 and art director from 1957, he was responsible for designing almost three thousand different decorations and patterns. He also designed new shapes, such as the 720 "Panda Cub," and was an outstanding glaze chemist. His experience with glazes was fundamental in the development of the matt glaze used initially on the top of the range *Connoisseur Series.*

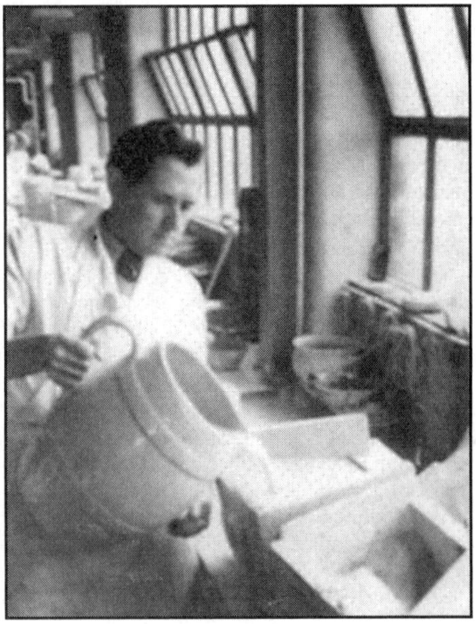

Mould making

When a complex model, such as an animal, is being manufactured, the mould it will be produced from is of vital importance. In this department Albert Hallam had exceptional skill. He joined Beswick in 1926 at age 14 as an apprentice mouldmaker and went on to become head of the mouldmaking department and also a modeller. The series of butterflies are Albert Hallam's creations, as are a number of horses, dogs and cats, which were modelled after Arthur Gredingtons retirement. These include at least one model that is very sought after today, number 2282 "Norwegian Fjord Horse."

There are several other modellers whose work is featured in this book. Very little is known about some of them as they tended to be employed on a freelance basis, for example, Mr. Garbet, who contributed cats, dogs and a sheep. Although small in number, significant contributions were also made by Alan Maslankowski, whose 2578 "Shire Horse" is quite magnificent, Colin Melbourne, who besides the unique "C.M." series also modelled most of the Peter Scott ducks, Graham Orwell whose models included the 1374 "Galloping Horse" and 1391 "Mounted Indian," and Pal Zalman whose one equine model, the 1549 "Horse, Head tucked," is still in production.

By the late 1960s, Ewart and Gilbert Beswick were nearing retirement, and as there was not another generation to follow them into the family business, the decision was made in 1969 to sell to Royal Doulton. Beswick animals continued to be produced, and although much rationalization took place, such as reducing the number of colourways of the horses and withdrawing many pieces, the ranges were also expanded by the regular introduction of new pieces.

Then in August 1989, the decision was implemented to make the vast majority of the remaining animals produced at the Beswick factory into *Doulton Animals*, and the pieces were all issued with DA numbers. At the same time, grey and palomino matts were withdrawn from the horses' colourways, and only a few continued to be available in grey and palomino glosses.

In September 1999, Royal Doulton moved their complete range of animals (with the exception of the limited edition models) to the Beswick backstamp. Confusion in pricing will exist for a while until the secondary market catches up.

Graham Tongue began work at Beswick in 1966, and became head modeller in 1973, when Albert Hallam retired. He concentrated on the modelling of animals, and his modelling skill is apparent in almost all the sections here.

Graham Tongue has the distinction of modelling the piece which holds the world-record price for a piece of Beswick, appropriately an equine model entitled the "Spirit of Whitfield." In 1987 he was commissioned by the Chatterley Mining Museum to model Kruger, the last pit pony used at the Staffordshire mine. The resulting model, based on the 2541 "Welsh Mountain Pony," was considerably adapted with incredible attention to detail. The result was superb. Only four models were made, one each for the Beswick and Chatterley Whitfield museums, one presented to HRH Princess Anne when she visited the museum, and one was auctioned in aid of the Princesss favourite charity. In April 1994 the mining museum was closed and everything was auctioned. The "Spirit of Whitfield" sold for £2,750, a far cry from one hundred years ago when Beswick was advertising pieces for 6 ½d.

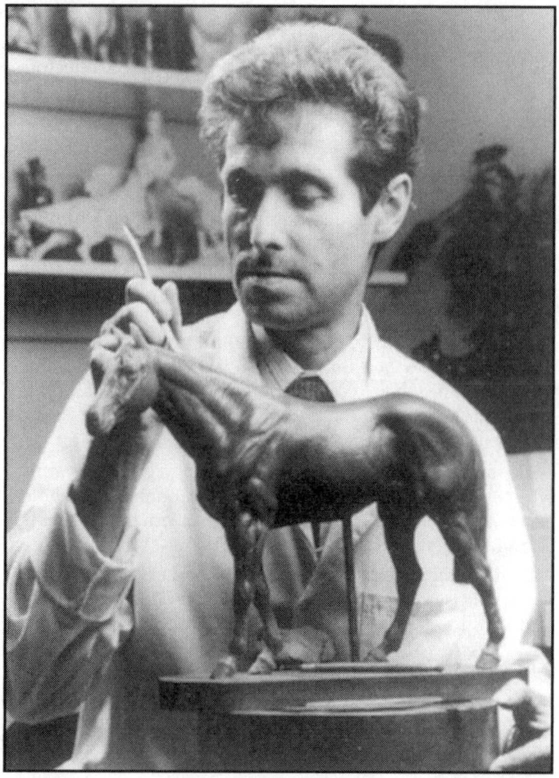

Graham Tongue at work

Although very few animals now carry the Beswick backstamp, this book illustrates the animal kingdom as seen through the eyes of the Beswick designers since the early 1930s. Cats and kittens with appealing eyes, birds and butterflies to fly across walls, a well-stocked zoo with animals from all over the world, everyday farm animals, animals which make you laugh, champion dogs, sleek horses and fish leaping from their pools are all lasting reminders of the Beswick story. The story will continue as more information emerges and the elusive models are discovered.

BACKSTAMPS AND SEALS

BACKSTAMPS

Backstamp 1, for the animal models, is the earliest printed stamp found.

1. Script Beswick Ware Made In England

2. Circular BESWICK ENGLAND

3. Oval BESWICK ENGLAND

4. Semi circular BESWICK ENGLAND

5. BESWICK CREST ENGLAND

SEALS

In addition to the first small gummed seal, green with gold lettering, an alternative oval style with gold lettering on a green background was used. The small green seal was replaced by the large oval style.

1. Small gummed seal (first style) green with gold lettering

2. Small gummed seal (second style) green with gold lettering

ROYAL DOULTON

INTERNATIONAL COLLECTORS CLUB

Founded in 1980, the Royal Doulton International Collectors Club provides an information service on all aspects of the company's products, past and present. A club magazine, *Gallery*, is published four times a year with information on new products and current events that will keep the collector up-to-date on the happenings in the world of Royal Doulton. Upon joining the club, each new member will receive a free gift and invitations to special events and exclusive offers throughout the year.

To join the Royal Doulton Collectors Club, please contact your local stockist, or contact the club directly by writing to the address opposite or calling the appropriate number.

International Collectors Club
Sir Henry Doulton House
Forge Lane, Etruria
Stoke-on-Trent, Staffordshire
ST1 5NN, England
Telephone:
U.K.: 8702 412696
Overseas: +44 1782 404045
U.K. Fax: +44 (0) 1782 404000
On-line at www.doulton-direct.co.uk
E-mail: icc@royal-doulton.com

VISITOR CENTRE

Opened in the Summer of 1996, the Royal Doulton Visitor Centre houses the largest collection of Royal Doulton figurines in the world. Demonstration areas offer the collector a first hand insight on how figurines are assembled and decorated. Also at the Visitor Centre is a restaurant and a retail shop offering both best quality ware and slight seconds.

Factory tours may be booked, Monday to Friday.

Royal Doulton Visitor Centre
Nile Street, Burslem
Stoke-on-Trent, ST6 2AJ, England

Visitor Centre: Tel.: +44 (0) 1782 292434
Fax: +44 (0) 1782 292424
Factory Store: Tel.: +44 (0) 1782 292451

WEBSITE AND E-MAIL ADDRESS

Web Sites:
www.royal-doulton.com
www.doulton-direct.com.au
www.royal-doulton-brides.com

E-mail:
Visitor Centre: visitor@royal-doulton.com
Consumer Enquiries: enquiries@royal-doulton.com
Museum Curator: heritage@royal-doulton.com
Doulton-Direct: direct@royal-doulton.com

ROYAL DOULTON FACTORY SHOPS

Royal Doulton Group Factory Shop
Lawley Street, Longton,
Stoke-on-Trent ST3 2PH, England
Tel.: +44 (0) 1782 291237

Royal Doulton Factory Shop
Forge Lane, Etruria
Stoke-on-Trent ST1 5NN, England
Tel.: +44 (0) 1782 284056

Royal Doulton Factory Shop
Victoria Road, Fenton,
Stoke-on-Trent ST4 2PJ, England
Tel.: +44 (0) 1782 291869

Beswick Factory Shop
Barford Street, Longton,
Stoke-on-Trent ST3 2JP England
Tel.: +44 (0) 1782 291237

COLLECTOR CLUB CHAPTERS

Detroit Chapter
Ronald Griffin, President
629 Lynne Avenue
Ypsilanti, MI., 48198-3829

Edmonton Chapter
Mildred's Collectibles
6813 104 Street, Edmonton, AB

New England Chapter
Robert Hicks, President
Lee Piper, Vice President
Michael Lynch, Secretary
Scott Reichenberg, Treasurer
E-mail doingantiq@aol.com

Northern California Chapter
Edward L. Khachadourian, President
P.O. Box 214, Moraga, Ca. 94556-0214
Tel.: (925) 376-2221 Fax: (925) 376-3581
E-mail: khack@pacbell.net

Northwest, Bob Haynes, Chapter
Alan Matthew, President
15202 93rd Place N.E., Bothell,
WA., 98011 Tel.: (425) 488-9604

Rochester Chapter
Judith L. Trost, President
103 Garfield Street, Rochester,
NY., 14611. Tel.: (716) 436-3321

Ohio Chapter
Reg Morris, President
5556 Whitehaven Avenue
North Olmstead, OH., 44070
Tel.: (216) 779-5554

Western Pennsylvania Chapter
John Re, President
9589 Parkedge Drive, Allison Park,
PA., 15101
Tel.: (412) 366-0201
Fax: (412) 366-2558

THE DOULTON MARKETS

LAND AUCTIONS

AUSTRALIA
Goodman's
7 Anderson Street,
Double Bay, Sydney, 2028, N.S.W. Australia
Tel.: +61 (0) 2 9327 7311; Fax: +61 (0) 2 9327 2917
Enquiries: Suzanne Brett
www.goodmans.com.au
E-mail: info@goodmans.com.au

Sotheby's
118-122 Queen Street, Woollahra,
Sydney, 2025, N.S.W., Australia
Tel.: +61 (0) 2 9362 1000; Fax: +61 (0) 2 9362 1100
www.sothebys.com

CANADA
Empire Auctions
Montreal
5500 Paré Street, Montreal, Quebec H4P 2M1
Tel.: (514) 737-6586; Fax: (514) 342-1352
Enquiries: Isadoe Rubinfeld
E-mail: montreal@empireauctions.com

Ottawa
1380 Cyrville Road, Gloucester, On
Tel.: (613) 748-5343; Fax: (613) 748-0354
Enquiries: Elliot Melamed
E-mail: ottawa@empireauctions.com

Toronto
165 Tycos Drive
Toronto, On, M6B 1W6
Tel.: (416) 784-4261; Fax: (416) 784-4262
Enquiries: Micheal Rogozinsky
www.empireauctions.com
E-mail: toronto@empireauctions.com

Maynard's Industries Ltd.
Arts / Antiques
415 West 2nd Avenue, Vancouver, BC, V5Y 1E3
Tel.: (604) 876-1311; Fax: (604) 876-1323
www.maynards.com
E-mail: antiques@maynards.com

Ritchie's
288 King Street East, Toronto, On, M5A 1K4
Tel.: (416) 364-1864; Fax: (416) 364-0704
Enquiries: Caroline Kaiser
www.ritchies.com
E-mail: auction@ritchies.com

Waddington's
111 Bathurst Street, Toronto, On, M5V 2R1
Tel.: (416) 504-9100; Fax: (416) 504-0033
Enquiries: Bill Kime
www.waddingtonsauctions.com
E-mail: info@waddingtonsauctions.com

UNITED KINGDOM
BBR Auctions
Elsecar Heritage Centre, Nr. Barnsley,
South Yorkshire S74 8HJ, England
Tel.: +44 (0) 1226 745156; Fax: +44 (0) 1226 351561
Enquiries: Alan Blakeman
www.bbrauctions.co.uk
E-mail: sales@bbrauctions.com

Bonhams
Bond Street:
101 New Bond Street, London, WI5 1SR, England

Chelsea:
65-69 Lots Road, Chelsea, London, SW10 0RN,
England

Knightsbridge:
Montpelier Street, Knightsbridge, London, SW7 1HH
Tel.: +44 (0) 20 7393 3900; Fax: +44 (0) 20 7393 3905
Enquiries:
Decorative Arts: Joy McCall
Tel.: +44 (0) 20 7393 3942
Comtemporary Ceramics: Gareth Williams
Tel.: +44 (0) 20 7393 3941
Doulton Beswick Wares: Mark Oliver
Tel.: +44 (0) 20 7468 8233
www.bonhams.com
E-mail: info@bonhams.com

Christie's
London
8 King Street, London, SW1 England
Tel.: +44 (0) 207-839-9060 ; Fax:+44 (0) 207-839-1611

South Kensington
85 Old Brompton Road, London, SW7 3LD, England
Tel.: +44 (0) 20 7581 7611; Fax: +44 (0) 20 7321 3321
Enquires:
Decorative Arts: Michael Jeffrey
Tel.: +44 (0) 20 7321 3237
www.christies.com; E-mail: info@christies.com

Potteries Specialist Auctions
271 Waterloo Road, Cobridge, Stoke-on-Trent
Staffordshire, ST6 3HR, England
Tel.: +44 (0) 1782 286622; Fax: +44 (0) 1782 213777
Enquiries: Stella Ashbrooke
www.potteriesauctions.com
E-mail: enquiries@potteriesauctions.com

Sotheby's
London
34-35 New Bond Street, London, W1A 2AA, England
Tel.: +44 (0) 20 7293 5000; Fax: +44 (0) 20 7293 5989

Olympia
Hammersmith Road, London WI4 8UX, England
Tel.: +44 (0) 20 7293 5555; Fax: +44 (0) 20 7293 6939

Sotheby's
Sussex
Summers Place, Billingshurst, Sussex,
RH14 9AF, England
Tel.: +44 (0) 1403 833500; Fax: +44 (0) 1403 833699
www.sothebys.com:
E-mail: info@sothebys.com

Louis Taylor
Britannia House,
10 Town Road, Hanley
Stoke-on-Trent, Staffordshire, England
Tel.: +44 (0) 1782 214111; Fax:+44 (0) 1782 215283
Enquiries: Clive Hillier

Thomson Roddick & Medcalf
60 Whitesands
Dumfries, DG1 2RS
Scotland
Tel.: +44 (0) 1387 279879; Fax: +44 (0) 1387 266236
Enquiries: C. R. Graham-Campbell

Peter Wilson Auctioneers
Victoria Gallery, Market Street
Nantwich, Cheshire, CW5 5DG, England
Tel.: +44 (0) 1270 610508; Fax: +44 (0) 1270 610508
Enquiries: Peter Wilson

UNITED STATES

Christie's East
219 East 67th Street, New York, NY 10021
Tel.: +1 212 606 0400
Enquiries: Timothy Luke
www.christies.com

William Doyle Galleries
175 East 87th Street, New York, N.Y. 10128
Tel.: +1 212 427 2730
Fax: +1 212 369 0892

Sotheby's Arcade Auctions
1334 York Avenue, New York, N.Y. 10021
Tel.: +1 212 606 7000
Enquiries: Andrew Cheney
www.sothebys.com

VIRTUAL AUCTIONS

Amazon.com ® Auctions
Main site: www.amazon.com
Plus 4 International sites.

AOL.com Auctions ®
Main site: www.aol.com
Links to - E-bay.com
ubid.com.

E-BAY ® The World's On-line Market Place ™
Main site: www.ebay.com
Plus 20 International sites.

YAHOO! Auctions ®
Main site: www.yahoo.com
Plus 15 International auction sites.

FAIRS, MARKETS AND SHOWS

AUSTRALIA

Royal Doulton and Antique Collectable Fair
Marina Hall, Civic Centre,
Hurstville, Sydney

CANADA

Canadian Art & Collectables Show and Sale
Kitchener Memorial Auditorium, Kitchener, Ontario
Usually early May.
For information on times and location contact:
Trajan Publishing Corp.
103 Lakeshore Road, Suite 202,
St. Catherines, Ontario L2N 2T6
Tel.: (905) 646-7744; Fax: (905) 646-0995

UNITED KINGDOM

20th Century Fairs
266 Glossop Road, Sheffield S10 2HS, England
Usually in May or June.
For information on times and dates:
Tel.: +44 (0) 114 275-0333; Fax:+44 (0) 114 275 4443

Doulton And Beswick Collectors Fair
National Motorcycle Museum, Meriden, Birmingham,
Usually March and August.
For information on times and dates:
Doulton and Beswick Dealers Association
Tel.: +44 (0) 181 303-3316

DMG Antiques Fairs Ltd.
Newark, the largest in the UK with usually six fairs annually. For information on times and dates for this and many other fairs contact:
DMG
Newark, P.O.Box 100, Newark,
Nottinghamshire, NG2 1DJ
Tel.: +44 (0) 1636 702326; Fax: +44 (0) 1636 707923
www.dmgantiquefairs.com
www.antiquesdirectory.co.uk

U.K. Fairs
Doulton and Beswick Fair for collectors
River Park Leisure Centre, Winchester
Usually held in October for information on times and dates contact:
Enquiries U.K. Fairs; Tel.; +44 (0) 20 8500 3505
www.portia.co.uk
E-mail: ukfairs@portia.co.uk

LONDON MARKETS

Alfies Antique Market
13-25 Church Street, London; Tuesday - Saturday

Camden Passage Market
London; Wednesday and Saturday

New Caledonia Market
Bermondsey Square, London; Friday morning

Portobello Road Market
Portobello Road, London; Saturday

UNITED STATES

Atlantique City

Atlantic City Convention Centre
Atlantic City, NJ

International Gift and Collectible Expo

Donald E. Stephens Convention Centre,
Rosemont, Illinois

For information on the above two shows contact:
Krause Publications
700 East State Street, Iola, WI, 54990-0001
Tel.: (877) 746-9757; Fax: (715) 445-4389
www.collectibleshow.com
E-mail: iceshow@krause.com

Doulton Convention and Sale International

Fort Lauderdale, Florida, U.S.A.
Usually February. For information on times and dates:
Pascoe & Company,
575 S.W. 22nd Ave., Miami, Florida 33135
Tel.: (305) 643-2550; Fax: (305) 643-2123
www.pascoeandcompany.com
E-mail: sales@pascoeandcompany.com

Royal Doulton Convention & Sale

John S. Knight Convention Centre
77 E. Mill Street, Akron, Ohio 44308
Usually August. For information on times and dates:
Colonial House Productions,
182 Front Street, Berea, Ohio 44017;
Tel.: (866) 885-9024; Fax: (905) 854-3117
www.Colonial-House-Collectibles.com
E-mail: yworry@aol.com

FURTHER READING

Storybook Figurines

The Charlton Standard Catalogue of Royal Doulton Beswick Storybook Figurines by Jean Dale
Cartoon Classics and other Character Figures by Louise Irvine
Royal Doulton Bunnykins Figures by Louise Irvine
Bunnykins Collectors Book by Louise Irvine
Beatrix Potter Figures and Giftware edited by Louise Irvine
The Beswick Price Guide by Harvey May

Animals, Figures and Character Jugs

Royal Doulton Figures by Desmond Eyles, Louise Irvine and Valerie Baynton
The Charlton Standard Catalogue of Beswick Animals, by Diana & John Callow and Marilyn & Peter Sweet
The Charlton Standard Catalogue of Royal Doulton Animals by Jean Dale
The Charlton Standard Catalogue of Royal Doulton Figurines by Jean Dale
The Charlton Standard Catalogue of Royal Doulton Jugs by Jean Dale
Collecting Character and Toby Jugs by Jocelyn Lukins
Collecting Doulton Animals by Jocelyn Lukins
Doulton Flambé Animals by Jocelyn Lukins
The Character Jug Collectors Handbook by Kevin Pearson
The Doulton Figure Collectors Handbook by Kevin Pearson

General

The Charlton Standard Catalogue of Beswick Pottery by Diana and John Callow
Discovering Royal Doulton by Michael Doulton
The Doulton Story by Paul Atterbury and Louise Irvine
Royal Doulton Series Ware by Louise Irvine (Vols. 1-5)
Limited Edition Loving Cups by Louise Irvine and Richard Dennis
Doulton for the Collector by Jocelyn Lukins
Doulton Kingsware Flasks by Jocelyn Lukins
Doulton Burslem Advertising Wares by Jocelyn Lukins
Doulton Lambeth Advertising Wares by Jocelyn Lukins
The Doulton Lambeth Wares by Desmond Eyles and Louise Irvine
The Doulton Burslem Wares by Desmond Eyles
Hannah Barlow by Peter Rose
George Tinwoth by Peter Rose
Sir Henry Doulton Biography by Edmund Gosse
Phillips Collectors Guide by Catherine Braithwaite
Royal Doulton by Jennifer Queree
John Beswick: A World of Imagination. Catalogue reprint (1950-1996)
Royal Doulton by Julie McKeown

Magazines and Newsletters

Rabbitting On (Bunnykins Newsletter) Contact Leah Selig: 2 Harper Street, Merrylands 2160, New South Wales, Australia. Tel./Fax 61 2 9637 2410 (International), 02 637 2410 (Australia)
Collecting Doulton Magazine, Contact Barry Hill, Collecting Doulton, P.O. Box 310, Richmond, Surrey TW10 7FU, England
Doulton News, published by Thorndon Antiques & Fine China Ltd., edited by David Harcourt, P.O. Box 12-076 (109 Molesworth Street), Wellington, New Zealand
Beswick Quarterly (Beswick Newsletter) Contact Laura J. Rock-Smith: 10 Holmes Court, Sayville, N.Y. 11782-2408, U.S.A. Tel./Fax (631) 589-9027
Cottontails (Newsletter of Bunnykins Collectors' Club), Contact Claire Green: 6 Beckett Way, Lewes, East Sussex, BN7 2EB, U.K. E-mail: claireg@2btinternet.com

Chapter One
BIRDS

The models of our "feathered friends" are a delight for any bird enthusiast, and there are plenty here to choose from.

They come in all sizes, from very small birds, such as the little wren, to the impressive and large pheasant from the Connoisseur Series. Some are expensive, some are not, and quite a few are still in production. The figures cover a wide range from the comic Fun Models to wall plaques to the precise realism of the Peter Scott Wildfowl collection. When displayed in groups, the colours of their plumage create an impressive display.

Among the birds in this group are species that you could see any day of the week in your garden and also more exotic or rare varieties, such as the bald eagle, penguin and kookaburra.

INDEX BY MODEL NUMBER

MODELS TRANSFERRED TO *THE CHARLTON STANDARD CATALOGUE OF BESWICK COLLECTABLES*

Model No.	Description
370	Ducks - Candleholder
497	Pelican - Match holder and ash-bowl
617	Duck - Ashtray
754	Pheasant - Ashtray
755	Duck - Ashtray
762	Duck on Skis
769	Duck - Night light holder
800	Penguin Chick
801	Penguin Chick
802	Penguin - With Umbrella
803	Penguin - With Walking Stick
1090	Cock and Hen - Salt and pepper
1212	Ducks (Three) - Ashtray

Model No. 317
DUCK - On pottery base

Designer: Miss Greaves
Height: 8 ¼″, 21.0 cm
Colours: See below
Issued: c.1936-1954
Series: Fun Models

Colourway	U.K. £	U.S. $	Can. $
1. Blue - gloss	135.00	195.00	300.00
2. Blue/green - matt	115.00	170.00	265.00
3. Green - gloss	115.00	170.00	265.00
4. Natural - satin	135.00	195.00	300.00
5. White - gloss	100.00	145.00	225.00

Model No. 450A
PENGUIN – Large

Designer: Mr. Owen
Height: 8″, 20.3 cm
Colours: 1. Black and white - gloss
2. Blue - gloss
Issued: 1936-by 1954

Description	U.K. £	U.S. $	Can. $
1. Black	300.00	425.00	650.00
2. Blue	225.00	300.00	500.00

Model No. 450B
PENGUIN – Small

Designer: Mr. Owen
Height: 3 ½″, 8.9 cm
Colours: 1. Black and white - gloss
2. Blue - gloss
Issued: 1936-by 1954

Description	U.K. £	U.S. $	Can. $
1. Black	125.00	200.00	300.00
2. Blue	125.00	200.00	300.00

Model No. 618
PUFFIN

Designer: Mr. Owen
Height: 9″, 22.9 cm
Colours: Blue - gloss
Issued: 1938-by 1954

Colourway	U.K. £	U.S. $	Can. $
Blue - gloss	250.00	350.00	550.00

Model No. 749
MALLARD DUCK - Rising

Designer: Arthur Gredington
Height: 6 ½", 16.5 cm
Colours: Browns, teal green and white - gloss
Issued: 1939-by 1965

Description	U.K. £	U.S. $	Can. $
Gloss	150.00	225.00	350.00

Model No. 750
MALLARD DUCK - Settling

Designer: Arthur Gredington
Height: 6 ½", 16.5 cm
Colours: Browns, teal green and white - gloss
Issued: 1939-by 1965

Description	U.K. £	U.S. $	Can. $
Gloss	150.00	225.00	350.00

Model No. 756
MALLARD DUCK - Standing

Designer: Mr. Watkin
Height: 756/1 - 7", 17.8 cm
756/2 - 5 ¾", 14.6 cm
756/2A - 4 ½", 11.9 cm
756/3 - 3 ½", 8.9 cm
Colours: 1. Brown, teal green and white - gloss
2. Blue - gloss
Issued: 1939-1973

Colourway	U.K. £	U.S. $	Can. $
1. 756/1 Brown	55.00	80.00	120.00
2. 756/1 Blue	115.00	170.00	265.00
3. 756/2 Brown	40.00	60.00	90.00
4. 756/2 Blue	85.00	125.00	190.00
5. 756/2A Brown	30.00	45.00	70.00
6. 756/2A Blue	75.00	110.00	165.00
7. 756/3 Brown	20.00	30.00	45.00
8. 756/3 Blue	65.00	95.00	145.00

Note: Model no. 756/3 has grass around feet.
Model no. 902 makes a set of five pieces.

Model No. 760
DUCK WITH LADYBIRD ON BEAK

Designer: Mr. Watkin
Height: 3 ¾", 9.5 cm
Colours: White with yellow beak, ladybird on beak - gloss
Issued: 1939-1971
Series: Fun Models

Description	U.K. £	U.S. $	Can. $
Gloss	45.00	65.00	100.00

Model No. 765
DUCK FAMILY

Designer: Arthur Gredington
Height: 2 ¾" x 7", 7.0 x 17.8 cm
Colours: White with yellow beaks - gloss
Issued: 1939-1971

Description	U.K. £	U.S. $	Can. $
Gloss	45.00	65.00	100.00

Model No. 767A
PHEASANT
First Version - Curved tail

Designer: Mr. Watkin
Height: 3", 7.6 cm
Colours: Red brown, teal green - gloss
Issued: 1939-1971

Description	U.K. £	U.S. $	Can. $
Gloss	25.00	40.00	60.00

Note: This model was used on 754 (pheasant ashtray).

Model No. 767B
PHEASANT
Second Version - Straight tail

Designer: Mr. Watkin
Height: 3", 7.6 cm
Colours: Red, brown and teal green - gloss or matt
Issued:
1. Gloss - 1971-1995
2. Matt - 1983-1989

Description	U.K. £	U.S . $	Can. $
1. Gloss	15.00	25.00	40.00
2. Matt	20.00	30.00	45.00

Model No. 768
SEAGULL ON ROCK

Designer: Arthur Gredington
Height: 8 ½", 21.6 cm
Colours: Cream and dark brown, green and yellow base - gloss
Issued: 1939-by 1954

Description	U.K. £	U.S. $	Can. $
Gloss	400.00	600.00	900.00

Model No. 817/1
MALLARD DUCK - Squatting

Designer: Mr. Watkin
Height: 7 ½", 19.1 cm
Colours: Brown, teal green and white - gloss
Issued: 1940-1954
Set: 817/2

Description:	U.K. £	U.S. $	Can. $
Gloss	190.00	275.00	400.00

Model No. 817/2
MALLARD DUCK - Squatting

Designer: Mr. Watkin
Height: 6 ¾", 17.2 cm
Colours: Brown, teal green and white - gloss
Issued: 1940-1970
Set: 817/1

Description	U.K. £	U.S. $	Can. $
Gloss	175.00	250.00	375.00

Model No. 820
GEESE (Pair)

Designer: Arthur Gredington
Height: 4", 10.1 cm
Colours: White with orange feet and beaks - gloss
Issued: 1940-1971
Series: Fun Models
Set: 821, 822

Description	U.K. £	U.S. $	Can. $
Gloss	30.00	45.00	65.00

Model No. 821
GOSLING - Facing left

Designer: Arthur Gredington
Height: 2 ¼", 5.7 cm
Colours: White with orange beak - gloss
Issued: 1940-1971
Series: Fun Models
Set: 820, 822

Description	U.K. £	U.S. $	Can. $
Gloss	15.00	25.00	40.00

Model No. 822
GOSLING - Facing right

Designer: Arthur Gredington
Height: 1 ¾", 4.3 cm
Colours: White with orange beak - gloss
Issued: 1940-1971
Series: Fun Models
Set: 820, 821

Description	U.K. £	U.S. $	Can. $
Gloss	15.00	25.00	40.00

Model No. 827
HARDY'S DUCK - Standing

Designer: Mr. Watkin
Height: Large - 7 ½", 19.1 cm
Medium - 6", 15.0 cm
Small - 5", 12.7 cm
Colours:
1. White; brown and yellow - gloss
2. White; solid decorated wing - gloss
3. White; solid decorated neck, wing - gloss
4. White; yellow bill, feet - gloss

Issued: 1940-by 1954

Description	U.K. £	U.S. $	Can. $
1. Large	110.00	160.00	250.00
2. Large	110.00	160.00	250.00
3. Large	110.00	160.00	250.00
4. Large	110.00	160.00	250.00
1. Medium	90.00	130.00	195.00
2. Medium	90.00	130.00	195.00
3. Medium	90.00	130.00	195.00
4. Medium	90.00	130.00	195.00
1. Small	80.00	115.00	175.00
2. Small	80.00	115.00	175.00
3. Small	80.00	115.00	175.00
4. Small	80.00	115.00	175.00

Model No. 849
PHEASANT ON BASE - Flying upwards

Designer: Arthur Gredington
Height: 6", 15.0 cm
Colours: Browns, teal green and yellow - gloss
Issued: 1940-1971

Description	U.K. £	U.S. $	Can. $
Gloss	100.00	150.00	250.00

Model No. 850
PHEASANT ON BASE - Settling

Designer: Arthur Gredington
Height: 5 ¾", 14.6 cm
Colours: Browns, teal green and yellow - gloss
Issued: 1940-1971

Description	U.K. £	U.S. $	Can. $
Gloss	100.00	150.00	250.00

Photograph not available.
Model number 862 possibly
not put into production.

Model No. 862
FANTAIL PIGEON

Designer: Miss Joachin
Height: Unknown
Colours: Unknown
Issued: 1940-Unknown

Description	U.K. £	U.S. $	Can. $
Fantail Pigeon		Extremely Rare	

Model No. 902
MALLARD DUCK - Standing

Designer: Arthur Gredington
Height: 10", 25.4 cm
Colours: 1. Brown and teal green - gloss
2. Brown, teal green or white - gloss
Issued: 1940-1970

Colourway	U.K. £	U.S. $	Can. $
1. Brown	130.00	175.00	250.00
2. Brown/white	130.00	175.00	250.00

Note: Makes a set of five with 756/1, 756/2, 756/2A, 756/3.

Model No. 919A
DUCK - Large

Designer: Mr. Watkin
Height: 3 ¾", 9.5 cm
Colours: 1. Brown, teal green, white and pink - gloss
2. White with yellow beak and feet - gloss
Issued: 1941-1971

Colourway	U.K. £	U.S. $	Can. $
1. Brown	30.00	45.00	65.00
2. White	30.00	45.00	65.00

Model No. 919B
DUCK - Medium

Designer: Mr. Watkin
Height: 2 ½", 6.4 cm
Colours: 1. Brown, teal green, white and pink - gloss
2. White with yellow beak and feet - gloss
Issued: 1941-1971

Colourway	U.K. £	U.S. $	Can. $
1. Brown	20.00	30.00	45.00
2. White	20.00	30.00	45.00

Model No. 919C
DUCK - Small

Designer: Mr. Watkin
Height: 2", 5.0 cm
Colours: 1. Brown, teal green, white and pink - gloss
2. White with yellow beak and feet - gloss
Issued: 1941-1971

Colourway	U.K. £	U.S. $	Can. $
1. Brown	20.00	30.00	45.00
2. White	20.00	30.00	45.00

Model No. 925
AMERICAN BLUE JAYS

Designer: Arthur Gredington
Height: 5", 12.7 cm
Colours: Blue and white - gloss
Issued: 1941-by 1965

Description	U.K. £	U.S. $	Can. $
Gloss	90.00	125.00	200.00

Model No. 926
BALTIMORE ORIOLES

Designer: Arthur Gredington
Height: 5", 12.7 cm
Colours: 1. Golden and dark brown with blue markings - gloss
2. Chestnut brown, green claws - gloss
Issued: 1941-by 1965

Colourway	U.K. £	U.S. $	Can. $
1. Golden	100.00	145.00	225.00
2. Chestnut	100.00	145.00	225.00

Model No. 927
CARDINAL

Designer: Arthur Gredington
Height: 5 ¾", 14.6 cm
Colours: Dark red - gloss
Issued: 1941-by 1959

Description	U.K. £	U.S. $	Can. $
Gloss	95.00	135.00	200.00

Model No. 928
TANAGER

Designer: Arthur Gredington
Height: 5 ¾", 14.6 cm
Colours: 1. Red - gloss
2. Various - gloss
3. Yellow, green and orange - gloss
Issued: 1941-1959

Colourway	U.K. £	U.S. $	Can. $
1. Red	90.00	125.00	185.00
2. Various	90.00	125.00	185.00
3. Yellow/green	90.00	125.00	185.00

Model No. 929
CHICKADEE

Designer: Arthur Gredington
Height: 5 ¾", 14.6 cm
Colours: Dark and light blue, white and yellow - gloss or lustre
Issued: 1941-1968

Description	U.K. £	U.S. $	Can. $
1. Gloss	75.00	110.00	165.00
2. Lustre	95.00	135.00	200.00

Model No. 930
PARAKEET

Designer: Arthur Gredington
Height: 6″, 15.0 cm
Colours: Green and yellow - gloss
Issued: 1941-1975

Description	U.K. £	U.S. $	Can. $
Gloss	80.00	110.00	175.00

Model No. 980A
ROBIN
First Version - Base is a green mound

Designer: Arthur Gredington
Height: 3″, 7.6 cm
Colours: Brown and red - gloss
Issued: 1942-1973

Description	U.K. £	U.S. $	Can. $
Gloss	30.00	45.00	65.00

Model No. 980B
ROBIN
Second Version - Base is a branch and leaf

Designer: Arthur Gredington
Remodelled: Albert Hallam
Height: 3″, 7.6 cm
Colours: Brown and red - gloss or matt
Issued: 1. Gloss - 1973 to the present
2. Matt - 1983-1992

Description	U.K. £	U.S. $	Can. $
1. Gloss	16.00	N/A	N/A
2. Matt	16.00	25.00	40.00

Model No. 991A
CHAFFINCH
First Version - Base is a green mound

Designer: Arthur Gredington
Height: 2 ¾″, 7.0 cm
Colours: Pink, brown and black - gloss
Issued: 1943-1973

Description	U.K. £	U.S. $	Can. $
Gloss	30.00	45.00	65.00

Model No. 991B
CHAFFINCH
Second Version - Base is a branch

Designer: Arthur Gredington
Remodelled: Albert Hallam
Height: 2 ¾", 7.0 cm
Colours: Pink, brown, black - gloss or matt
Issued: 1. Gloss - 1973 to the present
2. Matt - 1983-1992

Description	U.K. £	U.S. $	Can. $
1. Gloss	16.00	N/A	N/A
2. Matt	16.00	25.00	40.00

Model No. 992A
BLUE TIT
First Version - Base is a green mound

Designer: Arthur Gredington
Height: 2 ½", 6.4 cm
Colours: White, blue and green - gloss
Issued: 1943 - 1973

Description	U.K. £	U.S. $	Can. $
Gloss	30.00	45.00	65.00

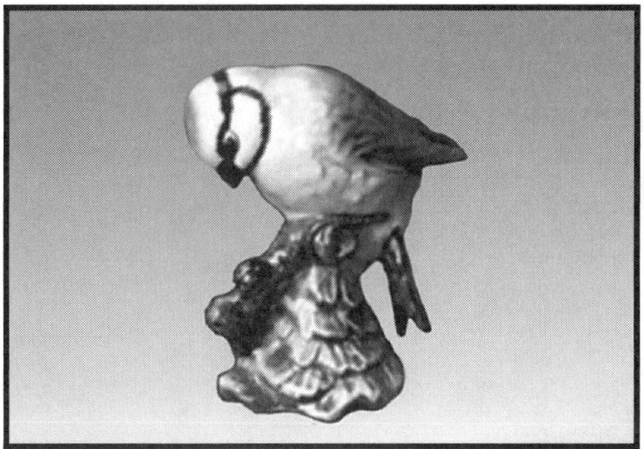

Model No. 992B
BLUE TIT
Second Version - Base is branch and leaves with ladybug

Designer: Arthur Gredington
Remodelled: Unknown
Height: 2 ¼", 5.7 cm
Colours: White, blue and green - gloss or matt
Issued: 1. Gloss - 1973 to the present
2. Matt - 1983-1992

Description	U.K. £	U.S. $	Can. $
1. Gloss	16.00	N/A	N/A
2. Matt	16.00	25.00	40.00

Model No. 993A
WREN
First Version - Base is a green mound

Designer: Arthur Gredington
Height: 2 ¼", 5.7 cm
Colours: Light brown, pink breast - gloss
Issued: 1943-1973

Description	U.K. £	U.S. $	Can. $
Gloss	30.00	45.00	65.00

Model No. 993B
WREN
Second Version - Base is a green leaf

Designer: Arthur Gredington
Remodelled: Graham Tongue
Height: 2 ¼", 5.7 cm
Colours: Dark and light brown - gloss or matt
Issued: 1. Gloss - 1973 to the present
2. Matt - 1983-1992

Description	U.K. £	U.S. $	Can. $
1. Gloss	16.00	N/A	N/A
2. Matt	16.00	25.00	40.00

Model No. 994
SHELLDRAKE - Rising (beak closed)

Designer: Arthur Gredington
Height: 6", 15.0 cm
Colours: White, brown and green - gloss
Issued: 1943-1965

Description	U.K. £	U.S. $	Can. $
Gloss	195.00	275.00	400.00

Model No. 995
SHELLDRAKE - Settling (beak open)

Designer: Arthur Gredington
Height: 6 ¼", 15.9 cm
Colours: White, brown and green - gloss
Issued: 1943-1965

Description	U.K. £	U.S. $	Can. $
Gloss	195.00	275.00	400.00

Model No. 1001
COCKEREL

Designer: Arthur Gredington
Height: 5 ¾", 14.6 cm
Colours: Green, red and yellow - gloss
Issued: 1944-by 1959
Series: Stylistic Models

Description	U.K. £	U.S. $	Can. $
Gloss	300.00	425.00	600.00

Model No. 1004
ROOSTER

Designer: Arthur Gredington
Height: 7", 17.8 cm
Colours: White, green, red, blue and black - gloss
Issued: 1944-by 1959
Series: Stylistic Model

Description	U.K. £	U.S. $	Can. $
Gloss	175.00	250.00	375.00

Model No. 1006
GREBIE

Designer: Arthur Gredington
Height: 5 ¼", 13.3 cm
Colours: Green and browns - gloss
Issued: 1945-by 1954
Series: Stylistic Model

Description	U.K. £	U.S. $	Can. $
Gloss	375.00	550.00	850.00

Model No 1015
COURTING PENGUINS

Designer: Arthur Gredington
Height: 5 ½", 14.0 cm
Colours: 1. Black and white with yellow markings - gloss
2. Blue - gloss
Issued: 1945-1965

Colourway	U.K. £	U.S. $	Can. $
1. Black/white	285.00	425.00	650.00
2. Blue	225.00	325.00	485.00

Model No. 1018
BALD EAGLE

Designer: Arthur Gredington
Height: 7 ¼", 18.4 cm
Colours: 1. Brown and white - gloss or matt
2. Bronze with black - satin
Issued: 1a. Gloss - 1945-1995
1b. Matt - 1983-1989
2. Britannia Collection - 1989-1992

Description	U.K. £	U.S. $	Can. $
1a. Gloss	100.00	150.00	225.00
1b. Matt	80.00	125.00	175.00
2. Satin	80.00	125.00	175.00

Model No. 1022
TURTLE DOVES

Designer: Arthur Gredington
Height: 7 ½", 19.1 cm
Colours: Browns, pale blue and pink, light brown and green base - gloss
Issued: 1945-1970

Description	U.K. £	U.S. $	Can. $
Gloss	250.00	350.00	550.00

Model No. 1041A
GREY WAGTAIL
First Version - Head down, light green base

Designer: Arthur Gredington
Height: 2 ½", 6.4 cm
Colours: Yellow, grey and black - gloss
Issued: 1945-1973

Description	U.K. £	U.S. $	Can. $
Gloss	30.00	45.00	65.00

Model No. 1041B
GREY WAGTAIL
Second Version - Head up, dark blue and green base

Designer: Arthur Gredington
Remodelled: Albert Hallam
Height: 2 ½", 6.4 cm
Colours: Yellow, grey and black - gloss or matt
Issued: 1. Gloss - 1973 to the present
2. Matt - 1983-1989

Description	U.K. £	U.S. $	Can. $
1. Gloss	16.00	N/A	N/A
2. Matt	16.00	25.00	40.00

Model No. 1042A
BULLFINCH
First Version - Yellow base and flowers

Designer: Arthur Gredington
Height: 2 ½", 6.4 cm
Colours: Red breast, dark brown feathers, yellow flowers and base - gloss
Issued: 1945-1973

Description	U.K. £	U.S. $	Can. $
Gloss	30.00	45.00	65.00

Model No. 1042B
BULLFINCH
Second Version - Base is a twig

Designer: Arthur Gredington
Remodelled: Graham Tongue
Height: 2 ½", 6.4 cm
Colours: Red, dark brown - gloss or matt
Issued: 1. Gloss - 1973-1998
2. Matt - 1983-1989

Description	U.K. £	U.S. $	Can. $
1. Gloss	18.00	30.00	45.00
2. Matt	18.00	30.00	45.00

Model No. 1046A
BARN OWL
First Version - Split tail feathers

Designer: Arthur Gredington
Height: 7 ¼", 18.4 cm
Colours: Golden brown and white - gloss
Issued: 1946-Unknown

Description	U.K. £	U.S. $	Can. $
Gloss	90.00	125.00	200.00

Model No. 1046B
BARN OWL
Second Version - Closed tail feathers

Designer: Arthur Gredington
Height: 7 ¼", 18.4 cm
Colours: Golden brown and white - gloss or matt
Issued: 1. Gloss - Unknown-1997
2. Matt - 1983-1989

Description	U.K. £	U.S. $	Can. $
1. Gloss	35.00	50.00	75.00
2. Matt	40.00	60.00	90.00

Model No. 1052
BARNACLE GOOSE

Designer: Arthur Gredington
Height: 6 ½", 16.5 cm
Colours: Dark grey-blue and white - gloss
Issued: 1943-1968

Description	U.K. £	U.S. $	Can. $
Gloss	550.00	775.00	1,200.00

Model No. 1159
KOOKABURRA

Designer: Arthur Gredington
Height: 5 ¾", 14.6 cm
Colours: Brown, blue and fawn - gloss
Issued: 1949-1976

Description	U.K. £	U.S. $	Can. $
Gloss	125.00	175.00	275.00

Model No. 1178
GOULDIAN FINCH - Wings out

Designer: Arthur Gredington
Height: 4", 10.1 cm
Colours: Purple, green and yellow - gloss
Issued: 1949-by 1959

Description	U.K. £	U.S. $	Can. $
Gloss	150.00	200.00	300.00

Model No. 1179
GOULDIAN FINCH - Wings in

Designer: Arthur Gredington
Height: 4 ½", 11.9 cm
Colours: Purple, green and yellow - gloss
Issued: 1949-by 1959

Description	U.K. £	U.S. $	Can. $
Gloss	150.00	200.00	300.00

Model No. 1180
COCKATOO - Small

Designer: Arthur Gredington
Height: 8 ½", 21.6 cm
Colours: 1. Pink and grey - gloss
2. Turquoise and yellow - gloss
Issued: 1949-1975

Colourway	U.K. £	U.S. $	Can. $
1. Pink/grey	115.00	170.00	265.00
2. Turquoise/yellow	125.00	180.00	275.00

Note: Large version is model no. 1818.

Model No. 1216A
BUDGERIGAR - Facing left
First Version - Flowers in high relief on base

Designer: Arthur Gredington
Height: 7", 17.8 cm
Colours: 1. Blue with dark brown markings - gloss
2. Green with yellow markings - gloss
3. Yellow - gloss
Issued: 1951-1967

Colourway	U.K. £	U.S. $	Can. $
1. Blue	400.00	550.00	850.00
2. Green	800.00	1,200.00	1,800.00
3. Yellow		Rare	

Model No. 1216B
BUDGERIGAR - Facing left
Second Version - No flowers on base

Designer: Arthur Gredington
Height: 7", 17.8 cm
Colours: Blue, green or yellow - gloss
Issued: 1. Blue - 1967-1975
2. Green - 1967-1972
3. Yellow - 1970-1972

Colourway	U.K. £	U.S. $	Can. $
1. Blue	175.00	225.00	350.00
2. Green	175.00	225.00	350.00
3. Yellow	1,000.00	1,500.00	2,250.00

Photograph not available at press time

Model No. 1217A
BUDGERIGAR - Facing right
First Version - Flowers in high relief on base

Designer: Arthur Gredington
Height: 7", 17.8 cm
Colours: 1. Blue - gloss
2. Green - gloss
Issued: 1951-1967

Colourway	U.K. £	U.S. $	Can. $
1. Blue	450.00	650.00	1,000.00
2. Green	550.00	775.00	1,200.00

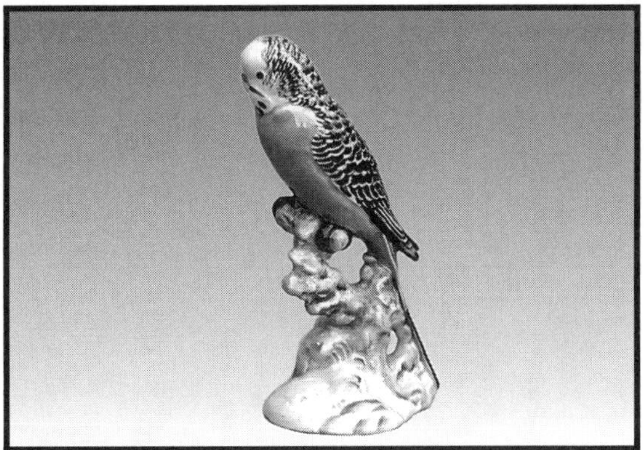

Model No. 1217B
BUDGERIGAR - Facing right
Second Version - No flowers on base

Designer: Arthur Gredington
Height: 7", 17.8 cm
Colours: 1. Blue - gloss
2. Green - gloss
3. Yellow - gloss
Issued: 1967-1970

Colourway	U.K. £	U.S. $	Can. $
1. Blue	175.00	225.00	350.00
2. Green	175.00	225.00	350.00
3. Yellow	2,000.00	3,000.00	4,500.00

Model No. 1218A
GREEN WOODPECKER
First Version - Flowers in high relief on base

Designer:	Arthur Gredington
Height:	9", 22.9 cm
Colours:	Green, red and white - gloss
Issued:	1951-1967

Description	U.K. £	U.S. $	Can. $
Gloss	200.00	300.00	450.00

Model No. 1218B
GREEN WOODPECKER
Second Version - No flowers on base

Designer:	Arthur Gredington
Height:	9", 22.9 cm
Colours:	Green, red and white - gloss or matt
Issued:	1. Gloss - 1967-1989 2. Matt - 1983-1988

Description	U.K. £	U.S. $	Can. $
1. Gloss	125.00	175.00	275.00
2. Matt	125.00	175.00	275.00

Model No. 1219A
JAY
First Version - Flowers in high relief on base

Designer: Arthur Gredington
Height: 6", 15.0 cm
Colours: Rust, blue, black and grey - gloss
Issued: 1951-1967

Description	U.K. £	U.S. $	Can. $
Gloss	325.00	475.00	700.00

Model No. 1219B
JAY
Second Version - No flowers on base

Designer: Arthur Gredington
Height: 6", 15.0 cm
Colours: Pink, blue and white - gloss
Issued: 1967-1971

Description	U.K. £	U.S. $	Can. $
Gloss	275.00	400.00	600.00

Model No. 1225A
PHEASANT
First Version - Flowers in high relief on base

Designer: Arthur Gredington
Height: 7 ¾", 19.7 cm
Colours: Red-brown, teal green, green base - gloss
Issued: 1951-1967

Description	U.K. £	U.S. $	Can. $
Gloss	175.00	255.00	385.00

Model No. 1225B
PHEASANT
Second Version - No flowers on base

Designer: Arthur Gredington
Height: 7 ¾", 19.7 cm
Colours: Red-brown, teal green, green base - gloss
Issued: 1967-1977

Description	U.K. £	U.S. $	Can. $
Gloss	125.00	175.00	275.00

Model No. 1226A
PHEASANT
First Version - Flowers in high relief on base

Designer: Arthur Gredington
Height: 6", 15.0 cm
Colours: Red-brown, teal green, green base - gloss
Issued: 1951-1967

Description	U.K. £	U.S. $	Can. $
Gloss	200.00	300.00	425.00

Model No. 1226B
PHEASANT
Second Version - No flowers on base

Designer: Arthur Gredington
Height: 6", 15.0 cm
Colours: Red-brown, teal green, green base - gloss
Issued: 1967-1977

Description	U.K. £	U.S. $	Can. $
Gloss	175.00	250.00	400.00

Model No. 1383A
PIGEON
First Version - Three stripes on wings

Designer: Mr. Orwell
Height: 5 ½", 14.0 cm
Colours: 1. Blue - gloss
2. Red - gloss
Issued: 1955-1972

Colourway	U.K. £	U.S. $	Can. $
1. Blue - gloss	125.00	180.00	275.00
2. Red - gloss	125.00	180.00	275.00

Model No. 1383B
PIGEON
Second Version - Two stripes on wings

Designer: Mr. Orwell
Height: 5 ½", 14.0 cm
Colours: Blue or red - gloss or matt
Issued: 1. Gloss - 1955-1989
2. Matt - 1983-1988

Colourway	U.K. £	U.S. $	Can. $
1a. Blue - gloss	100.00	150.00	225.00
1b. Blue - matt	100.00	150.00	225.00
2a. Red - gloss	100.00	150.00	225.00
2b. Red - matt	100.00	150.00	225.00

Model No. 1518
MALLARD DUCK

Designer: Arthur Gredington
Length: See below
Colours: Teal green, brown, white, yellow beak - gloss
Issued: See below
Series: Peter Scott Wildfowl

Description	Issued	Length	Price U.K. £	U.S. $	Can. $
1. Large	1958-1971	6 ½", 16.5 cm	150.00	225.00	350.00
2. Medium	1958-1971	5 ½", 14.0 cm	125.00	180.00	275.00
3. Small - First Version	1958-1962	4 ½", 11.9 cm	100.00	150.00	225.00
4. Small - Second Version	1962-1971	3 ¾", 11.9 cm	90.00	125.00	200.00

Model No. 1519
MANDARIN DUCK

Designer: Arthur Gredington
Length: 1. Large — 4 ½", 11.9 cm
2. Medium — 3 ¾", 9.5 cm
3. Small — 3", 7.6 cm
Colours: Tan-brown and blue with red beak - gloss
Issued: 1958-1971
Series: Peter Scott Wildfowl

Description	U.K. £	U.S. $	Can. $
1. Large	150.00	225.00	350.00
2. Medium	125.00	180.00	275.00
3. Small	100.00	150.00	225.00

Model No. 1520
POCHARD DUCK

Designer: Arthur Gredington
Length: 1. Large — 5 ½", 14.0 cm
2. Medium — 4 ½", 11.9 cm
3. Small — 3 ½", 8.9 cm
Colours: Brown, grey and black - gloss
Issued: 1958-1971
Series: Peter Scott Wildfowl

Description	U.K. £	U.S. $	Can. $
1. Large	150.00	225.00	350.00
2. Medium	125.00	180.00	275.00
3. Small	100.00	150.00	225.00

Model No. 1521
KING EIDER DUCK

Designer: Colin Melbourne
Length: 4", 10.1 cm
Colours: Dark grey with tan, brown, green and white - gloss
Issued: 1958-1971
Series: Peter Scott Wildfowl

Description	U.K. £	U.S. $	Can. $
Gloss	125.00	180.00	275.00

Model No. 1522
SMEW DUCK

Designer: Colin Melbourne
Length: 3", 7.6 cm
Colours: Grey, black and white - gloss
Issued: 1958-1971
Series: Peter Scott Wildfowl

Description	U.K. £	U.S. $	Can. $
Gloss	125.00	180.00	275.00

Model No. 1523
TUFTED DUCK

Designer: Colin Melbourne
Length: 2 ¾", 7.0 cm
Colours: Black and white - gloss
Issued: 1958-1971
Series: Peter Scott Wildfowl

Description	U.K. £	U.S. $	Can. $
Gloss	125.00	180.00	275.00

Model No. 1524
GOLDENEYE DUCK

Designer: Colin Melbourne
Length: 3 ½", 8.9 cm
Colours: Black, white and green - gloss
Issued: 1958-1971
Series: Peter Scott Wildfowl

Description	U.K. £	U.S. $	Can. $
Gloss	125.00	180.00	275.00

Model No. 1525
GOOSANDER

Designer: Colin Melbourne
Length: 4 ½", 11.9 cm
Colours: Pink, black and white, orange beak - gloss
Issued: 1958-1971
Series: Peter Scott Wildfowl

Description	U.K. £	U.S. $	Can. $
Gloss	125.00	180.00	275.00

Model No. 1526
WIDGEON DUCK

Designer: Colin Melbourne
Length: 3 ½", 8.9 cm
Colours: Pink, brown yellow, black and white - gloss
Issued: 1958-1971
Series: Peter Scott Wildfowl

Description	U.K. £	U.S. $	Can. $
Gloss	125.00	180.00	275.00

Model No. 1527
SHELDUCK

Designer: Colin Melbourne
Length: 4", 10.1 cm
Colours: Dark grey, tan, white, green and brown - gloss
Issued: 1958-1971
Series: Peter Scott Wildfowl

Description	U.K. £	U.S. $	Can. $
Gloss	125.00	180.00	275.00

Model No. 1528
SHOVELER

Designer: Colin Melbourne
Length: 3 ½", 8.9 cm
Colours: Tan, blue, white and dark brown - gloss
Issued: 1958-1971
Series: Peter Scott Wildfowl

Description	U.K. £	U.S. $	Can. $
Gloss	125.00	180.00	275.00

Model No. 1529
TEAL DUCK

Designer: Colin Melbourne
Length: 2 ¾", 7.0 cm
Colours: Tan, yellow, black, white with blue beak - gloss
Issued: 1958-1971
Series: Peter Scott Wildfowl

Description	U.K. £	U.S. $	Can. $
Gloss	125.00	180.00	275.00

Model No. 1614
FANTAIL PIGEON

Designer: Arthur Gredington
Height: 5", 12.7 cm
Colours: White - gloss
Issued: 1959-1969

Description	U.K. £	U.S. $	Can. $
Gloss	500.00	700.00	1,000.00

Model No. 1684
SWAN - Head up

Designer: Arthur Gredington
Height: 3", 7.6 cm
Colours: White - gloss
Issued: 1960-1973
Set: 1685, 1686, 1687

Description	U.K. £	U.S. $	Can. $
Gloss	75.00	110.00	165.00

Model No. 1685
SWAN - Head down

Designer: Arthur Gredington
Height: 2", 5.0 cm
Colours: White - gloss
Issued: 1960-1973
Set: 1684, 1686, 1687

Description	U.K £	U.S. $	Can. $
Gloss	75.00	110.00	165.00

BIRDS

Model 817
Mallard Duck, squatting

Model 749
Mallard Duck, rising

Model 750
Mallard Duck, settling

Model 1052
Barnacle Goose

Model 995
Shelldrake, beak open

Model 994
Shelldrake, beak closed

Model 850
Pheasant on base, settling

Model 849
Pheasant on base, flying upwards

Model 1225B
Pheasant, second version, no flowers on base

BIRDS

Model 1518
Mallard Duck

Model 1519
Mandarin Duck

Model 1520
Pochard Duck

Model 1521
King Eider Duck

Model 1524
Goldeneye Duck

Model 1525
Goosander

Model 1527
Shelduck

Model 1528
Shoveler

Model 1529
Teal Duck

BIRDS

Model 2188
Blue Jay

Model 1219B
Jay, second version

Model 1159
Kookaburra

Model 926
Baltimore Orioles

Model 925
American Blue Jays

Model 1022
Turtle Doves

Model 929
Chickadee

Model 1818
Cockatoo

Model 930
Parakeet

BUTTERFLIES

Model 1487
Purple Emperor Butterfly

Model 1488
Red Admiral Butterfly

Model 1489
Peacock Butterfly

Model 1490
Clouded Yellow Butterfly

Model 1491
Tortoiseshell Butterfly

Model 1492
Swallow-Tail Butterfly

Model 1493
Small Copper Butterfly

Model 1494
Purple Hairstreak Butterfly

Model 1495
Small Heath Butterfly

FISH

Model 1874
Roach

Model 1233
Atlantic Salmon

Model 1875
Perch

Model 1246
Golden Trout

Model 1266
Large-mouthed Black Bass

Model 1235
Barracuda

Model 1047
Angel Fish

Model 2066
Salmon

Model 1232
Oceanic Bonito

WILD ANIMALS

Model 845A
Zebra, first version

Model 845B
Zebra, second version

Model 1019
Bison

Model 2554A
Lion on Rock

Model 2725
Cheetah on Rock

Model 841
Leopard, seated

Model 998
Elephant, trunk stretching

Model 1720
Elephant and Tiger

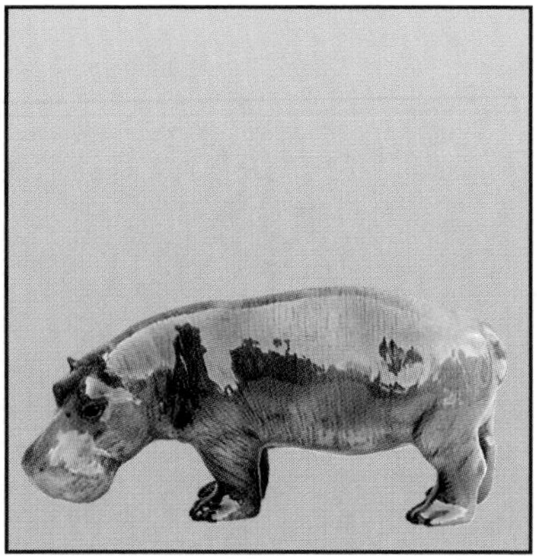

Model 1532
Hippopotamus

WILD ANIMALS

Model 368
Frog, on pottery base

Model 1534
Seal

Model 316
Rabbit, on pottery base

Model 1025
Hare, seated

Model 1024
Hare, running

Model 1021
Stoat

Model 1038
Koala Bear

Model 397
Monkey, on pottery base

Model 1049
Chimpanzee with pipe

WILD ANIMALS

Model 1308
Skunk

Model 3393
Badger, male

Model 2687
Badger, matt finish

Model 3399
Woodmouse

Model 3397
Harvest Mouse

Model 1678
Mouse

Model 1017
Fox, curled

Model 1943
Beaver on Log

Model 2194
Racoon on Log

Model No. 1686
CYGNET - Facing left

Designer:	Arthur Gredington
Height:	1", 2.5 cm
Colours:	Grey - gloss
Issued:	1960-1971
Set:	1684, 1685, 1687

Description	U.K. £	U.S. $	Can. $
Gloss	40.00	60.00	90.00

Model No. 1687
CYGNET - Facing right

Designer:	Arthur Gredington
Height:	1", 2.5 cm
Colours:	Grey - gloss
Issued:	1960-1971
Set:	1684, 1685, 1686

Description	U.K. £	U.S. $	Can. $
Gloss	40.00	60.00	90.00

Model No. 1774
PHEASANT - On pottery base

Designer:	Albert Hallam
Height:	4 ¾", 12.1 cm
Colours:	Red-brown, teal green and beige - gloss
Issued:	1961-1975

Description	U.K. £	U.S. $	Can. $
Gloss	100.00	150.00	225.00

Model No. 1818
COCKATOO - Large

Designer:	Albert Hallam
Height:	11 ½", 29.2 cm
Colours:	1. Pink and grey - gloss 2. Turquoise and yellow - gloss
Issued:	1962-1973

Colourway	U.K. £	U.S. $	Can. $
1. Pink/grey	150.00	250.00	350.00
2. Turquoise/yellow	225.00	300.00	450.00

Model No. 1892
LEGHORN COCKEREL

Designer: Arthur Gredington
Height: 9", 22.9 cm
Colours: Teal green, red, orange and yellow - gloss
Issued: 1963-1983

Description	U.K. £	U.S. $	Can. $
Gloss	275.00	400.00	600.00

Model No. 1899
SUSSEX COCKEREL

Designer: Arthur Gredington
Height: 7", 17.8 cm
Colours: Black, white and pink - gloss
Issued: 1963-1971

Description	U.K. £	U.S. $	Can. $
Gloss	1,000.00	1,500.00	2,250.00

Model No. 1957
TURKEY

Designer: Albert Hallam
Height: 7 ¼", 18.4 cm
Colours: 1. Bronze - gloss
2. White - gloss
Issued: 1964-1969

Colourway	U.K. £	U.S. $	Can. $
1. Bronze	350.00	500.00	750.00
2. White	700.00	1,000.00	1,500.00

Model No. 2026
OWL

Designer: Albert Hallam
Height: 4 ½", 11.9 cm
Colours: Golden brown and white - gloss
Issued: 1965 to the present

Description	U.K. £	U.S. $	Can. $
Gloss	19.00	N/A	N/A

Model No. 2059
GAMECOCK

Designer: Arthur Gredington
Height: 9 ½", 24.0 cm
Colours: Brown, teal green, cream and red - gloss
Issued: 1966-1975

Description	U.K. £	U.S. $	Can. $
Gloss	600.00	900.00	1,500.00

Model No. 2062
GOLDEN EAGLE

Designer: Graham Tongue
Height: 9 ½", 24.0 cm
Colours: Dark brown - gloss, matt, or satin matt
Issued: 1. 1966-1974 - Gloss
2. 1970-1972 - Matt
3. 1973-1989 - Satin matt
Series: 3. Connoisseur

Description	U.K. £	U.S. $	Can. $
1. Gloss	125.00	180.00	275.00
2. Matt	100.00	150.00	225.00
3. Satin matt	75.00	110.00	165.00

Model No. 2063
GROUSE (Pair)

Designer: Albert Hallam
Height: 5 ½", 14.0 cm
Colours: Red-brown - gloss
Issued: 1966-1975

Description	U.K. £	U.S. $	Can. $
Gloss	400.00	600.00	900.00

Model No. 2064
PARTRIDGE (Pair)

Designer: Albert Hallam
Height: 5 ½", 14.0 cm
Colours: Brown and blue - gloss
Issued: 1966-1975

Description	U.K. £	U.S. $	Can. $
Gloss	425.00	600.00	900.00

Model No. 2067
TURKEY

Designer: Albert Hallam
Height: 2 ½", 6.4 cm
Colours: 1. White and red - gloss
2. Bronze - gloss
Issued: 1966-1969

Colourway	U.K. £	U.S. $	Can. $
1. White	275.00	300.00	450.00
2. Bronze	175.00	250.00	400.00

Photograph not available at press time

Model No. 2071
OWL (Contemporary)

Designer: Graham Tongue
Height: 5", 12.7 cm
Colours: Unknown
Issued: 1966-Unknown
Series: Contemporary Models

Description	U.K. £	U.S. $	Can. $
Owl		Extremely Rare	

Model No. 2078
PHEASANTS (Pair)

Designer: Arthur Gredington
Height: 6 ¾", 17.2 cm
Colours: Red-brown and teal green with yellow markings - gloss
Issued: 1966-1975

Description	U.K. £	U.S. $	Can. $
Gloss	475.00	650.00	1,000.00

Model No. 2105A
GREENFINCH
First Version - Without flower on base

Designer: Graham Tongue
Height: 3", 7.6 cm
Colours: Natural - gloss
Issued: 1967-1973

Description	U.K. £	U.S. $	Can. $
Gloss	55.00	75.00	100.00

Model No. 2105B
GREENFINCH
Second Version - With flower on base

Designer: Graham Tongue
Remodelled: Albert Hallam
Height: 3", 7.6 cm
Colours: Green and yellow - gloss or matt
Issued: 1. Gloss - 1973-1998
2. Matt - 1983-1992

Description	U.K. £	U.S. $	Can. $
1. Gloss	30.00	50.00	75.00
2. Matt	30.00	50.00	75.00

Model No. 2106A
WHITETHROAT
First Version - Mouth open, base is a green mound

Designer: Graham Tongue
Height: 3", 7.6 cm
Colours: Dark grey, white and pink - gloss
Issued: 1967-1973

Description	U.K. £	U.S. $	Can. $
Gloss	55.00	75.00	100.00

Model No. 2106B
WHITETHROAT
Second Version - Mouth closed, base is a leaf

Designer: Graham Tongue
Remodelled: Albert Hallam
Height: 3", 7.6 cm
Colours: Natural - gloss or matt
Issued: 1. Gloss - 1973-1996
2. Matt - 1983-1992

Description	U.K. £	U.S. $	Can. $
1. Gloss	25.00	40.00	60.00
2. Matt	25.00	40.00	60.00

Model No. 2183
BALTIMORE ORIOLE

Designer: Albert Hallam
Height: 3 ½", 8.9 cm
Colours: Black and red - gloss or matt
Issued: 1. Gloss - 1968-1973
2. Matt - 1970-1972

Description	U.K. £	U.S. $	Can. $
1. Gloss	100.00	150.00	225.00
2. Matt	100.00	150.00	225.00

Model No. 2184
CEDAR WAXWING

Designer: Graham Tongue
Height: 4 ½", 11.9 cm
Colours: Brown, black and yellow - gloss or matt
Issued: 1. Gloss - 1968-1973
2. Matt - 1970-1972

Description	U.K. £	U.S. $	Can. $
1. Gloss	125.00	180.00	275.00
2. Matt	125.00	180.00	275.00

Model No. 2187
AMERICAN ROBIN

Designer: Graham Tongue
Height: 4", 10.1 cm
Colours: Dark grey and red - gloss or matt
Issued: 1. Gloss - 1968-1973
2. Matt - 1970-1972

Description	U.K. £	U.S. $	Can. $
1. Gloss	125.00	175.00	275.00
2. Matt	100.00	150.00	225.00

Model No. 2188
BLUE JAY

Designer: Albert Hallam
Height: 4 ½", 11.9 cm
Colours: Blue and white - gloss or matt
Issued: 1. Gloss - 1968-1973
2. Matt - 1970-1972

Description	U.K. £	U.S. $	Can. $
1. Gloss	150.00	225.00	350.00
2. Matt	125.00	180.00	275.00

Model No. 2189
BLACK CAPPED CHICADEE

Designer: Graham Tongue
Height: 4 ½", 11.9 cm
Colours: Yellow, white, grey, green and black - gloss or matt
Issued: 1. Gloss - 1968-1973
2. Matt - 1970-1972

Description	U.K. £	U.S. $	Can. $
1. Gloss	125.00	180.00	275.00
2. Matt	100.00	150.00	225.00

Model No. 2190
EVENING GROSBEAK

Designer: Albert Hallam
Height: 4", 10.1 cm
Colours: Black and yellow - gloss or matt
Issued: 1. Gloss - 1968-1973
2. Matt - 1970-1972

Description	U.K. £	U.S. $	Can. $
1. Gloss	150.00	225.00	350.00
2. Matt	125.00	180.00	275.00

Model No. 2191
QUAIL

Designer: Albert Hallam
Height: 5", 12.7 cm
Colours: Browns, black and white - gloss or matt
Issued: 1. Gloss - 1968-1971
2. Matt - 1970-1972

Description	U.K. £	U.S. $	Can. $
1. Gloss	175.00	250.00	375.00
2. Matt	150.00	225.00	350.00

Model No. 2200
CHICKEN - Running

Designer: Graham Tongue
Height: 1 ¼", 3.2 cm
Colours: Yellow - gloss
Issued: 1968-1973
Set: 2201, 2202

Description	U.K. £	U.S. $	Can. $
Gloss	125.00	180.00	275.00

Model No. 2201
CHICKEN - Pecking

Designer: Graham Tongue
Height: 1", 2.5 cm
Colours: Yellow - gloss
Issued: 1968-1973
Set: 2200, 2202

Description	U.K. £	U.S. $	Can. $
Gloss	100.00	150.00	225.00

Model No. 2202
CHICKEN - Seated

Designer: Graham Tongue
Height: 1 ½", 3.8 cm
Colours: Yellow - gloss
Issued: 1968-1973
Set: 2200, 2201

Description	U.K. £	U.S. $	Can. $
Gloss	125.00	180.00	275.00

Photograph not available at press time

Model No. 2238
OWL

Designer: Harry Sales
Height: 6 ¾", 17.2 cm
Colours: Unknown
Issued: 1968-1971
Series: Moda Range

Description	U.K. £	U.S. $	Can. $
Owl		Very Rare	

Model No. 2239
BIRD

Designer: Harry Sales
Height: 5", 12.7 cm
Colours: Unknown
Issued: 1968-1971
Series: Moda Range

Description	U.K. £	U.S. $	Can. $
Bird	250.00	350.00	525.00

Model No. 2240
COCKEREL

Designer: Harry Sales
Height: 6", 15.0 cm
Colours: 1. Blue - gloss
2. Brown - matt
Issued: 1968-1971
Series: Moda Range

Colourway	U.K. £	U.S. $	Can. $
1. Blue	150.00	225.00	350.00
2. Brown	125.00	180.00	275.00

Model No. 2273
GOLDFINCH

Designer: Graham Tongue
Height: 3", 7.6 cm
Colours: Brown, white, red and yellow - gloss or matt
Issued: 1. Gloss - 1969-1995
2. Matt - 1983-1992

Description	U.K. £	U.S. $	Can. $
1. Gloss	20.00	30.00	45.00
2. Matt	20.00	30.00	45.00

Model No. 2274
STONECHAT

Designer: Albert Hallam
Height: 3", 7.6 cm
Colours: Dark brown and white, red breast - gloss or matt
Issued: 1. Gloss - 1969-1997
2. Matt - 1983-1992

Description	U.K. £	U.S. $	Can. $
1. Gloss	20.00	30.00	45.00
2. Matt	20.00	30.00	45.00

Model No. 2305
MAGPIE

Designer: Albert Hallam
Height: 5", 12.7 cm
Colours: Black and white - gloss
Issued: 1970-1982

Description	U.K. £	U.S. $	Can. $
Gloss	100.00	150.00	225.00

Model No. 2307
EAGLE ON ROCK

Designer: Graham Tongue
Height: 3 ¾", 9.5 cm
Colours: Browns - gloss
Issued: 1970-1975

Description	U.K. £	U.S. $	Can. $
Gloss	100.00	150.00	225.00

Model No. 2308
SONGTHRUSH

Designer: Albert Hallam
Height: 5 ¾", 14.6 cm
Colours: Brown with yellow speckled breast - gloss and matt
Issued: 1. Gloss - 1970-1989
2. Matt - 1983-1989

Description	U.K. £	U.S. $	Can. $
1. Gloss	65.00	90.00	150.00
2. Matt	60.00	80.00	135.00

Model No. 2315
CUCKOO

Designer: Albert Hallam
Height: 5", 12.7 cm
Colours: Blue - gloss
Issued: 1970-1982

Description	U.K. £	U.S. $	Can. $
Gloss	125.00	180.00	275.00

Model No. 2316
KESTREL

Designer: Graham Tongue
Height: 6 ¾", 17.2 cm
Colours: Browns, white and blue - gloss or matt
Issued: 1. Gloss - 1970-1989
2. Matt - 1983-1989

Description	U.K. £	U.S. $	Can. $
1. Gloss	100.00	150.00	225.00
2. Matt	100.00	150.00	225.00

Model No. 2357
PENGUIN

Designer: Albert Hallam
Height: 12", 30.5 cm
Colours: Black and white - gloss
Issued: 1971-1976
Series: Fireside Model

Description	U.K. £	U.S. $	Can. $
Gloss	700.00	1,000.00	1,500.00

Model No. 2359
HERON - Stylistic

Designer:	Albert Hallam
Height:	10 ½", 26.7 cm
Colours:	Black - satin
Issued:	1971-Unknown

Description	U.K. £	U.S. $	Can. $
Satin	75.00	125.00	200.00

Model No. 2371
KINGFISHER

Designer:	Albert Hallam
Height:	5", 12.7 cm
Colours:	Blue and brown - gloss or matt
Issued:	1. Gloss - 1971-1998
	2. Matt - 1983-1989

Description	U.K. £	U.S. $	Can. $
1. Gloss	40.00	55.00	85.00
2. Matt	50.00	70.00	100.00

Model No. 2398
PENGUIN CHICK - Standing

Designer:	Graham Tongue
Height:	7", 17.8 cm
Colours:	Blue, black and white - gloss
Issued:	1971-1976

Description	U.K. £	U.S. $	Can. $
Gloss	300.00	425.00	650.00

Photograph not available.
Model number 2399 probably
not put into production.

Model No. 2399
PENGUIN CHICK

Designer:	Albert Hallam
Height:	6 ¾", 17.2 cm
Colours:	Black and white - gloss
Issued:	1972-Unknown

Description	U.K. £	U.S. $	Can. $
Gloss	Extremely Rare		

Model No. 2413
NUTHATCH

Designer: Graham Tongue
Height: 3", 7.6 cm
Colours: Dark blue and white - gloss or matt
Issued: 1. Gloss - 1972-1995
2. Matt - 1983-1989

Description	U.K. £	U.S. $	Can. $
1. Gloss	20.00	30.00	45.00
2. Matt	20.00	30.00	45.00

Model No. 2415
GOLDCREST

Designer: Graham Tongue
Height: 3", 7.6 cm
Colours: Green, yellow and grey - gloss or matt
Issued: 1. Gloss - 1972 to the present
2. Matt - 1983-1989

Description	U.K. £	U.S. $	Can. $
1. Gloss	16.00	N/A	N/A
2. Matt	40.00	60.00	90.00

Model No. 2416A
LAPWING
First Version - Tail feathers split

Designer: Albert Hallam
Height: 5 ½", 14.0 cm
Colours: Black, dark green and white - gloss
Issued: 1972-Unknown

Description	U.K. £	U.S. $	Can. $
Gloss	175.00	250.00	375.00

Model No. 2416B
LAPWING
Second Version - Tail feathers together

Designer: Albert Hallam
Height: 5 ½", 14.0 cm
Colours: Black, dark green and white - gloss
Issued: Unknown-1982

Description	U.K. £	U.S. $	Can. $
Gloss	100.00	150.00	225.00

Model No. 2417
JAY

Designer: Graham Tongue
Height: 5", 12.7 cm
Colours: Brown, white and blue - gloss
Issued: 1972-1982

Description	U.K. £	U.S. $	Can. $
Gloss	100.00	150.00	225.00

Model No. 2420
LESSER SPOTTED WOODPECKER

Designer: Graham Tongue
Height: 5 ½", 14.0 cm
Colours: Red, white and black - gloss
Issued: 1972-1982

Description	U.K. £	U.S. $	Can. $
Gloss	125.00	180.00	275.00

Model No. 2434
PENGUIN CHICK - Sliding

Designer: Graham Tongue
Height: 3 ¾" x 8", 9.5 x 20.3 cm
Colours: Blue, black and white - gloss
Issued: 1972-1976

Description	U.K. £	U.S. $	Can. $
Gloss	400.00	550.00	825.00

Model No. 2760
PHEASANT

Designer: Graham Tongue
Height: 10 ½", 26.7 cm
Issued:
1. Tan and brown - satin matt
   a. Beswick - 1982-1989
   b. Royal Doulton (DA38) - 1989-1994
2. Bronze; black shading - matt, 1989-1992

Series:
1. Connoisseur
2. Britannia Collection

Description	U.K. £	U.S. $	Can. $
1. Connoisseur	200.00	300.00	450.00
2. Britannia	250.00	350.00	525.00

Model No. 3272
TAWNY OWL

Designer: Mr. Sutton
Height: 3 ¼", 8.3 cm
Colours: Brown and white - gloss
Issued: 1990 to the present

Description	U.K. £	U.S. $	Can. $
Gloss	16.00	N/A	N/A

Model No. 3273
BARN OWL

Designer: Martyn Alcock
Height: 3 ¼", 8.3 cm
Colours: Light brown and white - gloss
Issued: 1990-1998

Description	U.K. £	U.S. $	Can. $
Gloss	20.00	30.00	45.00

Model No. 3274
GREAT TIT

Designer: Martyn Alcock
Height: 3", 7.6 cm
Colours: Black, yellow, white and grey - gloss
Issued: 1990-1995

Description	U.K. £	U.S. $	Can. $
Gloss	20.00	30.00	45.00

Model No. 3275
KINGFISHER

Designer: Mr. Sutton
Height: 2 ¾", 7.0 cm
Colours: Blue head and wings, orange breast - gloss
Issued: 1990-1998

Description	U.K. £	U.S. $	Can. $
Gloss	20.00	30.00	45.00

BIRD WALL PLAQUES

INDEX BY MODEL NUMBER

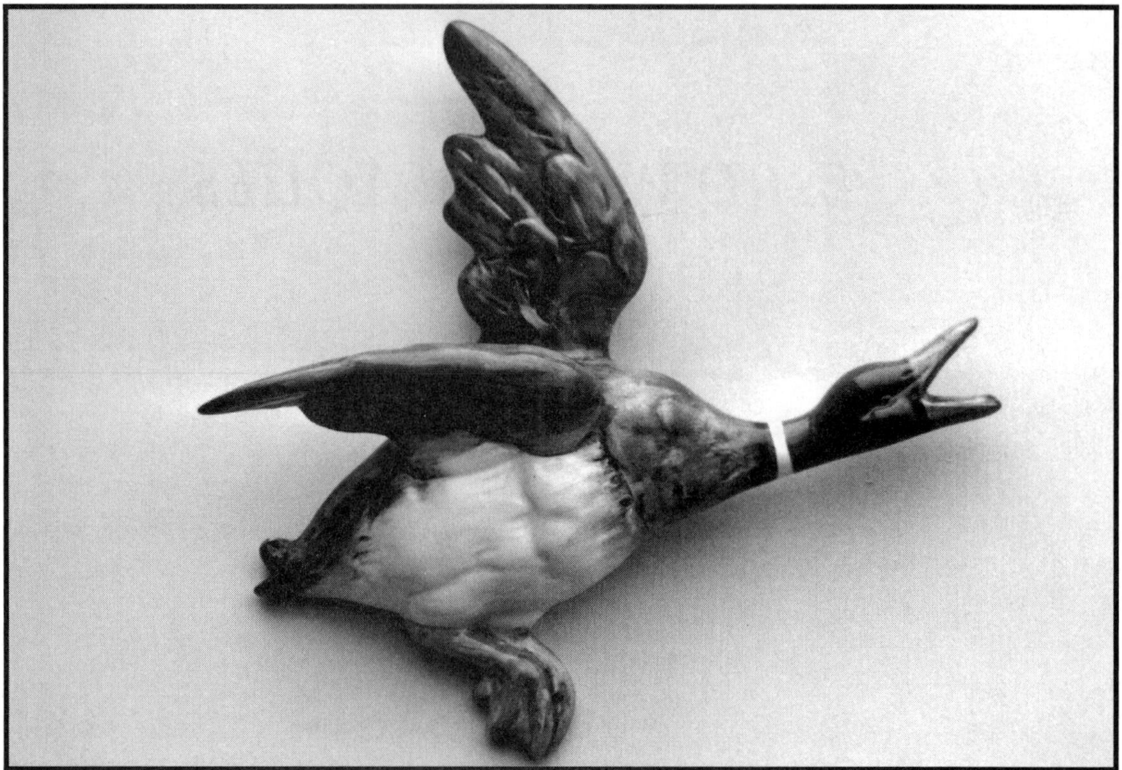

Model No. 596

MALLARD

Designer: Mr. Watkin
Length: See below
Issued: See below
Colours: 1. Brown, teal green and white - gloss
2. White with yellow beaks - matt

Model No.	Finish	Issued	Length	U.K. £	Price U.S. $	Can. $
1. 596/0	Gloss	1938-1971	11 ¾", 29.8 cm	100.00	150.00	225.00
2. 596/0	Matt	1938-1971	11 ¾", 29.8 cm	95.00	140.00	200.00
3. 596/1	Gloss	1938-1973	10", 25.4 cm	80.00	125.00	175.00
4. 596/1	Matt	1938-1973	10", 25.4 cm	75.00	120.00	150.00
5. 596/2	Gloss	1938-1973	8 ¾", 22.2 cm	60.00	90.00	135.00
6. 596/2	Matt	1938-1973	8 ¾", 22.2 cm	60.00	90.00	135.00
7. 596/3	Gloss	1938-1973	7", 17.8 cm	50.00	75.00	115.00
8. 596/3	Matt	1938-1973	7", 17.8 cm	50.00	75.00	115.00
9. 596/4	Gloss	1938-1971	5 ¾", 14.6 cm	45.00	65.00	100.00
10. 596/4	Matt	1938-1971	5 ¾", 14.6 cm	45.00	65.00	100.00

Note: These also exist with a small "pocket" between the wings.

Model No. 658

SEAGULL
Style One - Wings up, apart

Designer: Mr. Watkin
Length: See below
Colours: 1. White, black and yellow - gloss
2. White and yellow - matt
3. White - matt
Issued: 1938-1967

Model No.	Finish	Length	U.K. £	Price U.S. $	Can. $
1. 658/1	Gloss	14", 35.5 cm	100.00	150.00	225.00
2. 658/1	Matt	14", 35.5 cm	90.00	125.00	175.00
3. 658/1	Matt	14", 35.5 cm	65.00	100.00	150.00
4. 658/2	Gloss	11 ¾", 29.8 cm	90.00	125.00	175.00
5. 658/2	Matt	11 ¾", 29.8 cm	80.00	110.00	160.00
6. 658/2	Matt	11 ¾", 29.8 cm	55.00	80.00	120.00
7. 658/3	Gloss	10", 25.4 cm	80.00	110.00	160.00
8. 658/3	Matt	10", 25.4 cm	70.00	100.00	150.00
9. 658/3	Matt	10", 25.4 cm	45.00	65.00	100.00
10. 658/4	Gloss	8", 20.3 cm	70.00	100.00	150.00
11. 658/4	Matt	8", 20.3 cm	60.00	85.00	125.00
12. 658/4	Matt	8", 20.3 cm	35.00	50.00	75.00

Model No. 661

PHEASANT

Designer: Mr. Watkin
Length: See below
Colours: 1. Teal green, browns and white - gloss
2. White - matt
Issued: 1938-1971

Model No./Size	Finish	Length	Price U.K. £	Price U.S. $	Price Can. $
1. 661/1 Large	Gloss	12", 30.5 cm	100.00	150.00	225.00
2. 661/1 Large	Matt	12", 30.5 cm	95.00	140.00	200.00
3. 661/2 Medium	Gloss	10 ¼", 26.0 cm	85.00	120.00	180.00
4. 661/2 Medium	Matt	10 ¼", 26.0 cm	80.00	110.00	160.00
5. 661/3 Small	Gloss	8 ½", 21.6 cm	70.00	100.00	150.00
6. 661/3 Small	Matt	8 ½", 21.6 cm	65.00	90.00	135.00

Model No. 705
BLUE TIT - Flying to the right

Designer:	Mr. Watkin
Height:	4 ½", 11.9 cm
Size:	Large
Colours:	Blue and browns - gloss
Issued:	1939-1967
Set:	706, 707

Description	U.K. £	U.S. $	Can. $
Gloss	85.00	125.00	175.00

Model No. 706
BLUE TIT - Flying to the left

Designer:	Mr. Watkin
Height:	4 ½", 11.9 cm
Size:	Medium
Colours:	Blue and browns - gloss
Issued:	1939-1967
Set:	705, 707

Description	U.K. £	U.S. $	Can. $
Gloss	85.00	125.00	175.00

Model No. 707
BLUE TIT - Wings up, flying to the left

Designer:	Mr. Watkin
Height:	4 ½", 11.9 cm
Size:	Small
Colours:	Blue and browns - gloss
Issued:	1939-1967
Set:	705, 706

Description	U.K. £	U.S. $	Can. $
Gloss	85.00	125.00	175.00

Model No. 729

KINGFISHER - Flying to the right

Designer: Arthur Gredington
Height: See below
Colours: 1. Green and yellow - gloss
2. Blue - gloss
Issued: 1939-1971

Model No./Size	Colourway	Height	Price U.K. £	Price U.S. $	Price Can. $
1. 729/1 Large	Green	7 ½", 19.1 cm	75.00	110.00	165.00
2. 729/1 Large	Blue	7 ½", 19.1 cm	100.00	150.00	225.00
3. 729/2 Medium	Green	6", 15.0 cm	65.00	95.00	145.00
4. 729/2 Medium	Blue	6", 15.0 cm	100.00	150.00	225.00
5. 729/3 Small	Green	5", 12.7 cm	55.00	80.00	125.00
6. 729/3 Small	Blue	5", 12.7 cm	100.00	150.00	225.00

Note: Model no. 729/2 can be paired with no. 743 to make a facing pair.

Model No. 731
FLAMINGO

Designer: Mr. Watkin
Length: 15", 38.1 cm
Colours: 1. Pearl orange and black - gloss
2. White, yellow and black wing tips - satin
Issued: 1939-1954

Description	U.K. £	U.S. $	Can. $
1. Gloss	300.00	450.00	675.00
2. Satin	300.00	450.00	675.00

Model No. 743
KINGFISHER - Flying to the left

Designer: Arthur Gredington
Height: 6", 15.0 cm
Colours: Greens and yellow - gloss
Issued: 1939-1954

Description	U.K. £	U.S. $	Can. $
Gloss	100.00	150.00	175.00

Note: Model no. 743 can be paired with no. 729/2 to make a facing pair.

Model No. 757

SWALLOW

Designer: Arthur Gredington
Height: See below
Colours: 1. Blues - gloss
2. Golden brown; yellow tail - gloss
Issued: 1939-1973

Model No./Colourway	Size	Height	U.K. £	Price U.S. $	Can. $
1. 757/1 Blue	Large	7 ½", 19.1 cm	75.00	100.00	150.00
2. 757/1 Brown	Large	7 ½", 19.1 cm		Extremely Rare	
3. 757/2 Blue	Medium	6 ¼", 15.9 cm	65.00	95.00	145.00
4. 757/2 Brown	Medium	6 ¼", 15.9 cm		Extremely Rare	
5. 757/3 Blue	Small	5", 12.7 cm	55.00	75.00	110.00
6. 757/3 Brown	Small	5", 12.7 cm		Extremely Rare	

Model No. 922
SEAGULL
Style Two - Wings up, together

Designer: Arthur Gredington
Height: Large - 12", 30.5 cm
Medium - 10 ½", 26.7 cm
Small - 9 ½", 24.0 cm
Colours: White, grey and black - gloss or matt
Issued: 1941-1971

Description	U.K. £	U.S. $	Can. $
1. Large - gloss	75.00	100.00	150.00
2. Large - matt	65.00	95.00	145.00
3. Medium - gloss	65.00	95.00	145.00
4. Medium - matt	60.00	90.00	135.00
5. Small - gloss	55.00	75.00	110.00
6. Small - matt	50.00	75.00	110.00

Model No. 1023
HUMMING BIRD

Designer: Arthur Gredington
Height: Large - 5 ¾", 14.6 cm
Medium - 5", 12.7 cm
Small - 4 ¾", 12.1 cm
Colours: Browns, grey and red - gloss
Issued: 1944-1967

Description	U.K. £	U.S. $	Can. $
1. Large - gloss	90.00	125.00	175.00
2. Medium - gloss	80.00	110.00	160.00
3. Small - gloss	70.00	100.00	150.00

Model No. 1188

PINK LEGGED PARTRIDGE

Designer: Arthur Gredington
Length: See below
Colours: Browns, white and grey - gloss
Issued: 1950-1967

Model No.	Size	Length	U.K. £	Price U.S. $	Can. $
1. 1188/1	Large	10 ½", 26.7 cm	125.00	175.00	275.00
2. 1188/2	Medium	9", 22.9 cm	100.00	150.00	225.00
3. 1188/3	Small	7 ½", 19.1 cm	85.00	125.00	175.00

Model No. 1344

GREEN WOODPECKER

Designer: Mr. Orwell
Length: See below
Colours: Greens and brown, red head - gloss
Issued: 1954-1968

Model No.	Size	Length	Price U.K. £	Price U.S. $	Price Can. $
1. 1344/1	Large	7 ½", 19.1 cm	175.00	250.00	375.00
2. 1344/2	Medium	6", 15.0 cm	150.00	200.00	300.00
3. 1344/3	Small	5", 12.7 cm	125.00	175.00	250.00

Model No. 1530

TEAL

Designer: Arthur Gredington
Length: See below
Colours: Brown, grey and green - gloss
Issued: 1958-1968

Model No.	Size	Length	Price U.K. £	Price U.S. $	Price Can. $
1. 1530/1	Large	8 ¼", 21.0 cm	175.00	250.00	375.00
2. 1530/2	Medium	7 ¼", 18.4 cm	150.00	200.00	300.00
3. 1530/3	Small	6 ¼", 15.9 cm	125.00	175.00	250.00

Chapter Two

BUTTERFLY PLAQUES

Butterflies are an unusual choice for the medium of pottery, and these few wall plaques tend to be rare. It is also unusual to find them in perfect condition, as often the antennae have suffered from the passage of time. These butterfly wall plaques were modelled in large, medium and small sizes. The Beswick attention to detail is very apparent here.

At the present time, there have been no catalogues found in which these models are illustrated. Fortunately, each model is impressed on the back with the name of the butterfly and the shape number. If this were not the case, then identification would be a problem.

INDEX BY MODEL NUMBER

Model No. 1487

PURPLE EMPEROR BUTTERFLY

Designer: Albert Hallam
Height: 6 ¼" x 4", 15.9 x 10.1 cm
Size: Large

Colourway	Issued	U.K. £	Price U.S. $	Can. $
Blue and white - gloss	1957-by 1963	375.00	575.00	875.00

Note: Butterflies are priced as having the antennae intact, without them the price must be much lower.

Model No. 1488
RED ADMIRAL BUTTERFLY

Designer: Albert Hallam
Dimensions: 6 ¼" x 4", 15.9 x 10.1 cm
Size: Large
Colours: Browns, blue and white - gloss
Issued: 1957-by 1963

Description	U.K. £	U.S. $	Can. $
Gloss	375.00	575.00	875.00

Model No. 1489
PEACOCK BUTTERFLY

Designer: Albert Hallam
Dimensions: 6 ¼" x 4", 15.9 x 10.1 cm
Size: Large
Colours: Browns, black and yellow - gloss
Issued: 1957-by 1963

Description	U.K. £	U.S. $	Can. $
Gloss	375.00	575.00	875.00

Model No. 1490
CLOUDED YELLOW BUTTERFLY

Designer: Albert Hallam
Dimensions: 5 ¼" x 3 ½", 13.3 x 8.9 cm
Size: Medium
Colours: Yellow, black and red - gloss
Issued: 1957-by 1963

Description	U.K. £	U.S. $	Can. $
Gloss	325.00	450.00	675.00

Model No. 1491
TORTOISESHELL BUTTERFLY

Designer: Albert Hallam
Dimensions: 5 ¼" x 3 ½", 13.3 x 8.9 cm
Size: Medium
Colours: Yellow, blue and black - gloss
Issued: 1957-by 1963

Description	U.K. £	U.S. $	Can. $
Gloss	325.00	450.00	675.00

Model No. 1492
SWALLOW-TAIL BUTTERFLY

Designer: Albert Hallam
Dimensions: 5 ¼" x 3 ½", 13.3 x 8.9 cm
Size: Medium
Colours: Brown, green and blue wings - gloss
Issued: 1957-by 1963

Description	U.K. £	U.S. $	Can. $
Gloss	325.00	450.00	675.00

Model No. 1493
SMALL COPPER BUTTERFLY

Designer: Albert Hallam
Dimensions: 3 ¾" x 2 ¼", 9.5 x 5.7 cm
Size: Small
Colours: Browns - gloss
Issued: 1957-by 1963

Description	U.K. £	U.S. $	Can. $
Gloss	300.00	425.00	625.00

Model No. 1494
PURPLE HAIRSTREAK BUTTERFLY

Designer: Albert Hallam
Dimensions: 3 ¾" x 2 ¼", 9.5 x 5.7 cm
Size: Small
Colours: Browns and grey - gloss
Issued: 1957-by 1963

Description	U.K. £	U.S. $	Can. $
Gloss	300.00	425.00	625.00

Model No. 1495
SMALL HEATH BUTTERFLY

Designer: Albert Hallam
Dimensions: 3 ¾" x 2 ¼", 9.5 x 5.7 cm
Size: Small
Colours: Browns - gloss
Issued: 1957-by 1963

Description	U.K. £	U.S. $	Can. $
Gloss	300.00	425.00	625.00

Chapter Three

CATS

Cat lovers will appreciate the variety of felines offered here. Colours listed under individual cats are those on which they could be found. The Swiss roll decoration has two Swiss roll patterns, one on the shoulder and one on the hip.

Colourways	**Dates of Issue**
Black gloss	Model No. 1897 only
Black matt	1984 - 1988
British Blue (lead grey gloss)	1964 - 1966
Chocolate point gloss	1953 - 1963
Copper lustre	1971 only
Ginger matt	1984 - 1988
Ginger (dark) gloss	1945 - 1970
Ginger (pale) gloss	1959 - 1963
Ginger striped gloss	1965 - 1989
Ginger Swiss roll gloss	1964 - 1966
Grey matt	1984 - 1988
Grey (shaded) gloss	1965 - 1989
Grey (smokey blue) gloss	1945 - 1970
Grey striped gloss	1962 - 1973
Grey Swiss roll gloss	1964 - 1966
Royal blue gloss	Only one example known
Seal point gloss	1963 - 1989
Seal point matt	1984 - 1988
White (large eyes) gloss	1963 - 1989
White (small eyes) gloss	1945 - 1963
White matt	1984 - 1988
White Zodiac cat	1958 - 1970

INDEX BY MODEL NUMBER

MODEL NUMBERS TRANSFERRED TO *THE CHARLTON STANDARD CATALOGUE OF BESWICK COLLECTABLES*

Model No.	Description
1026	Cat Conductor
1027	Cat with Cello
1028	Cat with Fiddle
1029	Cat with Saxophone
2156/57	Cat Cruet, Salt and Pepper
2761	Cat on Chimney, Salt and Pepper
2805	Cat on Post Box, Money Box
3012	Sporting Cat
FF2	Mee-Ouch
FF3	Kitcat
FF4	Dribble
FF5	Throw In
FF6	Referee: Red Card

Model 1031 White gloss (large eyes) left, (small eyes) right

Model No. 1030
CAT - Seated, head looks up

Designer: Arthur Gredington
Height: 6 ¼", 15.9 cm

Colourway	Finish	Intro.	Disc.	Price U.K. £	Price U.S. $	Price Can. $
1. British Blue (lead grey)	Gloss	1964	1966	200.00	325.00	500.00
2. Ginger (dark)	Gloss	1945	1970	85.00	125.00	200.00
3. Ginger (pale)	Gloss	1959	1963	75.00	100.00	150.00
4. Ginger striped	Gloss	1965	1973	100.00	150.00	225.00
5. Ginger Swiss roll	Gloss	1964	1966	180.00	250.00	375.00
6. Grey (shaded)	Gloss	1971	1973	75.00	100.00	150.00
7. Grey (smokey blue)	Gloss	1945	1970	60.00	85.00	125.00
8. Grey striped	Gloss	1962	1973	100.00	150.00	225.00
9. Grey Swiss roll	Gloss	1964	1966	200.00	325.00	500.00
10. Royal blue	Gloss				**Unique***	
11. White (small eyes)	Gloss	1945	1963	70.00	100.00	150.00
12. White (large eyes)	Gloss	1963	1973	65.00	90.00	135.00

Note: * Only one example known.

Model No. 1031
CAT - Seated, head looks forward

Designer: Arthur Gredington
Height: 4 ½", 11.9 cm

Colourway	Finish	Intro.	Disc.	U.K. £	Price U.S. $	Can. $
1. British Blue (lead grey)	Gloss	1964	1966	200.00	300.00	450.00
2. Ginger (dark)	Gloss	1945	1970	70.00	100.00	150.00
3. Ginger (pale)	Gloss	1959	1963	60.00	85.00	125.00
4. Ginger striped	Gloss	1965	1973	80.00	125.00	175.00
5. Ginger Swiss roll	Gloss	1964	1966	185.00	260.00	400.00
6. Grey (shaded)	Gloss	1971	1973	65.00	90.00	135.00
7. Grey (smokey blue)	Gloss	1945	1970	55.00	75.00	110.00
8. Grey striped	Gloss	1962	1973	85.00	125.00	200.00
9. Grey Swiss roll	Gloss	1964	1966	200.00	325.00	500.00
10. White (small eyes)	Gloss	1945	1963	60.00	85.00	125.00
11. White (large eyes)	Gloss	1963	1971	55.00	75.00	110.00

Model No. 1296 / K1296
SIAMESE KITTENS - Curled together

Designer: Miss Granoska
Length: 2 ¾", 7.0 cm

Colours	Model Number	Issued	U.K. £	Price U.S. $	Can. $
1. Chocolate point, gloss	1296	1953-1963	55.00	75.00	110.00
2. Copper lustre, gloss (1)	1296	1971	65.00	95.00	145.00
3. One white/one pale grey, gloss (2)	1296	Unknown		**Unique**	
4. Seal point, gloss					
a. Beswick	1296	1964-1989	20.00	30.00	45.00
b. Royal Doulton	DA122	1990-1999	20.00	30.00	45.00
c. Beswick	K1296	1999-Current	17.50	N/A	60.00
5. Seal point - matt		1984-1989	55.00	75.00	110.00

Note: 1. Copper lustre was produced for export only.
2. Only one example known.

Model No. 1316
PERSIAN KITTENS - Seated

Designer: Miss Granoska
Height: 3 ½", 8.9 cm

Colourway	Finish	Intro.	Disc.	U.K. £	Price U.S. $	Can. $
1. British Blue (lead grey)	Gloss	1964	1966	150.00	200.00	300.00
2. Ginger (dark)	Gloss	1953	1970	60.00	90.00	135.00
3. Ginger (pale)	Gloss	1959	1963	50.00	70.00	125.00
4. Ginger striped	Gloss	1971	1973	70.00	100.00	150.00
5. Ginger Swiss roll	Gloss	1964	1966	125.00	175.00	300.00
6. Grey (shaded)	Gloss	1965	1973	45.00	65.00	100.00
7. Grey striped	Gloss	1962	1973	70.00	100.00	150.00
8. Grey Swiss roll	Gloss	1964	1966	175.00	250.00	375.00
9. White (large eyes)	Gloss	1963	1973	45.00	65.00	100.00

Model No. 1435
CAT - Seated

Designer: Colin Melbourne
Height: 5 ¼", 13.3 cm
Colours: Grey striped - gloss
Issued: 1956-1963

Colourway	U.K. £	U.S. $	Can. $
Grey striped, gloss	200.00	325.00	475.00

Note: A pewter example is known to exist.

Model No. 1436
KITTEN - Seated

Designer: Colin Melbourne
Height: 3 ¼", 8.3 cm

Colourway	Finish	Intro.	Disc.	Price U.K. £	Price U.S. $	Price Can. $
1. Black	Matt	1984	1989	35.00	50.00	75.00
2. British Blue (lead grey)	Gloss	1964	1966	95.00	140.00	200.00
3. Ginger	Matt	1984	1989	30.00	45.00	70.00
4. Ginger (dark)	Gloss	1956	1970	35.00	50.00	75.00
5. Ginger (pale)	Gloss	1959	1963	25.00	35.00	50.00
6. Ginger striped						
a. Beswick	Gloss	1965	1989	40.00	65.00	95.00
b. Doulton (DA123)	Gloss	1990	1999	15.00	25.00	35.00
7. Ginger Swiss roll	Gloss	1964	1966	95.00	140.00	200.00
8. Grey	Matt	1984	1989	40.00	60.00	90.00
9. Grey (shaded)						
a. Beswick	Gloss	1965	1989	25.00	45.00	70.00
b. Doulton (DA123)	Gloss	1990	1999	15.00	25.00	35.00
10. Grey striped	Gloss	1962	1973	35.00	50.00	75.00
11. Grey Swiss roll	Gloss	1964	1966	100.00	150.00	200.00
12. White (small eyes)	Gloss	1956	1963	45.00	65.00	95.00
13. White (large eyes)						
a. Beswick	Gloss	1963	1989	30.00	50.00	75.00
b. Doulton (DA123)	Gloss	1990	1999	15.00	25.00	35.00
14. White	Matt	1984	1989	45.00	65.00	95.00

Model No. 1437
CAT - Seated, looking up

Designer: Colin Melbourne
Height: 3 ¼", 8.3 cm
Colours: Grey striped - gloss
Issued: 1956-1963

Colourway	U.K. £	Price U.S. $	Can. $
Grey striped	200.00	300.00	450.00

Note: A ginger striped colourway is known to exist.

Model No. 1438
CAT - Standing, looking back

Designer: Colin Melbourne
Height: 3 ¾", 9.5 cm
Colours: Grey striped - gloss
Issued: 1956-1963

Colourway	U.K. £	Price U.S. $	Can. $
Grey striped	275.00	400.00	600.00

Photograph not
available at press time

Model No. 1541
CAT - Seated

Designer: Mr. Garbet
Height: Unknown
Colours: Dark pewter - Satin gloss
Issued: 1958-1961

Description	U.K. £	U.S. $	Can. $
Satin gloss	Extremely Rare		

Model No. 1542
CAT - Lying, left front paw up

Designer: Mr. Garbet
Height: Unknown
Colours: Dark pewter - Satin gloss
Issued: 1958-1961

Description	U.K. £	U.S. $	Can. $
Satin gloss	Sold February 27th, 1999 Potteries Specialist Auctions, £800.00.		

Model No. 1543
CAT - Seated, left front paw up

Designer: Mr. Garbet
Height: Unknown
Colours: Dark pewter- Satin gloss
Issued: 1958-1961

Description	U.K. £	U.S. $	Can. $
Satin gloss	Sold November 8th, 2001 Potteries Specialist Auctions, £715.00.		

Model No. 1558A
SIAMESE CAT - Lying, facing left
First Version -
Puffed out cheeks, short neck, fleshy body

Designer:	Pal Zalmen
Length:	7 ¼", 18.4 cm
Colours:	Chocolate point - gloss
Issued:	1958-c.1963

Description	U.K. £	U.S. $	Can. $
Gloss	75.00	125.00	175.00

Model No. 1558B
SIAMESE CAT - Lying, facing left
Second Version -
Sleek, tapering face, long neck and body

Designer:	Pal Zalmen
Remodelled:	Albert Hallam
Length:	7 ¼", 18.4 cm
Colours:	1. Copper lustre - gloss 2. Seal point - gloss or matt
Issued:	1. Copper lustre a. Gloss - 1971 (export only) 2. Seal point - gloss a. Beswick - c.1963-1989 b. Doulton (DA124) - 1990-1999 c. Beswick - 1999 to the present 3. Seal point a. Matt - 1984-1989

Description	U.K. £	U.S. $	Can. $
1. Copper lustre	100.00	150.00	225.00
2. Seal point - gloss			
a. Beswick - original	25.00	35.00	50.00
b. Doulton (DA124)	25.00	35.00	50.00
c. Beswick - reissued	23.50	N/A	75.00
3. Seal point - matt	50.00	75.00	100.00

Model No. 1559A
SIAMESE CAT - Lying, facing right
First Version -
Puffed out cheeks, short neck, fleshy body

Designer: Pal Zalmen
Length: 7 ¼", 18.4 cm
Colours: Chocolate point - gloss
Issued: 1958-c.1963

Description	U.K. £	U.S. $	Can. $
Gloss	65.00	100.00	150.00

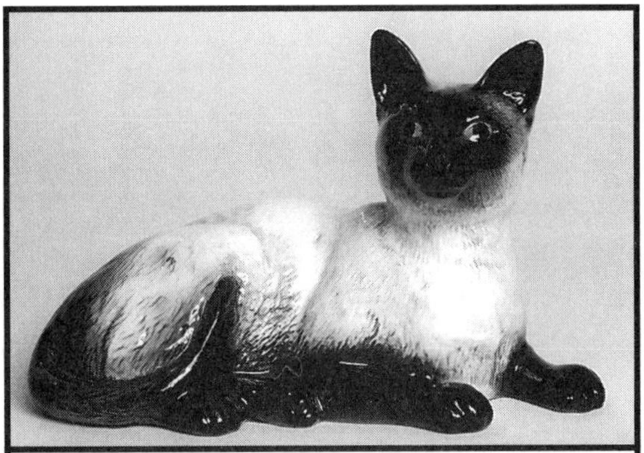

Model No. 1559B
SIAMESE CAT - Lying, facing right
Second Version -
Sleek, tapering face, long neck and body

Designer: Pal Zalmen
Remodelled: Albert Hallam
Length: 7 ¼", 18.4 cm
Colours:
1. Copper lustre - gloss
2. Seal Point - gloss or matt

Issued:
1. Copper lustre
   a. Gloss - 1971 (export only)
2. Seal point - gloss
   a. Beswick - c.1963-1989
   b. Doulton (DA125) - 1990-1999
   c. Beswick - 1999-to the present
3. Seal point
   a. Matt - 1984-1989

Description	U.K. £	U.S. $	Can. $
1. Copper lustre	90.00	125.00	200.00
2. Seal point - gloss			
a. Beswick - original	25.00	35.00	50.00
b. Doulton (DA125)	25.00	35.00	50.00
c. Beswick - reissued	23.50	N/A	N/A
3. Seal point - matt	45.00	65.00	95.00

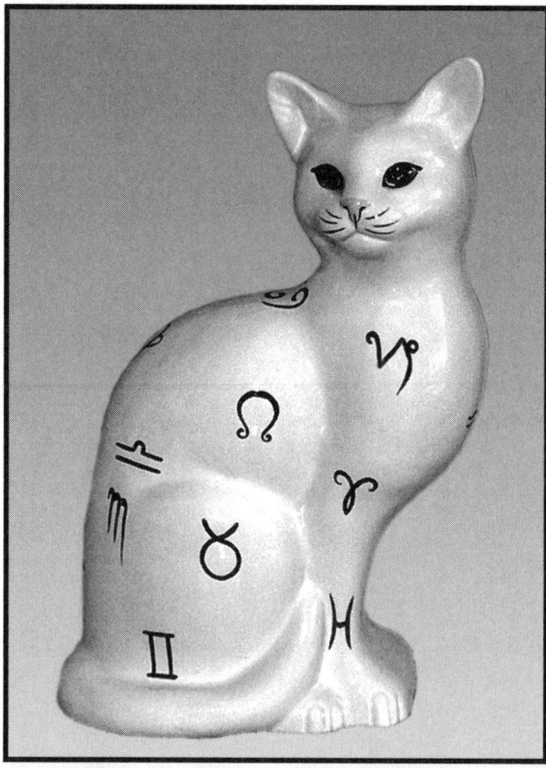

Model No. 1560
ZODIAC CAT - Seated, facing right

Designer: Pal Zalmen
Length: 11", 27.9 cm
Colours: 1. Black with gold details - gloss
2. White with zodiac symbols - gloss
Issued: 1958-1967
Set: Stylized model forming a pair with 1561

Colourway	U.K. £	U.S. $	Can. $
1. Black	250.00	350.00	525.00
2. White	200.00	300.00	450.00

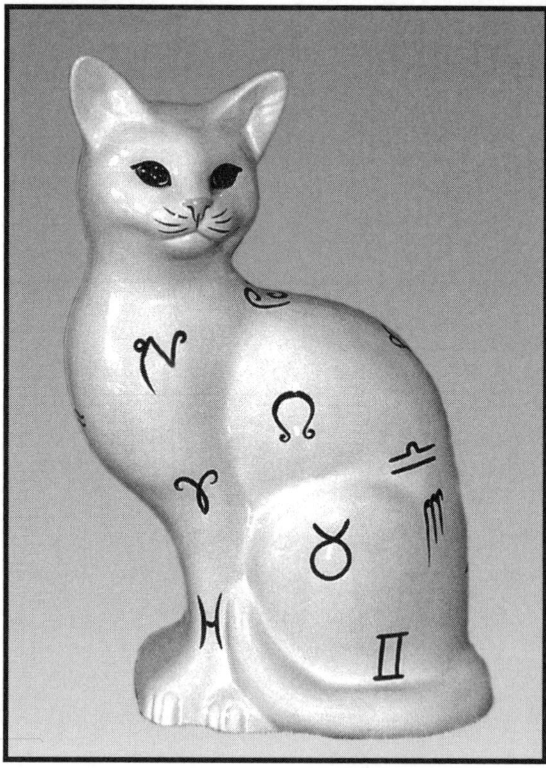

Model No. 1561
ZODIAC CAT - Seated, facing left

Designer: Pal Zalmen
Length: 11", 27.9 cm
Colours: 1. Black with gold details - gloss
2. White with zodiac symbols - gloss
Issued: 1958-1967
Set: Stylized model forming a pair with 1560

Colourway	U.K. £	U.S. $	Can. $
1. Black	250.00	350.00	525.00
2. White	200.00	300.00	450.00

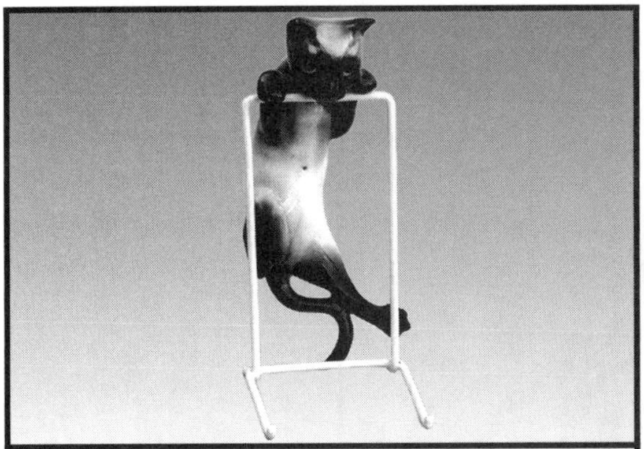

Model No. 1677
SIAMESE CAT - Climbing

Designer: Albert Hallam
Length: 6 ½", 16.5 cm
Colours: Seal point - gloss
Issued: 1960-1997

Description	U.K. £	U.S. $	Can. $
Gloss	20.00	30.00	45.00

Model No. 1803
CAT - Seated, looking up

Designer: Albert Hallam
Height: 1 ¼", 3.2 cm
Colours: Ginger striped - gloss
Issued: 1962-1971
Series: Bedtime Chorus

Description	U.K. £	U.S. $	Can. $
Gloss	50.00	75.00	115.00

Photograph not available at press time

Model No. 1857
SIAMESE CAT - Climbing

Designer: Albert Hallam
Length: 5 ½", 14.0 cm
Colours: Seal point - gloss
Issued: 1962-Unknown

Description	U.K. £	U.S. $	Can. $
Gloss		Extremely Rare	

Note: Similar in shape to model no. 1677.

Model No. 1867
PERSIAN CAT - Seated, looking up

Designer: Albert Hallam
Height: 8 ½", 21.6 cm

Colourway	Finish	Intro.	Disc.	U.K. £	Price U.S. $	Can. $
1. Black	Matt	1984	1989	60.00	90.00	135.00
2. British Blue (lead grey)	Gloss	1964	1966	225.00	325.00	500.00
3. Ginger	Matt	1984	1989	70.00	100.00	150.00
4. Ginger (dark)	Gloss	1963	1970	70.00	100.00	150.00
5. Ginger striped						
a. Beswick	Gloss	1965	1989	125.00	175.00	275.00
b. Doulton (DA126)	Gloss	1990	1996	55.00	80.00	120.00
6. Ginger Swiss roll	Gloss	1964	1966	150.00	225.00	325.00
7. Grey (shaded)						
a. Beswick	Gloss	1963	1989	55.00	80.00	120.00
b. Doulton (DA126)	Gloss	1990	1999	55.00	80.00	120.00
8. Grey	Matt	1984	1989	70.00	100.00	150.00
9. Grey striped	Gloss	1963	1973	150.00	225.00	325.00
10. Grey Swiss roll	Gloss	1964	1966	175.00	250.00	375.00
11. White (large eyes)						
a. Beswick	Gloss	1963	1989	55.00	80.00	120.00
b. Doulton (DA126)	Gloss	1990	1996	55.00	80.00	120.00
12. White	Matt	1984	1989	55.00	80.00	120.00

Model No. 1876
PERSIAN CAT - Lying

Designer: Albert Hallam
Height: 3 ½" x 6 ½", 8.0 x 6.5 cm

Colourway	Finish	Intro.	Disc.	Price U.K. £	Price U.S. $	Price Can. $
1. British Blue (lead grey)	Gloss	1964	1966	235.00	325.00	475.00
2. Ginger (dark)	Gloss	1963	1970	135.00	175.00	250.00
3. Ginger striped	Gloss	1965	1971	145.00	200.00	300.00
4. Ginger Swiss roll	Gloss	1964	1966	210.00	300.00	450.00
5. Grey (shaded)	Gloss	1963	1971	90.00	125.00	175.00
6. Grey striped	Gloss	1963	1971	150.00	200.00	300.00
7. Grey Swiss roll	Gloss	1964	1966	260.00	375.00	525.00
8. White (large eyes)	Gloss	1963	1971	90.00	125.00	175.00

Model No. 1877
CAT - Seated, scratching ear

Designer: Albert Hallam
Height: 6 ½", 16.5 cm
Issued: British Blue (lead grey), gloss – 1964-1966
Ginger (dark), gloss –1963-1970
Ginger striped, gloss –1965-1971
Ginger Swiss roll, gloss – 1964-1966
Grey (shaded), gloss – 1963-1971
Grey striped, gloss – 1963-1971
Grey Swiss roll, gloss – 1964-1966
White (large eyes), gloss – 1963-1971

Colourway	U.K. £	U.S. $	Can. $
1. British Blue (lead grey)	325.00	450.00	675.00
2. Ginger (dark)	150.00	200.00	300.00
3. Ginger striped	225.00	325.00	500.00
4. Ginger Swiss roll	325.00	450.00	675.00
5. Grey (shaded)	150.00	200.00	300.00
6. Grey striped	275.00	375.00	575.00
7. Grey Swiss roll	375.00	525.00	775.00
8. White (large eyes)	100.00	150.00	225.00

Model No. 1880
PERSIAN CAT - Seated, looking up

Designer: Albert Hallam
Height: 5 ¼", 13.3 cm
Issued:
1. British Blue (lead grey), gloss – 1964-1966
2. Ginger (dark), gloss –1963-1970
3. Ginger striped, gloss – 1965-1971
4. Ginger Swiss roll, gloss –1964-1966
5. Grey (shaded), gloss – 1963-1971
6. Grey striped, gloss –1963-1971
7. Grey Swiss roll, gloss –1964-1966
8. White (large eyes), gloss –1963-1971

Colourway	U.K. £	U.S. $	Can. $
1. British Blue (lead grey)	200.00	300.00	450.00
2. Ginger (dark)	150.00	200.00	300.00
3. Ginger striped	150.00	200.00	300.00
4. Ginger Swiss roll	175.00	250.00	375.00
5. Grey (shaded)	125.00	175.00	275.00
6. Grey striped	150.00	200.00	300.00
7. Grey Swiss roll	200.00	200.00	300.00
8. White (large eyes)	100.00	150.00	225.00

Model No. 1882
SIAMESE CAT - Seated, head forward

Designer: Albert Hallam
Height: 9 ½", 24.0 cm
Issued:
1. Black, gloss – 1986-1989
2. Black, matt – 1986-1989
3. Copper lustre, gloss – 1971-1971
4. Seal point, gloss
   a. Beswick – 1963-1989
   b. Doulton (DA127) – 1990-1999
5. Seal point, matt – 1984-1989

Series: Fireside Model

Colourway	U.K. £	U.S. $	Can. $
1. Black, gloss	75.00	100.00	150.00
2. Black, matt	85.00	125.00	175.00
3. Copper lustre, gloss	125.00	175.00	250.00
4. Seal point, gloss			
a. Beswick	75.00	100.00	150.00
b. Doulton (DA127)	55.00	80.00	120.00
5. Seal point, matt	85.00	125.00	175.00

Note: Copper lustre issued for export only.

Model No. 1883
PERSIAN CAT - On hind legs

Designer: Albert Hallam
Height: 6", 15.0 cm
Issued:
1. British Blue (lead grey), gloss – 1964-1966
2. Ginger (dark), gloss –1963-1970
3. Ginger striped, gloss – 1965-1971
4. Ginger Swiss roll, gloss – 1964-1966
5. Grey (shaded), gloss – 1963-1971
6. Grey striped, gloss – 1963-1971
7. Grey Swiss roll, gloss – 1964-1966
8. White (large eyes), gloss – 1963-1971

Colourway	U.K. £	U.S. $	Can. $
1. British Blue (lead grey)	250.00	350.00	525.00
2. Ginger (dark)	150.00	225.00	350.00
3. Ginger striped	175.00	250.00	375.00
4. Ginger Swiss roll	225.00	325.00	500.00
5. Grey (shaded)	200.00	300.00	450.00
6. Grey striped	175.00	250.00	375.00
7. Grey Swiss roll	275.00	400.00	600.00
8. White (large eyes)	125.00	175.00	250.00

Model No. 1885
PERSIAN KITTEN - Standing

Designer: Albert Hallam
Height: 4 ¾", 12.1 cm

Colourway	Finish	Intro.	Disc.	Price U.K. £	Price U.S. $	Price Can. $
1. British Blue (lead grey)	Gloss	1964	1966	225.00	325.00	500.00
2. Ginger (dark)	Gloss	1963	1970	95.00	125.00	175.00
3. Ginger striped	Gloss	1965	1973	125.00	175.00	250.00
4. Ginger Swiss roll	Gloss	1964	1966	175.00	250.00	375.00
5. Grey (shaded)	Gloss	1963	1973	95.00	125.00	175.00
6. Grey striped	Gloss	1963	1973	125.00	175.00	250.00
7. Grey Swiss roll	Gloss	1964	1966	225.00	325.00	500.00
8. White (large eyes)	Gloss	1963	1973	95.00	125.00	175.00

Model No 1886
PERSIAN KITTEN - Seated, looking up

Designer: Albert Hallam
Height: 4", 10.1 cm

Colourway	Finish	Intro.	Disc.	Price U.K. £	Price U.S. $	Price Can. $
1. Black	Matt	1984	1989	40.00	55.00	80.00
2. British Blue (lead grey)	Gloss	1964	1966	100.00	150.00	225.00
3. Ginger	Matt	1984	1989	35.00	50.00	75.00
4. Ginger (dark)	Gloss	1963	1970	35.00	50.00	75.00
5. Ginger striped						
a. Beswick	Gloss	1965	1989	50.00	70.00	100.00
b. Doulton (DA128)	Gloss	1990	1999	15.00	25.00	35.00
6. Ginger Swiss roll	Gloss	1964	1966	150.00	200.00	300.00
7. Grey						
a. Beswick	Gloss	1965	1989	15.00	25.00	35.00
b. Doulton (DA128)	Gloss	1990	1999	15.00	25.00	35.00
c. Beswick	Gloss	1999	Current	14.50	N/A	N/A
8. Grey	Matt	1984	1989	50.00	70.00	110.00
9. Grey striped	Gloss	1962	1973	60.00	85.00	125.00
10. Grey Swiss roll	Gloss	1964	1966	125.00	175.00	250.00
11. White						
a. Beswick	Gloss	1963	1989	15.00	25.00	35.00
b. Doulton (DA128)	Gloss	1990	1999	15.00	25.00	35.00
c. Beswick	Gloss	1999	Current	14.50	N/A	N/A
12. White	Matt	1984	1989	25.00	40.00	60.00

Model No. 1887
SIAMESE CAT - Seated, head turned back

Designer: Albert Hallam
Height: 4", 10.1 cm
Issued: 1. Copper lustre, gloss – 1971-1971
2. Seal point
a. Beswick, gloss – 1971-1989
b. Doulton (DA129), gloss, – 1990-1999
c. Beswick, gloss – 1999 to the present
3. Seal point, matt – 1984-1989

Colourway	U.K. £	U.S. $	Can. $
1. Copper lustre	85.00	125.00	175.00
2. Seal point			
a. Beswick - original	15.00	25.00	35.00
b. Doulton (DA129)	15.00	25.00	35.00
c. Beswick - reissued	14.50	N/A	N/A
3. Seal point	35.00	50.00	75.00

Note: Copper lustre produced for export only.

Model No. 1897
SIAMESE CAT - Standing

Designer: Albert Hallam
Height: 6 ½", 16.5 cm
Series: Fireside Model
Issued: 1. Black, gloss
a. Beswick – 1987-1989
b. Doulton (DA131) - 1990-1994
2. Black, matt – 1987-1989
3. Copper lustre, gloss – 1971-1971
4. Seal point, gloss
a. Beswick – 1963-1980
b. Doulton (DA130) – 1990-1997
5. Seal point, matt – 1984-1989

Colourway	U.K. £	U.S. $	Can. $
1. Black, gloss			
a. Beswick	60.00	85.00	125.00
b. Doulton (DA131)	60.00	85.00	125.00
2. Black, matt	65.00	90.00	135.00
3. Copper lustre, gloss	150.00	200.00	300.00
4. Seal point, gloss			
a. Beswick	30.00	45.00	65.00
b. Doulton (DA131)	30.00	45.00	65.00
5. Seal point, matt	45.00	65.00	100.00

Note: 1. In 1987 introduced as "Lucky Black Cat."
2. Copper lustre produced for export only.

Model No. 1898
PERSIAN CAT - Standing, tail erect

Designer: Albert Hallam
Height: 5", 12.7 cm

Colourway	Finish	Intro.	Disc.	Price U.K. £	Price U.S. $	Price Can. $
1. Black	Matt	1984	1989	50.00	75.00	115.00
2. British Blue (lead grey)	Gloss	1964	1966	175.00	250.00	375.00
3. Ginger	Matt	1984	1989	55.00	80.00	120.00
4. Ginger striped						
a. Beswick	Gloss	1965	1989	60.00	85.00	130.00
b. Doulton (DA132)	Gloss	1990	1994	30.00	45.00	65.00
5. Ginger Swiss roll	Gloss	1964	1966	175.00	250.00	375.00
6. Grey	Matt	1984	1989	30.00	45.00	65.00
7. Grey (shaded)						
a. Beswick	Gloss	1963	1989	30.00	45.00	65.00
b. Doulton (DA132)	Gloss	1990	1994	30.00	45.00	65.00
8. Grey Swiss roll	Gloss	1964	1966	200.00	300.00	450.00
9. White (large eyes)						
a. Beswick	Gloss	1963	1989	35.00	50.00	75.00
b. Doulton (DA132)	Gloss	1990	1994	30.00	45.00	65.00
10. White	Matt	1984	1989	35.00	50.00	75.00

Model No. 2100
CAT WITH MOUSE

Designer: Albert Hallam
Height: 3", 7.6 cm
Colours: Brown cat, white mouse - gloss
Issued: 1967-1973
Series: Fun Models

Description	U.K. £	U.S. $	Can. $
Gloss	75.00	110.00	165.00

Model No. 2101
CAT - Laughing

Designer: Albert Hallam
Height: 3", 7.6 cm
Colours: Grey - gloss
Issued: 1967-1973
Series: Fun Models

Description	U.K. £	U.S. $	Can. $
Gloss	65.00	90.00	135.00

Note: A white model is known to exist.

Model No. 2139
SIAMESE CAT - Seated, head up

Designer: Mr. Garbet
Height: 13 ¾", 34.9 cm
Issued: 1. Copper lustre - 1971 (export only)
2a. Seal point, gloss - Beswick – 1967-1989
2b. Seal point, gloss - Doulton - 1989-1996
Series: Fireside Models

Colourway	U.K. £	U.S. $	Can. $
1. Copper lustre	125.00	175.00	275.00
2. Seal point, gloss			
a. Beswick	90.00	125.00	175.00
b. Doulton (DA83)	90.00	125.00	175.00

Model No. 2233
CAT AND DOG WALL PLAQUE
Cat left, dog right

Designer: Graham Tongue
Height: 9" x 6 ¼", 23 x 15.9 cm (Concave)
Colours: Unknown - gloss
Issued: 1968-Unknown
Series: Wall Plaques

Description	U.K.£	U.S.$	Can.$
Gloss	65.00	90.00	135.00

Model No. 2236
CAT WALL PLAQUE

Designer: Graham Tongue
Height: 9" x 6 ¼", 23 x 15.9 cm (Concave)
Colours: Ginger cat with yellow eyes on dark pewter background - gloss
Issued: 1968-Unknown
Series: Wall Plaques

Description	U.K.£	U.S.$	Can.$
Gloss	65.00	90.00	135.00

Photograph not available.
Model number 2310 possibly not put into production.

Model No. 2301
CAT - Climbing

Designer: Albert Hallam
Height: 4 ½", 11.9 cm
Colours: Unknown
Issued: 1969-Unknown

Description	U.K. £	U.S. $	Can. $
Cat - Climbing	Extremely Rare		

Note: Similar to model no. 1677.

Photograph not available.
Model number 2311 possibly not put into production.

Model No. 2311
SIAMESE CAT

Designer: Graham Tongue
Length: 1 ½", 3.8 cm
Colours: Unknown
Issued: 1970-Unknown

Description	U.K. £	U.S. $	Can. $
Siamese Cat	Extremely Rare		

Note: Similar to model no. 2139.

Model No. 2480
CHESHIRE CAT

Designer: Graham Tongue
Height: 1 ½", 3.8 cm
Colours: Tabby - gloss
Issued: 1973-1982
Series: Alice in Wonderland

Description	U.K. £	U.S. $	Can. $
Gloss	375.00	525.00	775.00

Note: For the rest of the pieces in the Alice in Wonderland series see *The Charlton Standard Catalogue of Royal Doulton Beswick Storybook Figurines.*

Model No. K194
CAT - Seated

Designer: Marilyn Alcock
Height: 3 ¾", 9.5 cm
Colour: Black and white - gloss
Issued: a. Doulton (DA194) – 1999-1999
b. Beswick – 1999 to the present

Description	U.K. £	U.S. $	Can. $
a. Doulton (DA194)	20.00	30.00	45.00
b. Beswick	19.50	N/A	60.00

Model No. K229
QUIET PLEASE

Designer: Warren Platt
Height: 1 ¾", 4.4 cm
Colour: Grey and white kittens - gloss
Issued: a. Doulton (DA229) – 1995-1999
b. Beswick – 1999 to the present

Description	U.K. £	U.S. $	Can. $
a. Doulton (DA229)	20.00	30.00	45.00
b. Beswick	19.50	N/A	65.00

Chapter Four
DOGS

Beswick produced mantelpiece dogs of the old Staffordshire type from about 1898. In 1933, when the shape book was created — in which each model was illustrated by a sketch with details such as height, modeller and dates — these dogs, in various sizes, were the initial numbers. During the 1930s dogs of the novelty type were produced with several unrealistic-looking decorations, including blue and green gloss and mottled blue in a satin-type finish. In fact customers could order novelties in any decoration to match the domestic ware being made at the time. Then in 1941, Arthur Gredington, following his success with realistic models of horses, created the first of the champion dogs, the Dalmatian "Arnoldene," shape number 961. Seven other breeds were also produced in 1941, and four more the following year. These figures were all modelled in a show stance from champions of their particular breed, and almost all of them were modelled by Arthur Gredington.

Over the years most of the popular breeds joined the Beswick "kennel," and many were also produced in a smaller size. Action poses were added to the collection, such as the 1507 Spaniel running. This type of model was reintroduced with the Good Companions series in 1987, the same time several more medium-sized dogs were issued. These and the Good Companions, had a short production run with the Beswick backstamp (some for less than a year), as from August 1989 they were issued with Royal Doulton backstamps and given DA numbers. By 1994 all the Beswick medium-sized dogs had been withdrawn, leaving only the small dogs collection with Beswick backstamps. However, in October 1999 Royal Doulton announced that animal sculptures carrying their backstamp (except limited editions) would revert to the Beswick backstamp.

Many of the dogs share with the horses the distinction of being in continual production for four or five decades. During this time there has been a deterioration in the moulds and decorating processes; therefore, the quality of the models is variable. It is well worth looking out for the older figures that exhibit more mould detail and toning and shading in colour.

INDEX BY MODEL NUMBER

MODELS TRANSFERRED TO *THE CHARLTON STANDARD CATALOGUE OF BESWICK COLLECTIBLES*

Model No.	Description
87	Dog Standing in Armchair - Bookend
88	Scottie - Ashtray
624	Dog - Toothbrush Holder
810	Dog with Sailor's Hat - Ashtray
811	Dog Playing Accordian
812	Dog Asleep on Drum
831	Dog with Glasses Reading a Book
869	Five Puppy Ashtray
916	Three Puppy Ashtray
1918	Ashtray with Dog
1932	Dachshund - Ashtray
2130	Dog Praying

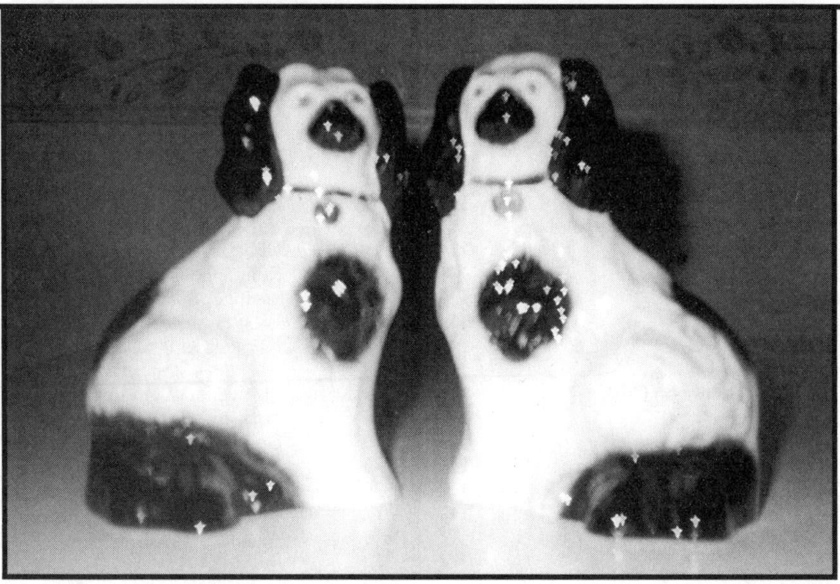

Model Nos. 1 to 6 **OLD STAFFORDSHIRE DOGS**

Designer: Unknown
Colours: Black and white
Issued: 1933-1955
Series: Mantelpiece Dogs

Model No.	1	2	3	4	5	6
Height:	13 ¾", 34.9 cm	11 ½", 29.2 cm	10", 25.4 cm	9", 22.9 cm	7 ½", 19.1 cm	5 ½", 14.0 cm

Price	Model No. 1	Model No. 2	Model No. 3	Model No. 4	Model No. 5	Model No. 6
U.K. £	100.00	85.00	75.00	65.00	55.00	45.00
U.S. $	150.00	120.00	100.00	90.00	80.00	65.00
Can. $	225.00	175.00	150.00	135.00	120.00	100.00

Note: Prices above are for singles, they are available in pairs, left and right facing.

Model No. 171
DOG - Begging

Designer:	Unknown
Height:	4 ¾", 12.1 cm
Colours:	White and tan - gloss
Issued:	1934-by 1954

Description	U.K. £	U.S. $	Can. $
Gloss	60.00	85.00	125.00

Model No. 286
DOG - Seated

Designer:	Mr. Watkin
Height:	6 ¼", 15.9 cm
Colours:	See below
Issued:	1. Blue, gloss – 1934-1967
	3. White, gloss – 1934-Unknown
	2. White and tan, gloss –1934-by 1954

Colourway	U.K. £	U.S. $	Can. $
1. Blue	70.00	100.00	150.00
2. White	70.00	100.00	150.00
3. White/tan	50.00	70.00	100.00

Model No. 301
SEALYHAM PLAQUE - Bow on right

Designer:	Unknown
Height:	7 ½", 19.1 cm
Colours:	Cream; blue bow - satin finish
Issued:	1936-1940
Series:	Wall Plaques

Description	U.K. £	U.S. $	Can. $
Satin finish	150.00	200.00	300.00

Model No. 302
SEALYHAM - Standing

Designer:	Mr. Watkin
Height:	6", 15.0 cm
Colours:	1. Blue - gloss
	2. White with dark ears - gloss
Issued:	1. 1936-1967
	2. 1936-by 1964

Colourway	U.K. £	U.S. $	Can. $
1. Blue	100.00	150.00	225.00
2. White/dark ears	80.00	125.00	175.00

Model No. 307
SEALYHAM PLAQUE

Designer:	Mr. Watkin
Height:	7", 17.8 cm
Colours:	Cream - satin finish
Issued:	1935-1940
Series:	Wall Plaques

Description	U.K. £	U.S. $	Can. $
Satin finish	150.00	200.00	300.00

Model No. 308
PUPPY - Seated

Designer:	Mr. Watkin
Height:	6 ¼", 15.9 cm
Colours:	1. Blue - gloss
	2. White with brown ears - gloss
Issued:	1. 1935-1967
	2. 1935-by 1954

Colourway	U.K. £	U.S. $	Can. $
1. Blue	75.00	100.00	150.00
2. White/brown	60.00	85.00	125.00

Note: Also issued as a money-box.

Model No. 324
Character Dog - Begging

Designer:	Miss Greaves
Height:	7", 17.8 cm
Colours:	1. Blue - gloss
	2. Cream - gloss
Issued:	1. 1936-by 1954
	2. 1936-by 1954
Series:	Fun Models

Colourway	U.K. £	U.S. $	Can. $
1. Blue	100.00	150.00	225.00
2. Cream	75.00	100.00	150.00

Model No. 361
DACHSHUND - Standing

Designer:	Mr. Watkin
Height:	5 ½", 14.0 cm
Issued:	1. Black/tan - gloss; 1936-1983
	2. Blue - gloss; 1936-by 1954
	3. Tan - gloss; 1936-1983

Colourway	U.K. £	U.S. $	Can. $
1. Black/tan	40.00	60.00	90.00
2. Blue	100.00	150.00	225.00
3. Tan	40.00	60.00	90.00

Model No. 373
SEALYHAM PLAQUE

Designer:	Unknown
Height:	7", 17.8 cm
Colours:	White dog with blue bow - satin matt
Issued:	1936-1940
Series:	Wall Plaques

Colourway	U.K. £	U.S. $	Can. $
White dog	150.00	200.00	300.00

Model No. 453
OLD ENGLISH SHEEPDOG - Seated

Designer:	Unknown
Height:	8 ½", 21.6 cm
Colours:	1. Blue - gloss
	2. Grey and white - gloss
Issued:	1. 1936-by 1954
	2. 1936-1973

Colourway	U.K. £	U.S. $	Can. $
1. Blue	125.00	175.00	275.00
2. Grey/white	90.00	125.00	200.00

Model No. 454
LOLLOPY DOG - Seated Puppy

Designer:	Miss Greaves
Height:	4 ¼", 10.8 cm
Issued:	1. Blue, gloss – 1936-1969
	2. Various, satin matt – 1936-by 1954
	3. White, gloss – 1936-1969
	4. White, matt – 1936-1969

Colourway	U.K. £	U.S. $	Can. $
1. Blue, gloss	30.00	45.00	70.00
2. Various, satin matt	25.00	35.00	55.00
3. White, gloss	25.00	35.00	55.00
4. White, matt	30.00	45.00	70.00

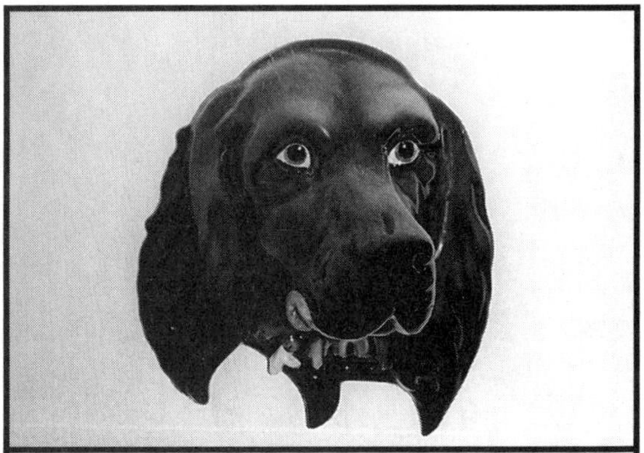

Model No. 668
DOG PLAQUE

Designer:	Mr. Symcox
Height:	11", 27.9 cm
Colours:	Deep red brown - gloss
Issued:	1938-1960
Series:	Wall Plaques

Description	U.K. £	U.S. $	Can. $
Gloss	100.00	150.00	225.00

Model No. 761
DOG WITH TOOTHACHE

Designer: Mr. Watkin
Height: 4 ¼", 10.8 cm
Colours: 1. White dog with red kerchief - gloss
2. White dog with green kerchief - gloss
Issued: 1939-1971
Series: Fun Models

Colourway	U.K. £	U.S. $	Can. $
1. Red kerchief	60.00	85.00	125.00
2. Green kerchief	75.00	100.00	150.00

Model No. 804
DOG WITH LADYBIRD ON NOSE

Designer: Mr. Watkin
Height: 4", 10.1 cm
Colours: White with red ladybird - gloss
Issued: 1940-1969
Series: Fun Models

Description	U.K. £	U.S. $	Can. $
Gloss	45.00	65.00	95.00

Model No. 805
DOG WITH LADYBIRD ON TAIL

Designer: Mr. Watkin
Height: 1. Large - 3 ¾", 9.5 cm
2. Small - 2 ½", 6.4 cm
Colours: White dog with red ladybird - gloss
Issued: 1940-1969
Series: Fun Models

Description	U.K. £	U.S. $	Can. $
1. Large	35.00	50.00	75.00
2. Small	25.00	35.00	60.00

Model No. 813
DOG WITH LADYBIRD ON NOSE

Designer: Mr. Watkin
Height: 4", 10.1 cm
Colours: White dog, red ladybird - gloss
Issued: 1940-1970
Series: Fun Models

Description	U.K. £	U.S. $	Can. $
Gloss	45.00	65.00	100.00

Model No. 907
DOG WITH LADYBIRD ON TAIL

Designer: Mr. Watkin
Height: 3 ¾", 9.5 cm
Colours: White dog, red ladybird - gloss
Issued: 1941-1971
Series: Fun Models

Description	U.K. £	U.S. $	Can. $
Gloss	35.00	50.00	75.00

Model No. 917
THREE PUPPIES

Designer: Mr. Watkin
Height: 2", 5.0 cm
Colours: Brown puppies - gloss
Issued: 1941-1965

Description	U.K. £	U.S. $	Can. $
Gloss	20.00	35.00	50.00

Note: The three dogs are same as used in model no. 916.

Model No. 941
FOXHOUND
First Version - Thick legs and tail

Designer: Mr. Watkin
Height: 2 ¾", 7.0 cm
Colours: White, tan and black - gloss
Issued: 1941-1969
Varieties: 2262

Description	U.K. £	U.S. $	Can. $
Gloss	35.00	50.00	75.00

Note: Remodelled in 1969 see also no. 2263.

Model No. 942
FOXHOUND
First Version - Thick legs and tail

Designer: Mr. Watkin
Height: 2 ¾", 7.0 cm
Colours: White, tan and black - gloss
Issued: 1941-1969
Varieties: 2263

Description	U.K. £	U.S. $	Can. $
Gloss	35.00	50.00	75.00

Note: Remodelled in 1969 see also no. 2262.

Model No. 943
FOXHOUND
First Version - Thick legs and tail

Designer: Mr. Watkin
Height: 2 ¾", 7.0 cm
Colours: White, tan and black - gloss
Issued: 1941-1969
Varieties: 2265

Description	U.K. £	U.S. $	Can. $
Gloss	35.00	50.00	75.00

Note: Remodelled in 1969 see also no. 2265.

Model No. 944
FOXHOUND
First Version - Thick legs and tail

Designer: Mr. Watkin
Height: 2 ¾", 7.0 cm
Colours: White, tan and black - gloss
Issued: 1941-1969
Varieties: 2264

Description	U.K. £	U.S. $	Can. $
Gloss	35.00	50.00	75.00

Note: Remodelled in 1969 see also no. 2264.

Model No. 961
DALMATION "ARNOLDENE" - Large

Designer: Arthur Gredington
Height: 5 ¾", 14.6 cm
Colours: White with black spot - gloss; matt
Issued: 1. Gloss - 1941-1994
2. Matt - 1970-1994

Description	U.K. £	U.S. $	Can. $
1. Gloss	40.00	60.00	90.00
2. Matt	40.00	60.00	90.00

Note: For the small size see no. 1763.

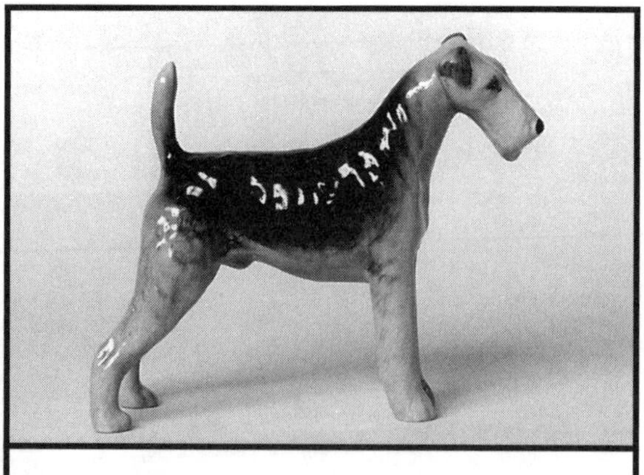

Model No. 962
AIREDALE TERRIER "CAST IRON MONARCH"

Designer: Arthur Gredington
Height: 5 ½", 14.0 cm
Colours: Black and tan - gloss; matt
Issued: 1. Gloss - 1941-1989
2. Matt - 1987-1989

Description	U.K. £	U.S. $	Can. $
1. Gloss	40.00	60.00	90.00
2. Matt	40.00	60.00	90.00

Model No. 963
WIRED-HAIRED TERRIER
"TALAVERA ROMULUS"

Designer: Arthur Gredington
Height: 5 ¾", 14.6 cm
Colours: White, light sandy brown and black - gloss
Issued: 1941-1984

Description	U.K. £	U.S. $	Can. $
Gloss	125.00	175.00	275.00

Model No. 964
SMOOTH-HAIRED TERRIER
"ENDON BLACK ROD"

Designer: Arthur Gredington
Height: 5 ½", 14.0 cm
Colours: White with black patches - gloss
Issued: 1941-1973

Description	U.K. £	U.S. $	Can. $
Gloss	350.00	500.00	750.00

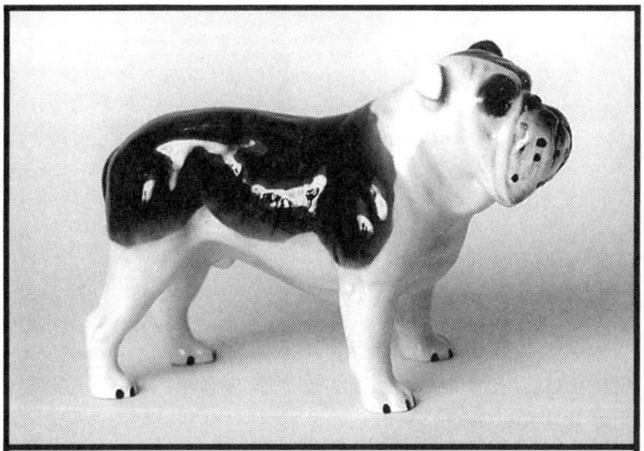

Model No. 965
BULLDOG "BASFORD BRITISH MASCOT" - Large

Designer: Arthur Gredington
Height: 5 ½", 14.0 cm
Colours: Brindle, tan and white - gloss; matt
Issued: 1. Gloss - 1941-1990
2. Matt - 1987-1989

Description	U.K. £	U.S. $	Can. $
1. Gloss	90.00	125.00	175.00
2. Matt	90.00	125.00	175.00

Note: For small size see no. 1731.

Model No. 966
IRISH SETTER "SUGAR OF WENDOVER"

Designer: Arthur Gredington
Height: 5 ¾", 14.6 cm
Colours: Red brown - gloss; matt
Issued: 1. Gloss - 1941-1989
2. Matt - 1987-1989

Description	U.K. £	U.S. $	Can. $
1. Gloss	60.00	85.00	125.00
2. Matt	50.00	75.00	110.00

Model No. 967
COCKER SPANIEL "HORSESHOE PRIMULA"

Designer: Arthur Gredington
Height: 5 ¾", 14.6 cm
Issued:
1. Black, gloss – 1965-1982
2. Black and white, gloss – 1970-1928
3. Golden brown, gloss – 1941-1929
3. Golden brown, gloss – 1941-1994
4. Golden brown, matt – 1987-1994
5. Liver and white, gloss – 1970-1994
6. Liver and white, matt – 1987-1994

Colourway	U.K. £	U.S. $	Can. $
1. Black, gloss	60.00	85.00	125.00
2. Black and white, gloss	60.00	85.00	125.00
3. Golden brown, gloss	40.00	60.00	90.00
4. Golden brown, matt	30.00	45.00	70.00
5. Liver and white, gloss	65.00	90.00	135.00
6. Liver and white, matt	65.00	90.00	135.00

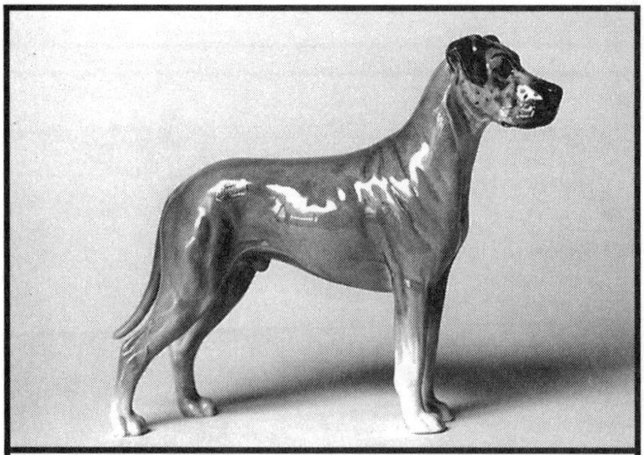

Model No. 968
GREAT DANE "RULER OF OUBOURGH"

Designer: Arthur Gredington
Height: 7", 17.8 cm
Colours: Light sandy brown - gloss; matt
Issued:
1. Gloss - 1941-1994
2. Matt - 1987-1994

Description	U.K. £	U.S. $	Can. $
1. Gloss	50.00	70.00	100.00
2. Matt	45.00	65.00	95.00

Model No. 969
ALSATIAN "ULRICA OF BRITTAS" - Large

Designer: Arthur Gredington
Height: 5 ¾", 14.6 cm
Colours: Black and light brown - gloss; matt
Issued:
1. 1942-1994
2. 1970-1994

Description	U.K. £	U.S. $	Can. $
1. Gloss	45.00	65.00	100.00
2. Matt	40.00	55.00	85.00

Note: For small size see no. 1762.

Model No. 970
BULL TERRIER "ROMANY RHINESTONE" - Large

Designer: Arthur Gredington
Height: 6 ½", 16.5 cm
Colours: 1. Brindle and white - gloss
2. White - gloss; matt
Issued: 1. Gloss - 1942-1975
2a. Gloss - 1942-1994
2b. Matt - 1987-1994

Colourway	U.K. £	U.S. $	Can. $
1. Brindle/white	175.00	250.00	375.00
2a. White - gloss	45.00	65.00	100.00
2b. White - matt	45.00	65.00	100.00

Model No. 971
SEALYHAM "FORESTEDGE FOXGLOVE"

Designer: Arthur Gredington
Height: 4 ¼", 10.8 cm
Colours: White - gloss
Issued: 1942-1967

Description	U.K. £	U.S. $	Can. $
Gloss	150.00	200.00	300.00

Model No. 972
GREYHOUND "JOVIAL ROGER"

Designer: Arthur Gredington
Height: 6", 15.0 cm
Colours: Light sandy brown - gloss; matt
Issued: 1. Gloss - 1942-1990
2. Matt - 1970-1990

Description	U.K. £	U.S. $	Can. $
1. Gloss	95.00	135.00	200.00
2. Matt	85.00	125.00	175.00

Model No. 973
ENGLISH SETTER "BAYLDONE BARONET"

Designer: Arthur Gredington
Height: 5 ½", 14.0 cm
Colours: Speckled grey - gloss; matt
Issued: 1. Gloss - 1942-1989
2. Matt - 1987-1989

Description	U.K. £	U.S. $	Can. $
1. Gloss	45.00	65.00	95.00
2. Matt	40.00	55.00	85.00

Model No. 1002
PUPPIT DOG

Designer: Arthur Gredington
Height: 4 ¾", 12.1 cm
Colours: White with black markings - gloss
Issued: 1944-1969
Series: Fun Models

Description	U.K. £	U.S. $	Can. $
Gloss	60.00	85.00	125.00

Model No. 1054
SPANIEL HOLDING "MY PLATE"

Designer: Arthur Gredington
Height: 4 ¼", 12.1 cm
Colours: White and brown - gloss
Issued: 1947-1967
Series: Fun Models

Description	U.K. £	U.S. $	Can. $
Gloss	70.00	100.00	150.00

Model No. 1055A
CAIRN TERRIER
First Version - With ball on left or right leg

Designer: Arthur Gredington
Height: 4", 10.1 cm
Colours: Beige with brown "stripes," red ball - gloss
Issued: 1946-1969

Description	U.K. £	U.S. $	Can. $
1. Ball on left leg	75.00	100.00	150.00
2. Ball on right leg	75.00	100.00	150.00

Model No. 1055B
CAIRN TERRIER
Second Version - Without ball

Designer: Arthur Gredington
Height: 4", 10.1 cm
Colours: Beige with brown "stripes" - gloss
Issued: 1946-1969

Description	U.K. £	U.S. $	Can. $
Without ball	85.00	125.00	175.00

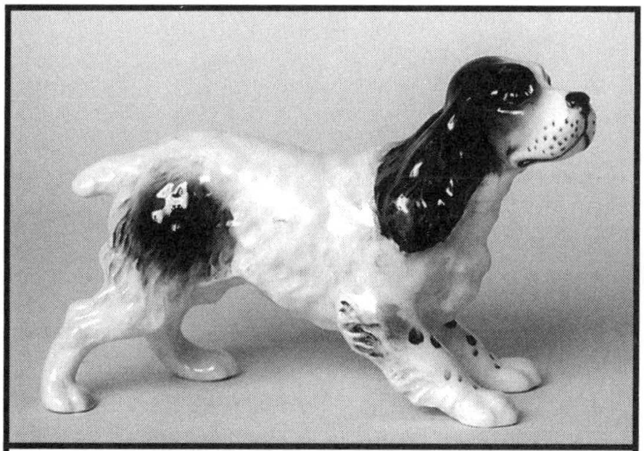

Model No. 1057
SPANIEL - Running

Designer: Arthur Gredington
Height: 3 ¾", 9.5 cm
Colours: 1. Blue, gloss
2. White with golden tan patches - gloss
Issued: 1. 1947-1954
2. 1946-1967

Description	U.K. £	U.S. $	Can. $
1. Blue		Rare	
2. White/tan	50.00	70.00	100.00

Model No. 1058
DOG WITH COLLAR "SCAMP"

Designer: Arthur Gredington
Height: 4 ½", 11.9 cm
Colours: Tan - gloss
Issued: 1948-1973
Seies: Fun Models

Description	U.K. £	U.S. $	Can. $
Gloss	50.00	70.00	100.00

Model No. 1059
PEKINESE - Begging

Designer: Arthur Gredington
Height: 4 ¼", 10.8 cm
Colours: Golden tan - gloss
Issued: 1946-1967

Description	U.K. £	U.S. $	Can. $
Gloss	50.00	70.00	100.00

Model No. 1060
RED SETTER - Lying

Designer: Arthur Gredington
Height: 3", 7.6 cm
Colours: Deep red brown - gloss
Issued: 1946-1973

Description	U.K. £	U.S. $	Can. $
Gloss	100.00	150.00	225.00

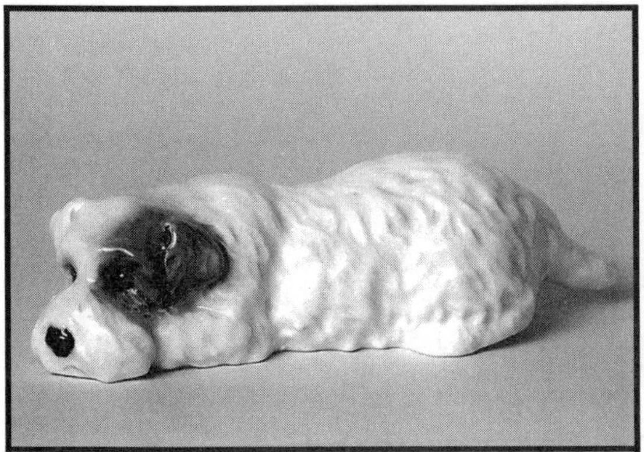

Model No. 1061
TERRIER - Lying

Designer: Arthur Gredington
Height: 2", 5.0 cm
Colours: White with light tan patches - gloss
Issued: 1946-1973

Description	U.K. £	U.S. $	Can. $
Gloss	85.00	125.00	175.00

Model No. 1062
TERRIER- Walking

Designer: Arthur Gredington
Height: 4", 10.1 cm
Colours: 1. Blue, gloss
2. White with light tan and black patches - gloss
Issued: 1. 1946-1954
2. 1946-1973

Description	U.K. £	U.S. $	Can. $
1. Blue		Rare	
2. White/tan	60.00	85.00	125.00

Model No. 1088
COMICAL DACHSHUND

Designer: Miss Jones
Height: 3 ½", 8.9 cm
Colours: White and brown - gloss
Issued: 1947-1973
Series: Fun Models

Description	U.K. £	U.S. $	Can. $
Gloss	45.00	65.00	95.00

Model No. 1202
BOXER "BLUE MOUNTAIN GRETA" - Large

Designer: Arthur Gredington
Height: 5 ½", 14.0 cm
Colours: 1. Brindle - gloss; matt
2. Tan - gloss
Issued: 1a. Gloss - 1950-1989
1b. Matt - 1987-1989
2. Gloss - 1973-1975

Colourway	U.K. £	U.S. $	Can. $
1a. Brindle - gloss	75.00	100.00	150.00
1b. Brindle - matt	45.00	65.00	100.00
2. Tan - gloss	65.00	90.00	135.00

Model No. 1220
ENGLISH SETTER

Designer: Arthur Gredington
Height: 8", 20.3 cm
Colours: Speckled grey - gloss
Issued: 1951-1973

Description	U.K. £	U.S. $	Can. $
Gloss	450.00	650.00	1,000.00

Model No. 1239
DOG WITH RUFF - Begging

Designer: Arthur Gredington
Height: 2 ½", 6.4 cm
Colours: White and light tan - gloss
Issued: 1952-1967

Description	U.K. £	U.S. $	Can. $
Gloss	45.00	65.00	100.00

Note: Originally issued in combination as model no. 1086 "Clown and Dog."

Model No. 1240
DOG - Seated

Designer: Arthur Gredington
Height: 2", 5.0 cm
Colours: White and light tan - gloss
Issued: 1952-1952

Description	U.K. £	U.S. $	Can. $
Gloss	45.00	65.00	100.00

Note: Originally produced in combination as model no. 1096 "Sportsman."

Model No. 1241
DOG - Howling

Designer: Arthur Gredington
Height: 1 ¼", 3.2 cm
Colours: White and light tan - gloss
Issued: 1952-1952

Description	U.K. £	U.S. $	Can. $
Gloss	35.00	50.00	75.00

Note: Originally produced in combination as model no. 909 "Puppy Love" (Hummel 1).

Model No. 1242
DOG - Barking

Designer: Arthur Gredington
Height: 1 ¼", 3.2 cm
Colours: White and light tan - gloss
Issued: 1952-1952

Description	U.K. £	U.S. $	Can. $
Gloss	35.00	50.00	75.00

Note: Originally issued in combination as model no. 906 "Strolling Along" (Hummel 5).

Model No. 1294
POODLE "EBONIT AV BARBETT"

Designer: Arthur Gredington
Height: 5 ¾", 14.0 cm
Colours: 1. Black - gloss; matt
2. White - gloss
Issued: 1. 1953-1967
2. 1953-1967

Colourway	U.K. £	U.S. $	Can. $
1a. Black - gloss	275.00	400.00	600.00
1b. Black - matt	250.00	350.00	525.00
2. White- gloss	300.00	425.00	650.00

Model No. 1299A
CORGI "BLACK PRINCE" - Large

Designer: Arthur Gredington
Height: 5 ½", 14.0 cm
Colours: Black, tan and white - gloss
Issued: 1953-1982
Varieties: 1299B

Description	U.K. £	U.S. $	Can. $
Gloss	60.00	85.00	125.00

Note: For small size see no. 1736.

Model No. 1299B
CORGI - Large

Designer: Arthur Gredington
Height: 5 ½", 14.0 cm
Colours: 1. Golden brown - gloss
2. Golden brown - matt
Issued: 1. 1953-1994
2. 1987-1994
Varieties: 1299A

Description	U.K. £	U.S. $	Can. $
1. Gloss	35.00	50.00	75.00
2. Matt	30.00	45.00	65.00

Note: For small size see no. 1736.

Model No. 1378/1/2/3/4/5/6
OLD ENGLISH DOGS - Left and right facing pairs

Designer: Unknown Series: Mantelpiece Dogs

Colourway	Model	Height	Issued	U.K. £	Price U.S. $	Can.
Red/gold	1378/1	13 ¼", 33.6 cm	1955-1973	100.00	150.00	225.00
Red/gold	1378/2	11 ½", 29.2 cm	1955-1972	90.00	125.00	200.00
Red/gold	1378/3	10", 25.4 cm	1955-1973	85.00	125.00	200.00
Red/gold	1378/4	9", 22.9 cm	1955-1973	80.00	115.00	175.00
Red/gold	1378/5	7 ½", 19.1 cm	1955-1973	75.00	110.00	175.00
Red/gold	1378/6	5 ½", 14.0 cm	1955-1973	65.00	100.00	160.00
Red/gold	1378/7	3 ½", 8.9 cm	1955-1973	55.00	90.00	130.00
White/gold	1378/1	13 ¼", 33.6 cm	1955-1976	75.00	110.00	165.00
White/gold	1378/2	11 ½", 29.2 cm	1955-1972	65.00	90.00	135.00
White/gold						
a. Beswick	1378/3	10", 25.4 cm	1955-1989	60.00	100.00	150.00
b. Doulton	DA89-90	10", 25.4 cm	1989-1997	60.00	100.00	150.00
White/gold						
a. Beswick	1378/4	9", 22.9 cm	1955-1989	50.00	75.00	110.00
b. Doulton	DA91-92	9", 22.9 cm	1989-1999	50.00	75.00	110.00
c. Beswick	1378/4	9", 22.9 cm	1999-Current	28.50	N/A	N/A
White/gold						
a. Beswick	1378/5	7 ½", 19.1 cm	1955-1989	35.00	60.00	85.00
b. Doulton	DA93-94	7 ½", 19.1 cm	1989-1997	35.00	60.00	85.00
White/gold						
a. Beswick	1378/6	5 ½", 14.0 cm	1955-1989	30.00	45.00	65.00
b. Doulton	DA95-96	5 ½", 14.0 cm	1989-1999	30.00	45.00	65.00
c. Beswick	1378/6	5 ½", 14.0 cm	1999-Current	18.00	N/A	N/A
White /gold						
a. Beswick	1378/7	3 ½", 8.9 cm	1955-1989	20.00	30.00	40.00
b. Doulton	DA97-98	3 ½", 8.9 cm	1989-1999	20.00	30.00	40.00
c. Beswick	1378/7	3 ½", 8.9 cm	1999-Current	13.00	N/A	N/A

Note: Also seen in Opaque white glaze.

Model No. 1386
POODLE

Designer: Arthur Gredington
Height: 3 ½", 8.9 cm
Issued:
1. Black, gloss – 1955-1990
2. Black, matt – 1988-1989
3. Chocolate, gloss – 1953-1973
4. White, gloss – 1955-1990
5. White, matt – 1984-1989

Colourway	U.K. £	U.S. $	Can. $
1. Black, gloss	30.00	45.00	65.00
2. Black, matt	30.00	45.00	65.00
3. Chocolate, gloss	65.00	90.00	135.00
4. White, gloss	30.00	45.00	65.00
5. White, matt	30.00	45.00	65.00

Note: A few examples are known in an apricot colourway.

Model No. 1460
DACHSHUND - Seated

Designer: Arthur Gredington
Height: 2 ¾", 7.0 cm
Colours:
1. Black and tan - gloss or matt
2. Tan - gloss or matt

Issued:
1a. Gloss - 1956 to the present
1b. Matt - 1984-1989
2a. Gloss - 1956-1990
2b. Matt - 1984-1990

Colourway	U.K. £	U.S. $	Can. $
1a. Black/tan - gloss	17.00	N/A	N/A
1b. Black/tan - matt	20.00	30.00	45.00
2a. Tan - gloss	25.00	35.00	50.00
2b. Tan - matt	20.00	30.00	45.00

Model No. 1461
DACHSHUND - Begging

Designer: Arthur Gredington
Height: 4", 10.1 cm
Colours:
1. Tan - gloss
2. Black and tan - gloss

Issued:
1. 1957-1975
2. 1957-1980

Colourway	U.K. £	U.S. $	Can. $
1. Tan	40.00	55.00	80.00
2. Black and tan	35.00	50.00	70.00

Model No. 1548
LABRADOR "SOLOMON OF WENDOVER"- Large

Designer: Arthur Gredington
Height: 5 ½", 14.0 cm
Issued: 1. Black, gloss – 1958-1994
2. Black, matt – 1987-1994
3. Golden yellow, gloss – 1958-1994
4. Golden yellow, matt – 1970-1994

Colourway	U.K. £	U.S. $	Can. $
1. Black, gloss	50.00	70.00	100.00
2. Black , matt	45.00	65.00	95.00
3. Golden yellow, gloss	50.00	70.00	100.00
4. Golden yellow, matt	45.00	65.00	95.00

Model No. 1731
BULLDOG "BOSUN" - Small

Designer: Unknown
Height: 2 ½", 6.4 cm
Colours: Tan and white - gloss; matt
Issued: 1. Gloss - 1960-1997
2. Matt - 1984-1989

Description	U.K. £	U.S. $	Can. $
1. Gloss	15.00	25.00	40.00
2. Matt	20.00	30.00	45.00

Note: For large size see no. 965.

Model No. 1736
CORGI - Small

Designer: Unknown
Height: 2 ¾", 7.0 cm
Colours: Golden brown - gloss; matt
Issued: 1. Gloss - 1961-1996
2. Matt - 1984-1989

Description	U.K. £	U.S. $	Can. $
1. Gloss	20.00	30.00	45.00
2. Matt	20.00	30.00	45.00

Note: For large size see no. 1299.

Model No. 1738
PUP WITH BONE

Designer: Harry Sales
Height: 3 ¾", 9.5 cm
Colours: White - gloss
Issued: 1961-1967
Series: Fun Models

Description	U.K. £	U.S. $	Can. $
Gloss	65.00	90.00	135.00

Model No. 1753
BULL TERRIER - Small

Designer: Arthur Gredington
Height: 3 ½", 8.9 cm
Colours: White with bright tan patches - gloss
Issued: 1961-1971

Description	U.K. £	U.S. $	Can. $
Gloss	90.00	150.00	225.00

Note: For large size see no. 970.

Model No. 1754
COCKER SPANIEL

Designer: Arthur Gredington
Height: 3", 7.6 cm
Issued:
1. Black and white, gloss – 1961-1996
2. Black and white, matt – 1984-1989
3. Liver and white, gloss – 1961-1997
4. Liver and white, matt – 1984-1989

Colourway	U.K. £	U.S. $	Can. $
1. Black and white, gloss	20.00	30.00	45.00
2. Black and white, matt	20.00	30.00	45.00
3. Liver and white, gloss	20.00	30.00	45.00
4. Liver and white, matt	20.00	30.00	45.00

Model No. 1762A
ALSATIAN - Small
First Version - 'Wolf-like,' tail not fully attached to leg

Designer: Mr. Garbet
Height: 3 ¼", 8.3 cm
Colours: Black and cream - gloss
Issued: 1961-1963

Description	U.K. £	U.S. $	Can. $
Gloss	45.00	65.00	100.00

Model No. 1762B
ALSATIAN - Small
Second Version - 'Fine head,' tail attached to leg

Designer: Arthur Gredington
Height: 3 ¼", 8.3 cm
Colours: Black and cream - gloss
Issued: 1963-1966

Description	U.K. £	U.S. $	Can. $
Gloss	40.00	60.00	90.00

Note: For large size see no. 969.

Model No. 1763
DALMATION - Small

Designer: Mr. Garbet
Height: 3 ½", 8.9 cm
Colours: White with black spots - gloss; matt
Issued: 1. Gloss - 1961 to the present
2. Matt - 1984-1989

Description	U.K. £	U.S. $	Can. $
1. Gloss	17.00	N/A	50.00
2. Matt	17.00	30.00	45.00

Note: For large size see no. 961.

Model No. 1786A
WHIPPET "WINGED FOOT MARKSMAN OF ALLWAYS"
First Version - Tail curls between legs

Designer: Arthur Gredington
Height: 4 ½", 11.9 cm
Colours: Light sandy brown - gloss
Issued: 1961-Unknown

Description	U.K. £	U.S. $	Can. $
Gloss	150.00	225.00	350.00

Model No. 1786B
WHIPPET "WINGED FOOT MARKSMAN OF ALLWAYS"
Second Version - Tail attached to leg

Designer: Arthur Gredington
Height: 4 ½", 11.9 cm
Colours: Light sandy brown - gloss; matt
Issued: 1. Gloss - Unknown-1989
2. Matt - 1987-1989

Description	U.K. £	U.S. $	Can. $
1. Gloss	65.00	90.00	135.00
2. Matt	65.00	90.00	135.00

Model No. 1791
COLLIE "LOCHINVAR OF LADYPARK" - Large

Designer: Arthur Gredington
Height: 5 ¾", 14.6 cm
Colours: Golden brown and white - gloss; matt
Issued: 1. Gloss - 1961-1994
2. Matt - 1970-1994

Description	U.K. £	U.S. $	Can. $
1. Gloss	40.00	55.00	85.00
2. Matt	35.00	50.00	75.00

Note: For small size see no. 1814.

Model No. 1792
SHEEPDOG - Large

Designer: Arthur Gredington
Height: 5 ½", 14.0 cm
Colours: Black and white - gloss; matt
Issued: 1. Gloss - 1961-1994
2. Matt - 1987-1994

Description	U.K. £	U.S. $	Can. $
1. Gloss	40.00	55.00	85.00
2. Matt	35.00	50.00	75.00

Note: For small size see no. 1854.

Model No. 1814
COLLIE - Small

Designer: Arthur Gredington
Height: 3 ¼", 8.3 cm
Colours: Golden brown and white - gloss
Issued: 1962-1975

Description	U.K. £	U.S. $	Can. $
Gloss	50.00	70.00	100.00

Note: For large size see no. 1791.

Model No. 1824
DOG - Singing

Designer: Albert Hallam
Height: 1 ½", 3.8 cm
Colours: Tan - gloss
Issued: 1962-1971
Series: Bedtime Chorus

Description	U.K. £	U.S. $	Can. $
Gloss	60.00	85.00	125.00

Model No. 1852
BOXER - Small

Designer: Arthur Gredington
Height: 3", 7.6 cm
Colours: Tan - gloss
Issued: 1962-1975

Description	U.K. £	U.S. $	Can. $
Gloss	45.00	65.00	100.00

Note: For large size see no. 1202.

Model No. 1854
SHEEPDOG - Small

Designer: Arthur Gredington
Height: 3″, 7.6 cm
Colours: Black and white - gloss; matt
Issued: 1. Gloss - 1962 to the present
2. Matt - 1987-1989

Description	U.K. £	U.S. $	Can. $
1. Gloss	19.00	N/A	N/A
2. Matt	15.00	25.00	40.00

Note: For large size see no. 1792.

Model No. 1855
RETRIEVER

Designer: Arthur Gredington
Height: 3 ¼″, 8.3 cm
Colours: 1. Black - gloss
2. Light golden brown - gloss
Issued: 1962-1975

Colourway	U.K. £	U.S. $	Can. $
1. Black	65.00	90.00	135.00
2. Light brown	45.00	65.00	100.00

Model No. 1871
POODLE

Designer: Arthur Gredington
Height: 4 ¼″, 10.8 cm
Colours: White, red bow - gloss
Issued: 1963-1967
Series: Advertising ware "Dubonnet"

Description	U.K. £	U.S. $	Can. $
Gloss	65.00	90.00	135.00

Model No. 1872
BULLDOG

Designer: Arthur Gredington
Height: 3 ¾″, 9.5 cm
Colours: White, pale tan ear and around eyes - gloss
Issued: 1963-1967
Series: Advertising ware "Dubonnet"

Description	U.K. £	U.S. $	Can. $
Gloss	65.00	90.00	135.00

Model No. 1933A
BEAGLE "WENDOVER BILLY" - Large

Designer: Arthur Gredington
Height: 5 ½", 14.0 cm
Colours: Black, tan and white - gloss or matt
Issued: 1. 1964-1989
2. 1987-1989
Varieties: 1933B

Description	U.K. £	U.S. $	Can. $
1. Gloss	45.00	65.00	100.00
2. Matt	40.00	55.00	80.00

Note: For small size see no. 1939.

Model No. 1933B
BEAGLE "WENDOVER BILLY" - on wooden plinth

Designer: Arthur Gredington
Height: 6", 15.0 cm
Colours: Black, tan and white - matt
Issued: 1970-1989
Series: Connoisseur Dogs
Varieties: 1933A

Description	U.K. £	U.S. $	Can. $
Matt	55.00	80.00	125.00

Model No. 1939
BEAGLE "WENDOVER BILLY" - Small

Designer: Arthur Gredington
Height: 3", 7.6 cm
Colours: Black, tan and white - gloss or matt
Issued: 1. Gloss - 1964 to the present
2. Matt - 1984-1989

Description	U.K. £	U.S. $	Can. $
1. Gloss	17.00	N/A	N/A
2. Matt	20.00	30.00	45.00

Note: For large size see no. 1933A.

Model No. 1944
YORKSHIRE TERRIER - Lying

Designer: Arthur Gredington
Height: 3 ½", 8.9 cm
Colours: Grey and tan - gloss
Issued: 1964-1976

Description	U.K. £	U.S. $	Can. $
Gloss	45.00	65.00	100.00

CATS

Model 1031
Cat – ginger striped

Model 1030
Cat – grey (smokey blue)

Model 1031
Cat – grey striped

Model 1880
Persian cat – ginger (dark)

Model 1880
Persian cat – British blue

Model 1867
Persian cat – grey (shaded)

Model 1436
Kitten – grey striped

Model 1877
Cat – grey swiss roll

Model 1436
Kitten – ginger (pale), gloss

CATS

Model 1885
Persian Kitten – grey striped

Model 1876
Persian cat – ginger (dark)

Model 1885
Persian kitten – grey swiss roll

Model 1437
Cat – grey striped

Model 1898
Persian cat – grey shaded, gloss

Model 1438
Cat – grey striped

Model 1435
Cat – grey striped

CATS

Model 1296
Siamese kittens – chocolate point

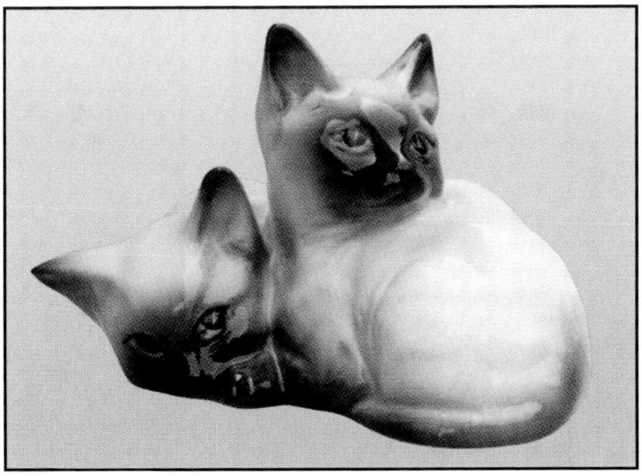

Model 1296
Siamese kittens – seal point

Model 1558
Siamese cat – chocolate point

Model 1558
Siamese cat – seal point

Model 1559A
Siamese cat – chocolate point

Model 1559B
Siamese cat – seal point

CATS

Model 1031
White, large eyes

Model 1031
White, small eyes

Model 1316
Persian kittens – white, large eyes

Model 1883
Persian cat – white, large eyes

Model 2101
Cat, laughing

Model 1886
Persian kitten – white

Model 1882
Siamese cat – copper lustre

Model 1542
Cat – satin gloss

Model 1543
Cat – satin gloss

DOGS

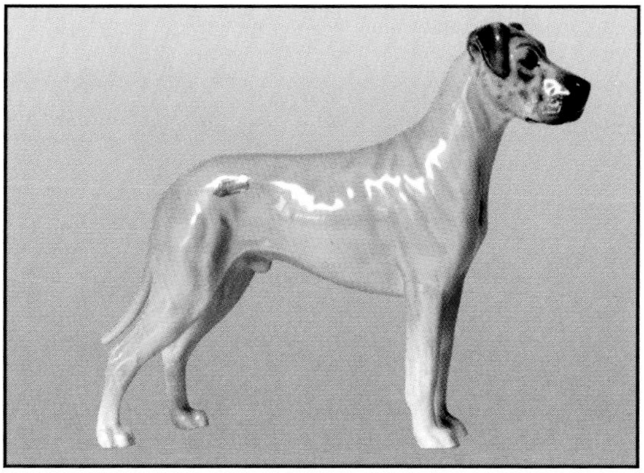

Model 968
Great Dane – gloss

Model 1062
Terrier – gloss

Model 1736
Corgi – small, gloss

Model 972
Greyhound – gloss

Model 1386
Poodle – brown, gloss

Model 1791
Collie – gloss

DOGS

Model 1202
Boxer – brindle, gloss

Model 1202
Boxer – dark tan, gloss

Model 1202
Boxer – light tan, gloss

Model 1852
Boxer – small, gloss

Model 1762
Alsatian, first version

Model 1762
Alsatian, second version

DOGS

Model 1002
Puppit Dog

Model 1054
"My Plate"

Model 1738
Pup with Bone

Model 1058
"Scamp"

Model 1088
Comical Dachshund

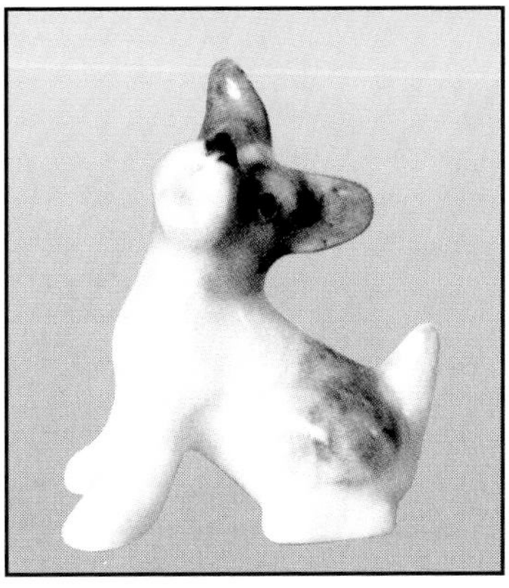

Model 1241
"Howling"

Model 1239
"Begging"

Model 1242
"Barking"

DOGS

Model 1786A
Whippet, first version

Model 1786B
Whippet, second version

Model 970
Bull Terrier – brindle and white

Model 1753
Bull Terrier – white and tan

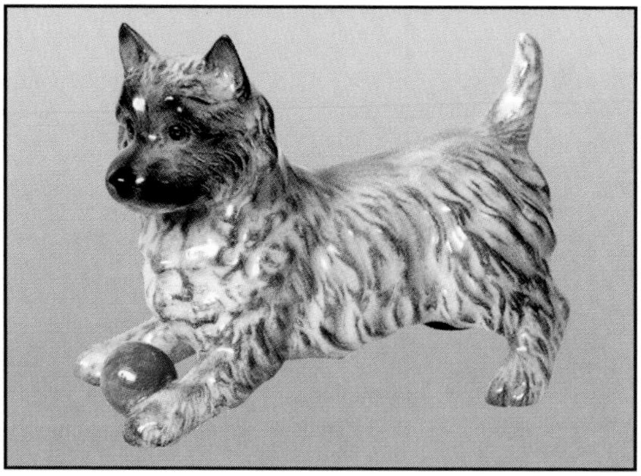

Model 1055A
Cairn Terrier, first version, with ball

Model 1055B
Cairn Terrier, second version, without ball

Model No. 1956
LABRADOR - Small

Designer: Arthur Gredington
Height: 3 ¼", 8.3 cm
Issued:
1. Black, gloss – 1964 - current
2. Black, matt – 1984 - 1989
3. Golden brown, gloss – 1964- current
4. Golden brown, matt – 1984-1989

Colourway	U.K. £	U.S. $	Can. $
1. Black, gloss	17.00	N/A	N/A
2. Black, matt	20.00	30.00	45.00
3. Golden brown, gloss	17.00	N/A	N/A
4. Golden brown, matt	20.00	30.00	45.00

Model No. 1982A
STAFFORDSHIRE BULL TERRIER
"BANDITS BRINTIGA"

Designer: Arthur Gredington
Height: 4 ¾", 12.1 cm
Colours: Dark brindle - gloss
Issued: 1964-1969

Description	U.K. £	U.S. $	Can. $
Gloss	300.00	425.00	650.00

Model No. 1982B
STAFFORDSHIRE BULL TERRIER

Designer: Arthur Gredington
Height: 4 ¾", 12.1 cm
Colours: Tan and white - gloss
Issued: 1964-1969

Description	U.K. £	U.S. $	Can. $
Gloss	300.00	425.00	650.00

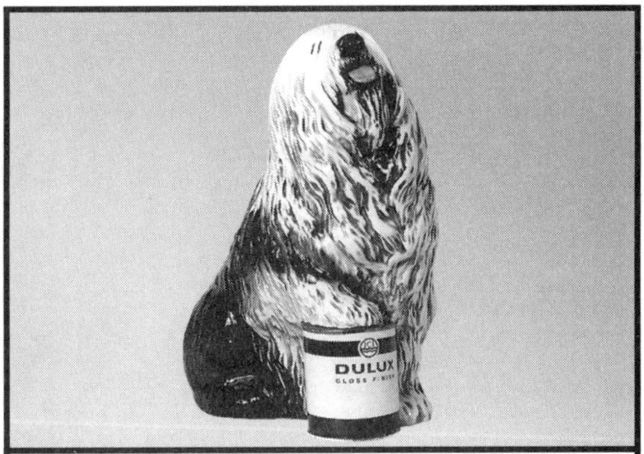

Model No. 1990
OLD ENGLISH SHEEPDOG

Designer: Mr. Mortimer
Height: 12 ½", 31.7 cm
Colours: Black, grey and white - gloss
Issued: 1964-1970
Series: Advertising ware "Dulux"

Description	U.K. £	U.S. $	Can. $
Gloss	550.00	800.00	1,200.00

Model No. 1997
PUG "CUTMIL CUTIE" - Large

Designer: Arthur Gredington
Height: 4 ½", 11.9 cm
Colours: Light sandy brown - gloss or matt
Issued: 1. Gloss - 1965-1982
2. Matt - 1970-1982

Description	U.K. £	U.S. $	Can. $
1. Gloss	60.00	85.00	125.00
2. Matt	50.00	70.00	100.00

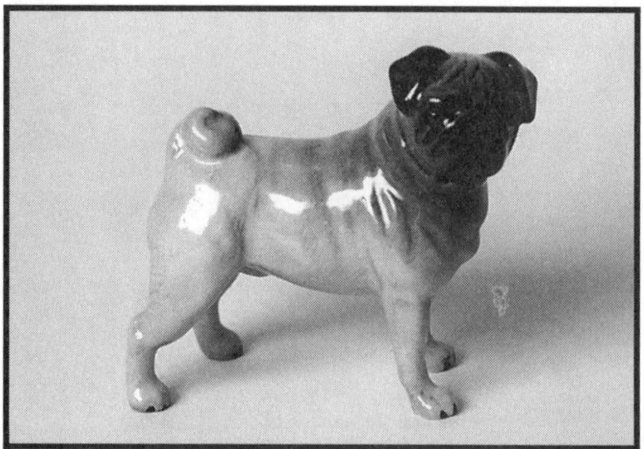

Model No. 1998
PUG - Small

Designer: Arthur Gredington
Height: 2 ½", 6.4 cm
Colours: Light sandy brown - gloss or matt
Issued: 1. Gloss - 1966-1990
2. Mattt - 1984-1989

Description	U.K. £	U.S. $	Can. $
1. Gloss	25.00	35.00	55.00
2. Matt	25.00	35.00	55.00

Note: This model has also been seen with head forward.

Model No. 2023
JACK RUSSELL TERRIER - Large

Designer: Arthur Gredington
Height: 5", 12.7 cm
Colours: White body, tan/black head - gloss or matt
Issued: 1. Gloss - 1965-1994
2. Matt - 1987-1994

Description	U.K. £	U.S. $	Can. $
1. Gloss	45.00	65.00	100.00
2. Matt	40.00	55.00	90.00

Note: For small size see no. 2109.

Model No. 2037
SCOTTIE

Designer: Arthur Gredington
Height: 4 ½", 11.9 cm
Colours: Black - gloss or matt
Issued: 1. Gloss - 1965-1990
2. Matt - 1987-1989

Description	U.K. £	U.S. $	Can. $
1. Gloss	45.00	65.00	100.00
2. Matt	40.00	55.00	90.00

Model No. 2038
WEST HIGHLAND TERRIER

Designer: Arthur Gredington
Height: 4 ¾", 12.1 cm
Colours: White - gloss or matt
Issued: 1. Gloss - 1965-1994
2. Matt - 1987-1989

Description	U.K. £	U.S. $	Can. $
1. Gloss	50.00	70.00	100.00
2. Matt	40.00	55.00	80.00

Model No. 2045A
BASSET HOUND "FOCHNO TRINKET"

Designer: Arthur Gredington
Height: 5", 12.7 cm
Colours: Black, white and tan - gloss or matt
Issued: 1. Gloss - 1965-1994
2. Matt - 1987-1994

Description	U.K. £	U.S. $	Can. $
1. Gloss	60.00	85.00	125.00
2. Matt	55.00	75.00	100.00

Model No. 2045B
BASSET HOUND "FOCHNO TRINKET"
- on wooden plinth

Designer: Arthur Gredington
Height: 6", 15.0 cm
Colours: Black, white and tan - matt
Issued: 1970-1989
Series: Connoisseur Dogs

Description	U.K. £	U.S. $	Can. $
Matt	65.00	100.00	150.00

Model No. 2102
YORKSHIRE TERRIER LAUGHING

Designer: Albert Hallam
Height: 3", 7.6 cm
Colours: Tan - gloss
Issued: 1967-1972
Series: Fun Models

Description	U.K. £	U.S. $	Can. $
Gloss	45.00	65.00	95.00

Model No. 2107A
KING CHARLES SPANIEL "BLENHEIM"

Designer: Arthur Gredington
Height: 5 ¼", 13.3 cm
Colours: Tan and white - gloss or matt
Issued: 1. Gloss - 1967-1994
2. Matt - 1987-1994

Description	U.K. £	U.S. $	Can. $
1. Gloss	70.00	100.00	150.00
2. Matt	65.00	90.00	135.00

Model No. 2107B
KING CHARLES SPANIEL "JOSEPHINE OF BLAGREAVES"

Designer: Arthur Gredington
Height: 5 ¼", 13.3 cm
Colours: Black, tan and white - gloss or matt
Issued: 1. Gloss - 1967-1994
2. Matt - 1987-1994

Description	U.K. £	U.S. $	Can. $
1. Gloss	70.00	100.00	150.00
2. Matt	65.00	90.00	135.00

Model No. 2108
POODLE "IVANOLA GOLD DIGGER"

Designer: Arthur Gredington
Height: 5 ¾", 14.6 cm
Colours: White, blue bow - gloss
Issued: 1967-1971

Description	U.K. £	U.S. $	Can. $
Gloss	300.00	450.00	675.00

Model No. 2109
JACK RUSSELL TERRIER - Small

Designer: Arthur Gredington and Albert Hallam
Height: 2 ½", 6.4 cm
Colours: White with tan head - gloss or matt
Issued: 1. Gloss - 1967 to the present
2. Matt - 1984-1989

Description	U.K. £	U.S. $	Can. $
1. Gloss	17.00	N/A	50.00
2. Matt	20.00	30.00	45.00

Note: For large size see no. 2023.

Model No. 2112
CAIRN TERRIER

Designer: Arthur Gredington and Albert Hallam
Height: 2 ¾", 7.0 cm
Colours: Dark cream - gloss or matt
Issued: 1. Gloss - 1967-1995
2. Matt - 1984-1989

Description	U.K. £	U.S. $	Can. $
1. Gloss	20.00	30.00	45.00
2. Matt	15.00	20.00	30.00

Model No. 2221
ST. BERNARD "CORNA GARTH STROLLER"

Designer: Albert Hallam
Height: 5 ½", 14.0 cm
Colours: Dark brown, tan and white - gloss or matt
Issued: 1. Gloss - 1968-1989
2. Matt - 1970-1989

Description	U.K. £	U.S. $	Can. $
1. Gloss	50.00	70.00	100.00
2. Matt	50.00	70.00	100.00

Model No. 2232
OLD ENGLISH SHEEPDOG

Designer: Albert Hallam
Height: 11 ½", 29.2 cm
Colours: Grey and white - gloss
Issued: a. Beswick – 1968-1989
b. Doulton (DA84) – 1989-1994
Series: Fireside Models

Description	U.K. £	U.S. $	Can. $
a. Beswick	150.00	225.00	325.00
b. Doulton (DA84)	150.00	225.00	325.00

Model No. 2235
BASSETHOUND - Wall Plaque

Designer: Graham Tongue
Height: 6 ¼" x 4 ½", 15.9 x 11.9 cm (concave)
Colours: Tan and white head
black satin surround - gloss
Issued: 1968-Unknown
Series: Wall Plaques

Description	U.K. £	U.S. $	Can. $
Gloss	75.00	110.00	165.00

Model No. 2262
FOXHOUND
Second Version - Thin legs and tail

Designer: Graham Tongue
Height: 2 ½", 6.4 cm
Colours: White, tan and black - gloss or matt
Issued: 1. Gloss - 1969-1997
2. Matt - 1984-1989
Varieties: 941

Description	U.K. £	U.S. $	Can. $
1. Gloss	15.00	25.00	40.00
2. Matt	15.00	25.00	40.00

Model No. 2263
FOXHOUND
Second Version - Thin legs and tail

Designer: Graham Tongue
Height: 3", 7.6 cm
Colours: White, tan and black - gloss or matt
Issued: 1. Gloss - 1969-1997
2. Matt - 1984-1989
Varieties: 942

Description	U.K. £	U.S. $	Can. $
1. Gloss	15.00	25.00	40.00
2. Matt	15.00	25.00	40.00

Model No. 2264
FOXHOUND
Second Version - Thin legs and tail

Designer: Graham Tongue
Height: 3", 7.6 cm
Colours: White, tan and black - gloss or matt
Issued: 1. Gloss - 1969-1997
2. Matt - 1984-1989
Varieties: 944

Description	U.K. £	U.S. $	Can. $
1. Gloss	15.00	25.00	40.00
2. Matt	15.00	25.00	40.00

Model No. 2265
FOXHOUND
Second Version - Thin legs and tail

Designer: Graham Tongue
Height: 2 ¾", 7.0 cm
Colours: White, tan and black - gloss or matt
Issued: 1. Gloss - 1969-1997
2. Matt - 1984-1989
Varieties: 943

Description	U.K. £	U.S. $	Can. $
1. Gloss	15.00	25.00	40.00
2. Matt	15.00	25.00	40.00

Model No. 2268
POODLE - Wall Plaque

Designer: Graham Tongue
Height: 6" x 4 ½", 15.9 x 11.9 cm (Concave)
Colours: Unknown - gloss
Issued: 1968-Unknown
Series: Wall Plaques

Description	U.K. £	U.S. $	Can. $
Gloss	95.00	135.00	200.00

Model No. 2271
DALMATIAN

Designer: Graham Tongue
Height: 13 ¾", 34.9 cm
Colours: White with black spots - gloss
Issued: a. Beswick – 1969-1989
b. Doulton (DA85) – 1989-1996
Series: Fireside Models

Description	U.K. £	U.S. $	Can. $
a. Beswick	175.00	250.00	375.00
b. Doulton (DA85)	175.00	250.00	375.00

Model No. 2285
AFGHAN HOUND "HAJUBAH OF DAVIEN"

Designer: Graham Tongue
Height: 5 ½", 14.0 cm
Colours: Golden and dark brown - gloss or matt
Issued: 1. Gloss - 1969-1994
2. Matt - 1987-1989

Description	U.K. £	U.S. $	Can. $
1. Gloss	45.00	65.00	100.00
2. Matt	40.00	55.00	85.00

Model No. 2286
DACHSHUND

Designer: Albert Hallam
Height: 10 ½", 26.7 cm
Colours: 1. Black and tan - gloss
2. Tan - gloss
Issued: 1. 1969-1981
2. 1969-1981
Series: Fireside Models

Colourway	U.K. £	U.S. $	Can. $
1. Black/tan	100.00	175.00	250.00
2. Tan	100.00	175.00	250.00

Model No. 2287
GOLDEN RETRIEVER "CABUS CADET"

Designer: Graham Tongue
Height: 5 ½", 14.0 cm
Colours: Light golden brown - gloss or matt
Issued: 1. Gloss - 1969-1994
2. Matt - 1987-1994

Description	U.K. £	U.S. $	Can. $
1. Gloss	45.00	65.00	100.00
2. Matt	40.00	55.00	85.00

Model No. 2299
DOBERMAN PINSCHER "ANNASTOCK LANCE"

Designer: Graham Tongue
Height: 5 ¾", 14.6 cm
Colours: Black and tan - gloss or matt
Issued: 1. Gloss - 1970-1994
2. Matt - 1987-1994

Description	U.K. £	U.S. $	Can. $
1. Gloss	45.00	65.00	100.00
2. Matt	40.00	55.00	85.00

Model No. 2300
BEAGLE

Designer: Albert Hallam
Height: 12 ¾", 32.4 cm
Colours: Black, tan and white - gloss
Issued: 1969-1983
Series: Fireside Models

Description	U.K. £	U.S. $	Can. $
Gloss	175.00	250.00	375.00

Model No. 2314
LABRADOR

Designer: Graham Tongue
Height: 13 ½", 34.3 cm
Colours: 1. Black - gloss
2. Golden brown - gloss
Issued: a. Beswick – 1970-1989
b. Doulton (DA86) – 1989-1996
Series: Fireside Models

Description	U.K. £	U.S. $	Can. $
a. Beswick	125.00	200.00	300.00
b. Doulton (DA86)	125.00	200.00	300.00

Model No. 2339
POODLE

Designer: Graham Tongue
Height: 5 ¾", 14.6 cm
Colours: 1. Black - gloss
2. White - gloss
Issued: 1971-1983

Colourway	U.K. £	U.S. $	Can. $
1. Black	60.00	85.00	125.00
2. White	60.00	85.00	125.00

Model No. 2377
YORKSHIRE TERRIER

Designer: Graham Tongue
Height: 10 ¼", 26.0 cm
Colours: Grey and tan - gloss
Issued: a. Beswick – 1971-1989
b. Doulton (DA87) – 1989-1994
Series: Fireside Models

Description	U.K. £	U.S. $	Can. $
a. Beswick	175.00	250.00	375.00
b. Doulton (DA87)	175.00	250.00	375.00

Model No. 2410
ALSATIAN

Designer: Graham Tongue
Height: 14", 35.5 cm
Colours: Dark and sandy brown - gloss
Issued: a. Beswick – 1972-1989
b. Doulton (DA88) – 1989-1996
Series: Fireside Models

Description	U.K. £	U.S. $	Can. $
a. Beswick	150.00	225.00	325.00
b. Doulton (DA88)	150.00	225.00	325.00

Model No. 2448
LAKELAND TERRIER

Designer: Albert Hallam
Height: 3 ¼", 8.3 cm
Colours: Pale tan and black - gloss or matt
Issued: 1. Gloss - 1973-1998
2. Matt - 1984-1989

Description	U.K. £	U.S. $	Can. $
1. Gloss	20.00	30.00	45.00
2. Matt	20.00	30.00	45.00

Model No. 2454
CHIHUAHUA - Lying on cushion

Designer: Albert Hallam
Height: 2 ¾", 7.0 cm
Colours: Cream dog, maroon cushion - gloss or matt
Issued: 1. Gloss - 1973-1996
2. Matt - 1984-1989

Description	U.K. £	U.S. $	Can. $
1. Gloss	25.00	40.00	60.00
2. Matt	25.00	40.00	60.00

Model No. 2581
COLLIE - on wooden plinth

Designer: Graham Tongue
Height: 8", 20.3 cm
Colours: Golden brown and white - matt
Issued: a. Beswick – 1979-1989
b. Doulton (DA24) – 1989-1994
Series: Connoisseur Dogs

Description	U.K. £	U.S. $	Can. $
a. Beswick	75.00	110.00	175.00
b. Doulton (DA24)	100.00	150.00	225.00

Model No. 2587
ALSATIAN - on wooden plinth

Designer: Graham Tongue
Height: 9", 22.9 cm
Colours: Dark and sandy brown - matt
Issued: a. Beswick – 1979-1989
b. Doulton (DA26) – 1989-1994
Series: Connoisseur Dogs

Description	U.K. £	U.S. $	Can. $
a. Beswick	75.00	110.00	175.00
b. Doulton (DA26)	100.00	150.00	225.00

Model No. 2929
COLLIE - Wall Plaque

Designer: Unknown
Height: Unknown
Colours: Golden brown and white - matt
Issued: 1986-1989
Series: Best of Breed

Description	U.K. £	U.S. $	Can. $
Matt	65.00	100.00	150.00

Note: Head from model no. 2581 mounted on wood.

Model No. 2932
ALSATIAN - Wall Plaque

Designer: Unknown
Height: Unknown
Colours: Black and cream - matt
Issued: 1986-1989
Series: Best of Breed

Description	U.K. £	U.S. $	Can. $
Matt	65.00	100.00	150.00

Note: Head from model no. 2587 mounted on wood.

Model No. 2946
MEAL TIME

Designer: Unknown
Height: 3 ½″, 8.9 cm
Colours: White and tan - gloss
Issued: 1986-1989
Series: Playful Puppies

Description	U.K. £	U.S. $	Can. $
Gloss	60.00	85.00	135.00

Note: Taken from Royal Doulton HN 1158.

Model No. 2947
GNAWING

Designer: Unknown
Height: 4 ¼″, 10.8 cm
Colours: White and tan - gloss
Issued: 1986-1989
Series: Playful Puppies

Description	U.K. £	U.S. $	Can. $
Gloss	60.00	85.00	135.00

Note: Taken from Royal Doulton HN 1159.

Model No. 2948
PLAY TIME

Designer: Unknown
Height: 3 ¾″, 9.5 cm
Colours: White and tan - gloss
Issued: 1986-1989
Series: Playful Puppies

Description	U.K. £	U.S. $	Can. $
Gloss	60.00	85.00	135.00

Note: Taken from Royal Doulton HN 2654.

Model No. 2949
JUGGLING

Designer: Unknown
Height: 3", 7.6 cm
Colours: White and tan - gloss
Issued: 1986-1989
Series: Playful Puppies

Description	U.K. £	U.S. $	Can. $
Gloss	60.00	85.00	135.00

Note: Taken from Royal Doulton HN 1103.

Model No. 2950
NAP TIME

Designer: Unknown
Height: 4 ½", 11.9 cm
Colours: White and tan - gloss
Issued: 1986-1989
Series: Playful Puppies

Description	U.K. £	U.S. $	Can. $
Gloss	60.00	85.00	135.00

Note: Taken from Royal Doulton HN 1099.

Model No. 2951
CAUGHT IT

Designer: Unknown
Height: 2 ¾", 7.0 cm
Colours: White and tan - gloss
Issued: 1986-1989
Series: Playful Puppies

Description	U.K. £	U.S. $	Can. $
Gloss	60.00	85.00	135.00

Note: Taken from Royal Doulton HN 1097.

Model No. 2980
SPANIEL - on plinth

Designer: Alan Maslankowski
Height: 8 ¼", 21.0 cm
Colours:
1. Black - matt
2. Black and white - matt
3. Golden - matt
4. Liver and white - matt
5. White - matt

Issued: See below
Series: Spirited Dogs

Colourway	Issued	U.K. £	U.S. $	Can. $
1. Black	1987-1989	100.00	175.00	250.00
2. Black/white				
a. Beswick	1987-1989	100.00	175.00	250.00
b. Doulton (DA108)	1990-1995	100.00	175.00	250.00
3. Golden				
a. Beswick	1987-1989	100.00	175.00	250.00
b. Doulton (DA108)	1990-1995	100.00	175.00	250.00
4. Liver/white				
a. Beswick	1987-1989	100.00	175.00	250.00
b. Doulton (DA108)	1990-1995	100.00	175.00	250.00
5. White		100.00	175.00	250.00

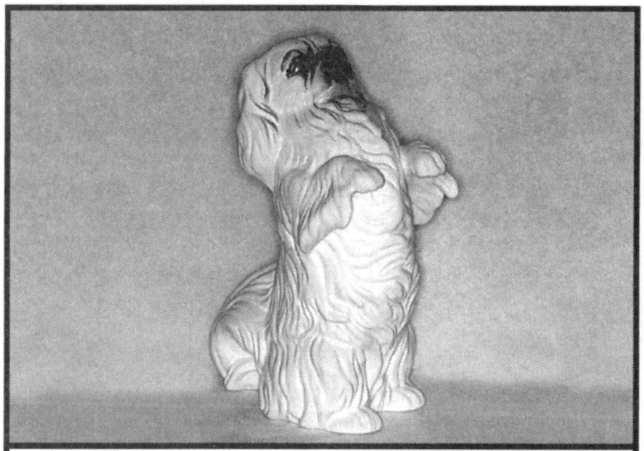

Model No. 2982
PEKINESE - Begging

Designer: Alan Maslankowski
Height: 5 ½", 14.0 cm
Colours: Cream - gloss or matt
Issued:
a. Beswick – 1987-1989
b. Doulton (DA113) – 1990-1995

Series: Good Companions

Description	U.K. £	U.S. $	Can. $
a. Beswick	50.00	75.00	110.00
b. Doulton (DA113)	40.00	60.00	90.00

Model No. 2984
NORFOLK TERRIER

Designer: Alan Maslankowski
Height: 4", 10.1 cm
Colours: Brown - gloss or matt
Issued:
a. Beswick – 1987-1989
b. Doulton (DA114) – 1990-1995

Series: Good Companions

Description	U.K. £	U.S. $	Can. $
a. Beswick	60.00	90.00	130.00
b. Doulton (DA114)	40.00	60.00	90.00

Model No. 2985
POODLE - on cushion

Designer: Alan Maslankowski
Height: 5 ½", 14.0 cm
Colours: White poodle, turquoise cushion - gloss or matt
Issued: a. Beswick – 1987-1989
b. Doulton (DA115) – 1990-1995
Series: Good Companions

Description	U.K. £	U.S. $	Can. $
a. Beswick			
Gloss	75.00	100.00	150.00
Matt	65.00	90.00	135.00
b. Doulton (DA115), gloss	65.00	90.00	135.00

Model No. 2986
SETTER - on ceramic plinth

Designer: Graham Tongue
Height: 8 ½", 21.6 cm
Colours: 1. Black, matt
2. Bronze finish
3. English Setter – Liver/white, matt
4. Gordon Setter – Black/tan, matt
5. Red Setter – Deep red brown, matt
6. White, matt
Issued: See below
Series: See below

Colourway	Issued	Series	U.K. £	U.S. $	Can. $
1. Black, matt	1987-1989	Spirited Dogs	125.00	175.00	250.00
2. Bronze	1989-1993	Britannia	125.00	175.00	250.00
3. English Setter					
a. Beswick	1987-1989	Spirited Dogs	125.00	175.00	250.00
b. Doulton (DA109)	1990-1995	Spirited Dogs	125.00	175.00	250.00
4. Gordon Setter					
a. Beswick	1988-1989	Spirited Dogs	125.00	175.00	250.00
b. Doulton (DA109)	1990-1995	Spirited Dogs	125.00	175.00	250.00
5. Red Setter					
a. Beswick	1987-1989	Spirited Dogs	125.00	175.00	250.00
b. Doulton (DA109)	1990-1995	Spirited Dogs	125.00	175.00	250.00
6. White	1987-1989	Spirited Dogs	100.00	150.00	225.00

Note: This model is found on an oval ceramic plinth and on a grass/rock ceramic mound.

Model No. 3011
POINTER

Designer: Graham Tongue
Height: 8 ½", 21.6 cm
Colour: See below
Issued: See below
Series: See below

Colourway	Issued	Series	U.K. £	U.S. $	Can. $
1. Black, matt	1987-1989	Spirited Dogs	90.00	125.00	200.00
2. Bronze finish	1989-1993	Britannia	90.00	125.00	200.00
3. White, matt	1987-1989	Spirited Dogs	75.00	100.00	150.00
4. White/brown, matt					
a. Beswick	1987-1989	Spirited Dogs	90.00	125.00	200.00
b. Doulton (DA 110)	1990-1995	Spirited Dogs	90.00	125.00	200.00

Note: This model is found on an oval ceramic plinth and on a grass/rock ceramic mound.

Model No. 3013
DACHSHUND - Standing

Designer: Alan Maslankowski
Height: 4 ¼", 10.8 cm
Colours: 1. Black and tan - gloss or matt
2. Tan - gloss or matt
Issued: a. Beswick – 1987-1989
b. Doulton (DA116) – 1990-1995
Series: Good Companions

Colourway	U.K. £	U.S. $	Can. $
a. Beswick	45.00	65.00	95.00
b. Doulton (DA116)	35.00	50.00	75.00

Model No. 3056 / (DA99)
ROTTWEILER

Designer: Alan Maslankowski
Height: 5 ¼", 13.3 cm
Colours: Black and tan - gloss or matt

Description	U.K. £	U.S. $	Can. $
a. Beswick	60.00	85.00	125.00
b. Doulton	40.00	60.00	90.00

Model No. 3058 / (DA100)
OLD ENGLISH SHEEP DOG - Walking

Designer: Warren Platt
Height: 5 ½", 14.0 cm
Colours: Grey and white - gloss or matt

Description	U.K. £	U.S. $	Can. $
1. Gloss			
a. Beswick, 1988-1989	45.00	65.00	95.00
b. Doulton, 1990-1999	45.00	65.00	95.00
c. Beswick, 1999 - Cur.	41.00	N/A	N/A
2. Matt			
a. Beswick, 1988-1989	60.00	90.00	135.00
b. Doulton, 1990-1995	60.00	90.00	135.00

Model No. 3060
STAFFORDSHIRE BULL TERRIER

Designer: Alan Maslankowski
Height: 4", 10.1 cm
Colours: 1. White and tan - gloss or matt
2. Brindle - gloss or matt
Issued: See below

Colourway	Issued	U.K. £	U.S. $	Can. $
1a. White/tan - gloss				
a. Beswick	1988-1989	70.00	100.00	150.00
b. Doulton (DA101)	1990-1995	65.00	95.00	140.00
1b. White/tan - matt				
a. Beswick	1988-1989	70.00	100.00	150.00
b. Doulton (DA101)	1990-1997	65.00	95.00	140.00
2a. Brindle - gloss				
a. Beswick	1988-1989	70.00	100.00	150.00
b. Doulton (DA101)	1990-1996	65.00	95.00	140.00
2b. Brindle - matt				
a. Beswick	1988-1989	70.00	100.00	150.00
b. Doulton (DA101)	1990-1996	65.00	95.00	140.00

Model No. 3062A
LABRADOR - on ceramic plinth

Designer:	Alan Maslankowski	
Height:	6 ½", 16.5 cm	
Colours:	1.	Black - matt
	2.	Golden - matt
Issued:	a.	Beswick – 1988-1989
	b.	Doulton (DA111) – 1990-1995
Series:	Spirited Dogs	
Varieties:	3062B	

Description	U.K. £	U.S. $	Can. $
a. Beswick	95.00	150.00	225.00
b. Doulton (DA111)	85.00	125.00	200.00

Model No. 3062B
LABRADOR - Walking

Designer:	Alan Maslankowski
Height:	5", 12.7 cm
Colours:	Chocolate brown - gloss
Issued:	1993 in a limited edition of 93
Varieties:	3062A

Description	U.K. £	U.S. $	Can. $
Gloss	225.00	350.00	525.00

Note: Produced for the B.C.C. with a special BCC backstamp.

Model No. 3066
RETRIEVER - on ceramic plinth

Designer:	Graham Tongue	
Height:	7 ½", 19.1 cm	
Colours:	See below	
Issued:	a.	Beswick, matt – 1988-1989
		Beswick, bronze – 1989-1989
	b.	Doulton (DA112) – 1990-1995
Series:	1.	Spirited Dogs
	2.	Britannia

Colourway	U.K. £	U.S. $	Can. $
a. Beswick	100.00	150.00	225.00
b. Doulton (DA112)	100.00	150.00	225.00

Model No. 3070
AFGHAN HOUND - Running

Designer:	Alan Maslankowski	
Height:	5 ½", 14.0 cm	
Colours:	Light brown and cream - gloss or matt	
Issued:	a.	Beswick – 1988-1989
	b.	Doulton (DA102) – 1990-1996

Description	U.K. £	U.S. $	Can. $
a. Beswick	90.00	125.00	200.00
b. Doulton (DA102)	60.00	90.00	125.00

Model No. 3073 / (DA103)
ALSATIAN - Standing

Designer: Alan Maslankowski
Height: 5 ¾", 14.6 cm
Colours: Black and light brown - gloss or matt
Issued: See below

Description	U.K. £	U.S. $	Can. $
1a. Beswick, gloss, 1988-89	45.00	60.00	90.00
1b. Doulton, gloss, 1990-99	40.00	60.00	90.00
1c. Beswick, gloss, 1999-curr.	41.00	N/A	140.00
2a. Beswick, matt, 1988-89	60.00	90.00	135.00
2b. Doulton, matt, 1990-96	50.00	75.00	110.00

Model No. 3080
SHETLAND SHEEPDOG - Seated

Designer: Alan Maslankowski
Height: 5 ½", 14.0 cm
Colours: Golden brown and white - gloss or matt
Issued: a. Beswick – 1988-1989
b. Doulton (DA117) – 1990-1995
Series: Good Companions

Description	U.K. £	U.S. $	Can. $
a. Beswick	85.00	125.00	200.00
b. Doulton (DA117)	40.00	60.00	90.00

Model No. 3081 / (DA104)
BOXER - Standing

Designer: Alan Maslankowski
Height: 5 ½", 14.0 cm
Colours: Golden brown and white - gloss or matt
Issued: See below

Description	U.K. £	U.S. $	Can. $
1a. Beswick, gloss - 1988-89	45.00	60.00	90.00
1c. Doulton, gloss - 1990-99	40.00	60.00	90.00
1c. Beswick, gloss - 1999-2001	40.00	55.00	85.00
2a. Beswick, matt - 1988-89	50.00	70.00	100.00
2b. Doulton, matt - 1990-95	50.00	75.00	100.00

Model No. 3082
CAIRN TERRIER - Standing

Designer: Warren Platt
Height: 4 ¾", 12.1 cm
Colours: Light brown - gloss or matt
Issued: a. Beswick – 1988-1989
b. Doulton (DA118) – 1990-1995
Series: Good Companions

Description	U.K. £	U.S. $	Can. $
a. Beswick	65.00	100.00	150.00
b. Doulton (DA118)	40.00	60.00	90.00

Model No. 3083
YORKSHIRE TERRIER - Seated

Designer: Warren Platt
Height: 5 ½", 14.0 cm
Colours: Grey and light brown - gloss and matt
Issued: a. Beswick – 1988-1989
b. Doulton (DA119) – 1990-1995
Series: Good Companions

Description	U.K. £	U.S. $	Can. $
a. Beswick	65.00	100.00	150.00
b. Doulton (DA119)	40.00	55.00	85.00

Model No. 3121
DOBERMAN

Designer: Alan Maslankowski
Height: 5 ¼", 13.3 cm
Colours: Black and tan - gloss or matt
Issued: a. Beswick – 1988-1989
b. Doulton (DA105) – 1990-1996

Description	U.K. £	U.S. $	Can. $
a. Beswick	55.00	80.00	125.00
b. Doulton (DA105)	55.00	80.00	125.00

Model No. 3129
ROUGH COLLIE

Designer: Warren Platt
Height: 5 ½", 14.0 cm
Colours: Golden brown and white - gloss or matt
Issued: a. Beswick – 1988-1989
b. Doulton (DA106), gloss – 1990-1995; matt – 1990-1996

Description	U.K. £	U.S. $	Can. $
a. Beswick	60.00	90.00	135.00
b. Doulton (DA106)	60.00	90.00	135.00

Model No. 3135
SPRINGER SPANIEL

Designer: Amanda Hughes-Lubeck
Height: 5", 12.7 cm
Colours: Dark brown and white - gloss or matt
Issued: See below

Description	U.K. £	U.S. $	Can. $
1a. Beswick, gloss, 1988-89	45.00	60.00	90.00
1b. Doulton, gloss, 1990-99	40.00	60.00	90.00
1c. Beswick, gloss, 1999-curr.	41.00	N/A	140.00
2a. Beswick, matt, 1988-89	60.00	90.00	135.00
2b. Doulton, matt, 1990-96	55.00	80.00	120.00

Model No. 3149
WEST HIGHLAND TERRIER - Seated

Designer: Martyn Alcock
Height: 5", 12.7 cm
Colours: White - gloss or matt
Issued: a. Beswick – 1989-1989
b. Doulton (DA120) – 1990-1995
Series: Good Companions

Description	U.K. £	U.S. $	Can. $
a. Beswick	60.00	90.00	135.00
b. Doulton (DA120)	40.00	60.00	90.00

Model No. 3155
CAVALIER KING CHARLES SPANIEL - Standing

Designer: Warren Platt
Height: 5 ½", 14.0 cm
Colours: 1. Black/tan/white - gloss or matt
2. Tan/white - gloss or matt
Issued: a. Beswick – 1989-1989
b. Doulton (DA121) – 1990-1995
Series: Good Companions

Description	U.K. £	U.S. $	Can. $
a. Beswick	70.00	100.00	150.00
b. Doulton (DA121)	40.00	60.00	90.00

Model No. 3258
ALSATIAN - Standing

Designer: Unknown
Height: 3 ¼", 8.3 cm
Colours: Black and cream - gloss
Issued: 1991-1997

Description	U.K. £	U.S. $	Can. $
Gloss	20.00	30.00	45.00

Model No. 3260
ROTTWEILER - Standing

Designer: Unknown
Height: 3 ½", 8.9 cm
Colours: Black and tan - gloss
Issued: 1991-1998

Description	U.K. £	U.S. $	Can. $
Gloss	20.00	30.00	45.00

Model No. 3262
YORKSHIRE TERRIER - Standing

Designer: Unknown
Height: 3 ½", 8.9 cm
Colours: Grey and sandy brown - gloss
Issued: 1991-1997

Description	U.K. £	U.S. $	Can. $
Gloss	20.00	30.00	45.00

Model No. 3270
GOLDEN RETRIEVER - Standing

Designer: Unknown
Height: 2 ¾", 7.0 cm
Colours: Pale golden brown - gloss
Issued: 1991 to the present

Description	U.K. £	U.S. $	Can. $
Gloss	17.00	N/A	N/A

Model No. 3375
HOUNDS - Seated

Designer: Martyn Alcock
Height: 2 ¼", 5.7 cm
Colours: Black, tan and white - gloss
Issued: 1993-1997

Description	U.K. £	U.S. $	Can. $
Gloss	20.00	30.00	45.00

Model No. 3376
GOLDEN RETRIEVERS - Seated

Designer: Martyn Alcock
Height: 2", 5.0 cm
Colours: Golden brown - gloss
Issued: 1993-1997

Description	U.K. £	U.S. $	Can. $
Gloss	20.00	30.00	45.00

Model No. 3377
COCKER SPANIEL - Standing

Designer: Amanda Hughes-Lubeck
Height: 3", 7.6 cm
Colours: Golden brown - gloss
Issued: 1993-1997

Description	U.K. £	U.S. $	Can. $
Gloss	20.00	30.00	45.00

Model No. 3378
ALSATIAN - Lying

Designer: Amanda Hughes-Lubeck
Height: 2 ½", 6.4 cm
Colours: Black and cream - gloss
Issued: 1993 to the present

Description	U.K. £	U.S. $	Can. $
Gloss	17.00	N/A	N/A

Model No. 3379
BULLDOG - Seated

Designer: Warren Platt
Height: 2 ½", 6.4 cm
Colours: White with pale tan patch - gloss
Issued: 1993 to the present

Description	U.K. £	U.S. $	Can. $
Gloss	16.00	N/A	50.00

Model No. 3380
JACK RUSSELL TERRIER - Standing

Designer: Warren Platt
Height: 2 ½", 6.4 cm
Colours: White with pale brown ears and patches on head - gloss
Issued: 1993-1997

Description	U.K. £	U.S. $	Can. $
Gloss	20.00	30.00	45.00

Model No. 3381
RETRIEVER - Standing

Designer: Warren Platt
Height: 2", 5.0 cm
Colours: Golden brown - gloss
Issued: 1993-1997

Description	U.K. £	U.S. $	Can. $
Gloss	20.00	30.00	45.00

Model No. 3382
SCOTTISH TERRIER - Standing

Designer: Martyn Alcock
Height: 3", 7.6 cm
Colours: Black - gloss
Issued: 1993 to the present

Description	U.K. £	U.S. $	Can. $
Gloss	16.00	N/A	50.00

Model No. 3383
COCKER SPANIELS - Seated

Designer: Martyn Alcock
Height: 2", 5.0 cm
Colours: Golden brown - gloss
Issued: 1993-1997

Description	U.K. £	U.S. $	Can. $
Gloss	20.00	30.00	45.00

Model No. 3384
BULLDOGS - Seated

Designer: Martyn Alcock
Height: 2 ¼", 5.7 cm
Colours: White with pale tan patches - gloss
Issued: 1994 to the present

Description	U.K. £	U.S. $	Can. $
Gloss	17.00	N/A	50.00

Model No. 3385
DALMATIAN - Standing

Designer: Amanda Hughes-Lubeck
Height: 3", 7.6 cm
Colours: White with black spots - gloss
Issued: 1994-1997

Description	U.K. £	U.S. $	Can. $
Gloss	20.00	30.00	45.00

Model No. 3436
CAVALIER KING CHARLES SPANIEL - Seated

Designer: Amanda Hughes-Lubeck
Height: 2 ½", 6.4 cm
Colours: White with golden brown patches - gloss
Issued: 1994 to the present

Description	U.K. £	U.S. $	Can. $
Gloss	16.00	N/A	50.00

Model No. 3467
WEST HIGHLAND WHITE TERRIERS - Seated

Designer: Amanda Hughes-Lubeck
Height: 2", 5.0 cm
Colours: White - gloss
Issued: 1994 to the present

Description	U.K. £	U.S. $	Can. $
Gloss	17.00	N/A	50.00

Model No. 3468
OLD ENGLISH SHEEPDOGS - Seated

Designer: Warren Platt
Height: 2", 5.0 cm
Colours: Grey and white - gloss
Issued: 1995 to the present

Description	U.K. £	U.S. $	Can. $
Gloss	17.00	N/A	50.00

Model No. 3475
BOXERS - One seated, one lying

Designer: Amanda Hughes-Lubeck
Height: 2 ¼", 5.7 cm
Colours: Tan - gloss
Issued: 1995-1998

Description	U.K. £	U.S. $	Can. $
Gloss	20.00	30.00	45.00

Model No. 3490
ROTTWEILERS - One seated, one lying

Designer: Warren Platt
Height: 2", 5.0 cm
Colours: Black and tan - gloss
Issued: 1995-1997

Description	U.K. £	U.S. $	Can. $
Gloss	20.00	30.00	45.00

Model No. D142
GOLDEN RETRIEVER

Designer: Amanda Hughes-Lubeck
Height: 5", 12.7 cm
Colours: Golden brown - gloss
Issued: a. Doulton (DA142) – 1990-1999
b. Beswick – 1999 to the present

Description	U.K. £	U.S. $	Can. $
a. Doulton (DA142)	45.00	65.00	100.00
b. Beswick	41.00	N/A	140.00

Model No. D145
LABRADOR - standing

Designer: Warren Platt
Height: 5", 12.7 cm
Issued: a. Doulton (DA145) – 1990-1999
b. Beswick – 1999 to the present

Colourway	U.K. £	U.S. $	Can. $
Black			
1a. Doulton (DA145)	45.00	65.00	100.00
1b. Beswick	41.00	N/A	140.00
Golden			
2a Doulton (Da145)	45.00	65.00	100.00
2b. Beswick	41.00	N/A	140.00

Model No. D222
BULLDOG

Designer: Warren Platt
Height: 5", 12.7 cm
Colours: White with tan patches
Issued: a. Doulton (DA222) – 1993-1999
b. Beswick – 1999 to the present

Description	U.K. £	U.S. $	Can. $
a. Doulton (DA222)	30.00	45.00	65.00
b. Beswick	31.00	N/A	N/A

Chapter Five

FARM ANIMALS - CATTLE

As the number of Beswick collectors grows dramatically, this particular section of Beswick animals has become more popular. This is mainly due to the accurate reproduction of champion-stock animals, where meticulous attention to detail by the designers and modellers at the Beswick factory, and now the Beswick Studio of Royal Doulton, has produced some superb models over the years.

This is very noticeable with the Hereford Cattle, since as the breed standard has changed, the models have been updated. Just compare the models of the early Herefords with the ones that followed; they are very different in shape.

It is also interesting to note that when the calves were discontinued in the mid 1970s, with the exception of the Friesian, public pressure brought about their reintroduction ten years later. Although the later models were altered from the originals, they can all live together as one happy family. Thus, for example, Aberdeen Angus Cattle becomes a set of four rather than just three.

As with all models that have had long production periods the cattle will be found, on the lighter coloured models, with various degrees of shading. It may be attributed to changes in glazing application and/or composition. Earlier models are more sought after due to better colouring and definition.

The models of the best-known breeds have survived to the present, but the lesser-known breeds, such as the Galloways, sadly had a short production run and now, as a result, are highly sought after by collectors.

The Connoisseur Range of cattle on polished wooden bases is truly impressive. With a satin matt finish, more detail can generally be achieved than on the gloss models—this, of course, was reflected in the retail price.

In 2001 Beswick introduced the Rare Breeds Series, which included three new cattle models.

INDEX BY MODEL NUMBER

MODELS TRANSFERRED TO *THE CHARLTON STANDARD CATALOGUE OF BESWICK COLLECTABLES*

Model No.	Description
2103	Laughing Pigs
2792	Daisy the Cow Creamer

Model No. 854
HEREFORD CALF

Designer: Arthur Gredington
Height: 4 ½", 11.9 cm
Colour: 1. Brown and white - gloss
2. Roan - gloss
3. Blue
Issued: 1940-c.1957

Colourway	U.K. £	U.S. $	Can. $
1. Brown/white	75.00	100.00	150.00
2. Roan	600.00	850.00	1,250.00
3. Blue	250.00	350.00	525.00

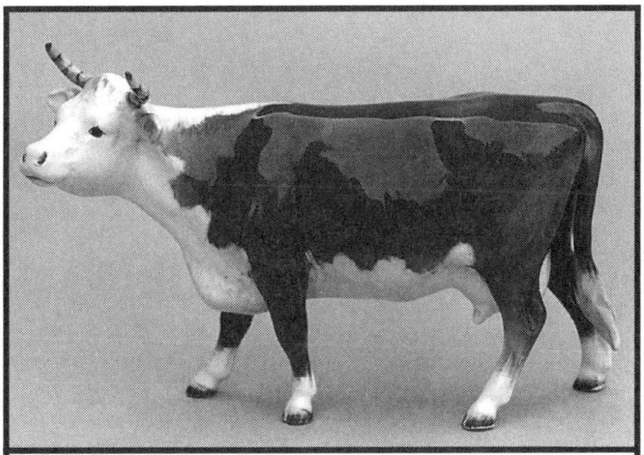

Model No. 899
HEREFORD COW
First Version - Horns are upright

Designer: Arthur Gredington
Height: 5", 12.7 cm
Colour: Brown and white - gloss
Issued: 1941-1941
Varieties: 948 (Horns point forward)

Colourway	U.K. £	U.S. $	Can. $
Brown/white	500.00	700.00	1,050.00

Note: Model no. 899 was remodelled in 1941 and became model no. 948.

Model No. 901A
HEREFORD CALF
First Version - Mouth open

Designer: Arthur Gredington
Height: 4", 10.1 cm
Colour: 1. Roan and white - gloss
2. Tan and white - gloss
Issued: 1940-Unknown
Varieties: 901B (mouth closed)

Colourway	U.K. £	U.S. $	Can. $
1. Roan/white	750.00	1,100.00	1,650.00
2. Tan/white	200.00	300.00	450.00

Model No. 901B
HEREFORD CALF
Second Version - Mouth closed

Designer: Arthur Gredington
Height: 3 ¾", 9.5 cm
Colour: See below - gloss
Issued: Unknown-c.1957
Varieties: 901A (mouth open)

Colourway	U.K. £	U.S. $	Can. $
1. Brown/white	75.00	100.00	150.00
2. Roan/white	675.00	950.00	1,400.00
3. White		Rare	

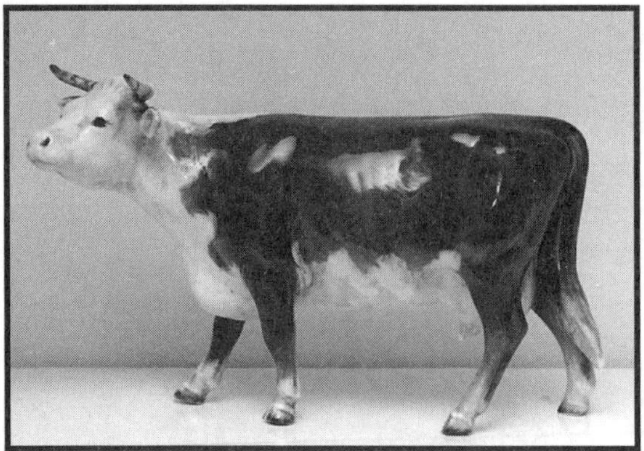

Model No. 948
HEREFORD COW
Second Version - Horns point forward

Designer: Arthur Gredington
Height: 5", 12.7 cm
Colour: 1. Brown and white - gloss
2. Roan and white - gloss
Issued: 1941-c.1957
Varieties: 899 (horns are upright)

Colourway	U.K. £	U.S. $	Can. $
1. Brown/white	575.00	800.00	1,200.00
2. Roan/white		Extremely Rare	

Model No. 949
HEREFORD BULL

Designer: Arthur Gredington
Height: 5 ¾", 14.6 cm
Colour: Brown and white - gloss
Issued: 1941-c.1957

Colourway	U.K. £	U.S. $	Can. $
Brown/white	175.00	250.00	375.00

Model No. 1248A
GUERNSEY COW
First Version - Horns and ears separate

Designer: Arthur Gredington
Height: 4 ¼", 10.8 cm
Colour: Golden brown and white - gloss
Issued: 1952-1953
Varieties: 1248B (Horns and ears moulded together)

Colourway	U.K. £	U.S. $	Can. $
Golden Brown	200.00	300.00	450.00

Note: Modelled from the Standard of the Guernsey Cattle Society.

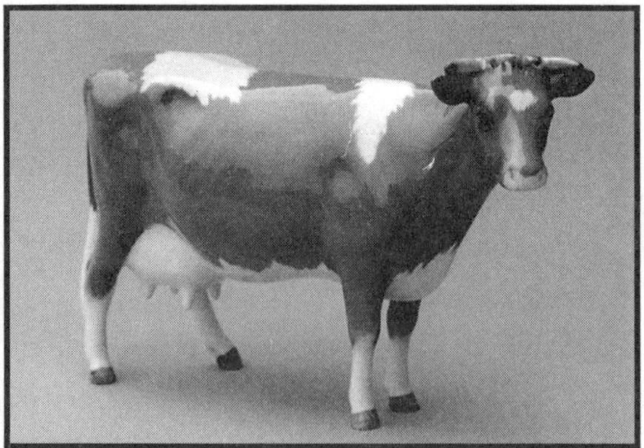

Model No. 1248B
GUERNSEY COW
Second Version - Horns and ears are moulded together

Designer: Arthur Gredington
Height: 4 ¼", 10.8 cm
Colour: Golden brown and white - gloss or matt
Issued: 1. Gloss - 1953-1989
2. Matt - 1985-1989
Varieties: 1248A (Horns and ears separate)

Description	U.K. £	U.S. $	Can. $
1. Gloss	80.00	125.00	175.00
2. Matt	70.00	100.00	150.00

Model No. 1248B/1249A
GUERNSEY COW AND CALF - on wooden plinth

Designer: Arthur Gredington
Height: 4 ¼", 10.8 cm
Colour: Golden brown and white - matt
Issued: c.1988

Description	U.K. £	U.S. $	Can. $
Matt	185.00	250.00	375.00

Note: Cow is no. 1248B; Calf is no. 1249A. Issued as a special commission for the Guernsey Cattle Society c.1988

Model No. 1249A
GUERNSEY CALF

Designer: Arthur Gredington
Height: 2 ¾", 7.0 cm
Colour: Golden brown and white - gloss or matt
Issued: 1. Gloss - 1952-1975
2. Matt - 1987-1989
Reissued: 3. Gloss - 1985-1989

Description	U.K. £	U.S. $	Can. $
1. Gloss	90.00	125.00	175.00
2. Matt	30.00	45.00	65.00
3. Gloss reissued	30.00	45.00	65.00

Model No. 1249B
AYRSHIRE CALF

Designer: Arthur Gredington
Height: 2 ¾", 7.0 cm
Colour: Brown and white - gloss or matt
Modelled: 1952
Issued: 1. Gloss - 1956-1975
2. Matt - 1987-1989
Reissued: 3. Gloss - 1985-1990

Description	U.K. £	U.S. $	Can. $
1. Gloss	90.00	125.00	175.00
2. Matt	30.00	45.00	65.00
3. Gloss reissued	30.00	45.00	65.00

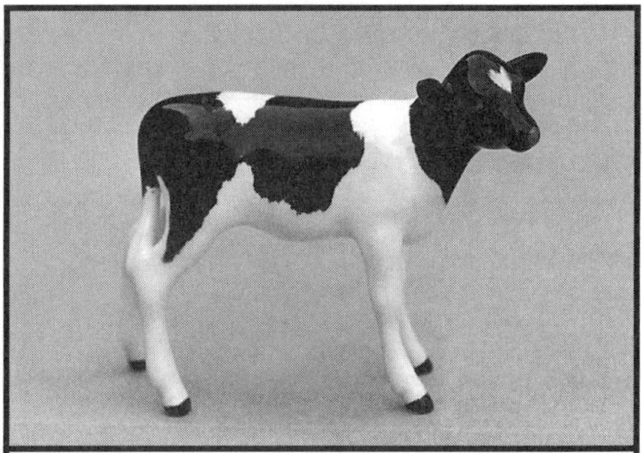

Model No. 1249C
FRIESIAN CALF

Designer: Arthur Gredington
Height: 2 ¾", 7.0 cm
Colour: Black and white - gloss or matt
Modelled: 1952
Issued: 1. Gloss - 1956-1997
2. Matt - 1987-1989

Description	U.K. £	U.S. $	Can. $
1. Gloss	40.00	55.00	80.00
2. Matt	30.00	45.00	70.00

Note: A Red Fresian Calf is known to exist.

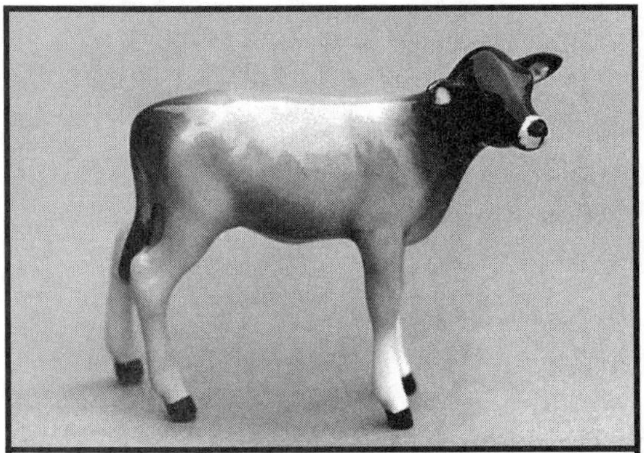

Model No. 1249D
JERSEY CALF

Designer: Arthur Gredington
Height: 2 ¾", 6.4 cm
Colour: Light brown with shading darker around the head - gloss or matt
Issued: 1. 1956-1975
2. 1987-1989
Reissued: 3. 1985-1997

Description	U.K. £	U.S. $	Can. $
1. Gloss	60.00	85.00	125.00
2 Matt	35.00	50.00	75.00
3. Gloss reissued	50.00	70.00	100.00

Model No. 1249E
HEREFORD CALF

Designer: Arthur Gredington
Height: 2 ¾", 7.0 cm
Colour: Brown and white - gloss
Modelled: 1952
Issued: This model was especially commissioned, sometime between 1975 and 1985, when the only calf in production was the Friesian.

Description	U.K. £	U.S. $	Can. $
Brown/white	100.00	150.00	225.00

Model No. 1345
JERSEY COW CH. "NEWTON TINKLE"

Designer: Arthur Gredington
Height: 4 ¼", 10.8 cm
Colour: Light brown with shading darker around the head - gloss or matt
Issued: 1. Gloss - 1954-1997
2. Matt - 1985-1989

Description	U.K. £	U.S. $	Can. $
1. Gloss	85.00	125.00	175.00
2. Matt	60.00	185.00	125.00

Model No. 1345/1249D
JERSEY COW AND CALF - on wooden plinth

Designer: Arthur Gredington
Height: 5 ¼", 13.3 cm
Colour: Light brown with shading especially around the head - gloss
Issued: 1993-1996
Series: Plinthed Animals

Description	U.K. £	U.S. $	Can. $
Light Brown	120.00	175.00	250.00

Note: Cow is no. 1345; Calf is no. 1249D.

Model No. 1350
AYRSHIRE COW CH. "ICKHAM BESSIE"

Designer: Arthur Gredington
Height: 5", 12.7 cm
Colour: Brown and white - gloss or matt
Issued: 1. Gloss - 1954-1990
2. Matt - 1985-1989

Description	U.K. £	U.S. $	Can. $
1. Gloss	175.00	250.00	375.00
2. Matt	150.00	200.00	300.00

Model No. 1360
HEREFORD COW

Designer: Arthur Gredington
Height: 4 ¼", 10.8 cm
Colour: Brown and white - gloss or matt
Issued: 1. Gloss - 1954-1997
2. Matt - 1985-1989

Description	U.K. £	U.S. $	Can. $
1. Gloss	60.00	85.00	125.00
2. Matt	80.00	115.00	175.00

Note: Modelled from the standard of the Hereford Cattle Society.

Model No. 1360/1827C
HEREFORD COW AND CALF - on wooden plinth

Designer: Graham Tongue
Height: 7", 17.8 cm
Colour: Brown and white - gloss
Issued: 1993-1996
Series: Plinthed Animals

Description	U.K. £	U.S. $	Can. $
Gloss	100.00	150.00	225.00

Note: Cow is no. 1360; Calf is no. 1827C.

Model No. 1362A
FRIESIAN COW
CH. "CLAYBURY LEEGWATER"

Designer: Arthur Gredington
Height: 4 ½", 11.9 cm
Colour: Black and white - gloss or matt
Issued: 1. Gloss - 1954-1997
2. Matt - 1985-1989
Varieties: 1362B

Description	U.K. £	U.S. $	Can. $
1. Gloss	90.00	135.00	200.00
2. Matt	110.00	150.00	225.00

Model No. 1362B
RED FRIESIAN COW

Designer: Arthur Gredington
Height: 4 ½", 11.9 cm
Colour: Brown and white - gloss
Modelled: 1954
Issued: 1992 in an edition of 130
Varieties: 1362A

Colourway	U.K. £	U.S. $	Can. $
Brown/white	*1,000.00*	*1,500.00*	*2,250.00*

Note: Produced for the Beswick Collectors Circle with special B.C.C. and Beswick backstamps.

Model No. 1362/1249C
FRIESIAN COW AND CALF - on wooden plinth

Designer: Graham Tongue
Height: 5 ½", 14.0 cm
Colour: Black and white - gloss
Issued: 1993-1996
Series: Plinthed Animals

Colourway	U.K. £	U.S. $	Can. $
Black/white	100.00	150.00	225.00

Note: Cow is no. 1362; Calf is no. 1249C.

Model No. 1363A
HEREFORD BULL
First Version - Horns protrude from ears

Designer: Arthur Gredington
Height: 4 ½", 10.8 cm
Colour: Brown and white - gloss or matt
Issued: 1. Gloss - 1955-unknown
2. Matt - 1985-unknown

Description	U.K. £	U.S. $	Can. $
1. Gloss	150.00	200.00	300.00
2. Matt	150.00	200.00	300.00

Model No. 1363B
HEREFORD BULL
Second Version - Horns flush to ears

Designer: Arthur Gredinton
Height: 4 ½", 10.8 cm
Colour: Brown and white - gloss or matt
Issued: 1. Gloss - Unknown-1997
2. Matt - 1985-1989

Description	U.K. £	U.S. $	Can. $
1. Gloss	75.00	100.00	150.00
2. Matt	95.00	135.00	200.00

Note: Modelled from the standard of the Hereford Cattle Society. This model has also appeared as a money-box.

Model No. 1363C
HEREFORD BULL - on wooden plinth

Designer:	Arthur Gredington
Height:	5 ½", 14.0 cm
Colour:	Brown and white - satin matt
Modelled:	1955
Issued:	1968-1975
Series:	Connoisseur

Colourway	U.K. £	U.S. $	Can. $
Brown/white	200.00	300.00	450.00

Note: Issued on a teak stand. The base was changed to polished wood in 1974.

Model No. 1406A
ABERDEEN ANGUS CALF

Designer:	Arthur Gredington
Height:	3", 7.6 cm
Colour:	Black - gloss
Issued:	1956-1975

Colourway	U.K. £	U.S. $	Can. $
Black	325.00	450.00	675.00

Model No. 1406B
HEREFORD CALF

Designer:	Arthur Gredington
Height:	3", 7.6 cm
Colour:	Brown and white - gloss
Issued:	1956-1975

Colourway	U.K. £	U.S. $	Can. $
Brown/white	200.00	300.00	450.00

Model No. 1406C
DAIRY SHORTHORN CALF

Designer:	Arthur Gredington
Height:	3", 7.6 cm
Colour:	Brown and white with shading - gloss
Issued:	1956-1973

Colourway	U.K. £	U.S. $	Can. $
Brown/white	500.00	700.00	1,100.00

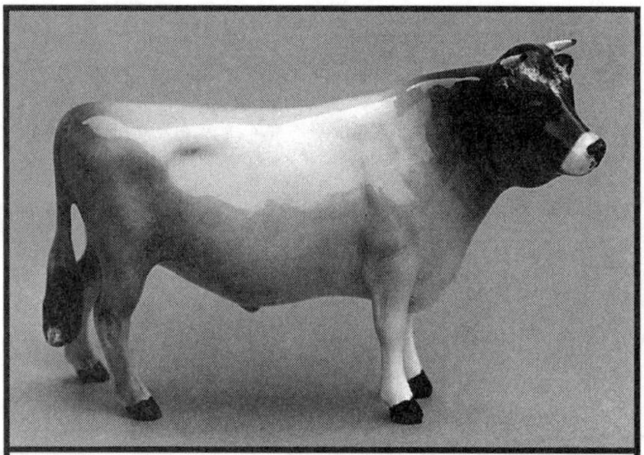

Model No. 1422
JERSEY BULL CH. "DUNSLEY COY BOY"

Designer: Arthur Gredington
Height: 4 ½", 11.9 cm
Colour: Light brown with shading and darker head - gloss or matt
Issued 1. Gloss - 1956-1997
2. Matt - 1985-1989

Description	U.K. £	U.S. $	Can. $
1. Gloss	85.00	120.00	175.00
2. Matt	60.00	85.00	125.00

Model No. 1439A
FRIESIAN BULL
CH. "CODDINGTON HILT BAR"

Designer: Arthur Gredington
Height: 4 ¾", 12.1 cm
Colour: Black and white - gloss or matt
Issued: 1. Gloss - 1956-1997
2. Matt - 1985-1989

Description	U.K. £	U.S. $	Can. $
1. Gloss	100.00	150.00	225.00
2. Matt	100.00	150.00	225.00

Model No. 1439B
FRIESIAN BULL - on teak plinth

Designer: Arthur Gredington
Height: 5 ½", 14.0 cm
Colour: Black and white - satin matt
Modelled: 1956
Issued: 1968-1973
Varieties: 1439A
Series: Connoisseur Cattle

Description	U.K. £	U.S. $	Can. $
Satin matt	150.00	200.00	300.00

Model No. 1439C
RED FRIESIAN BULL

Designer: Arthur Gredington
Height: 4 ¾", 12.1 cm
Colour: Brown and white - gloss
Modelled: 1956
Issued: 1992 in an edition of 129

Description	U.K. £	U.S. $	Can. $
Gloss	*600.00*	*950.00*	*1,500.00*

Note: Produced for the Beswick Collectors Circle with special B.C.C. and Beswick backstamps.

Model No. 1451
GUERNSEY BULL
CH. "SABRINA'S SIR RICHMOND 14th"

Designer: Colin Melbourne
Height: 4 ¾", 11.9 cm
Colour: Tan/brown and white - gloss or matt
Issued: 1. Gloss - 1956-1989
2. Matt - 1985-1989

Description	U.K. £	U.S. $	Can. $
1. Gloss	175.00	250.00	375.00
2. Matt	175.00	250.00	375.00

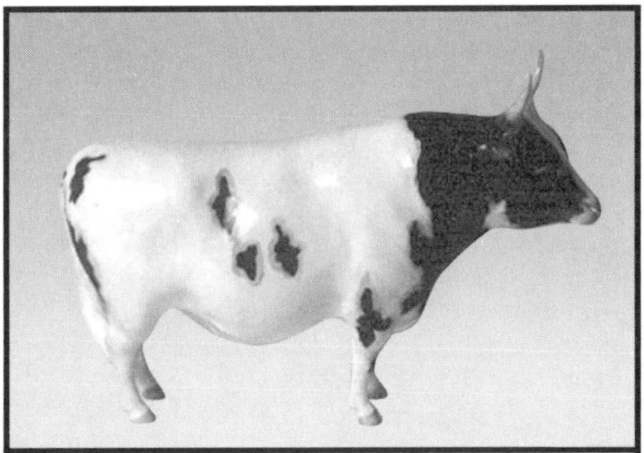

Model No. 1454A
AYRSHIRE BULL CH. "WHITEHILL MANDATE"
First Version

Designer: Colin Melbourne
Height: 5 ¼", 13.3 cm
Colour: Brown and white with shading - gloss
Issued: 1956-1957

Colourway	U.K. £	U.S. $	Can. $
Brown/white	*1,000.00*	*1,500.00*	*2,250.00*

Note: The First Version was modelled with noticably thinner legs and a narrow tail.

Model No. 1454B
AYRSHIRE BULL CH. "WHITEHILL MANDATE"
Second Version

Designer: Colin Melbourne
Height: 5 ¼", 13.3 cm
Colour: Brown, white and shaded - gloss or matt
Issued: 1. Gloss - 1957-1990
2. Matt - 1985-1989

Description	U.K. £	U.S. $	Can. $
1. Gloss	400.00	575.00	875.00
2. Matt	400.00	575.00	875.00

Model No. 1504
DAIRY SHORTHORN BULL
CH. "GWERSYLT LORD OXFORD 74th"

Designer: Arthur Gredington
Height: 5", 12.7 cm
Colour: Brown and white with shading - gloss
Issued: 1957-1973

Colourway	U.K. £	U.S. $	Can. $
Brown/white	*600.00*	*950.00*	*1,500.00*

Model No. 1510
DAIRY SHORTHORN COW
CH. "EATON WILD EYES 91 ST"

Designer: Arthur Gredington
Height: 4 ¾", 12.1 cm
Colour: Brown and white with shading - gloss
Issued: 1957-1973

Description	U.K. £	U.S. $	Can. $
Gloss	*900.00*	*1,250.00*	*1,800.00*

Model No. 1562
ABERDEEN ANGUS BULL

Designer: Arthur Gredington
Height: 4 ½", 11.9 cm
Colour: Black - gloss or matt
Issued: 1. Gloss - 1958-1989
2. Matt - 1985-1989

Description	U.K. £	U.S. $	Can. $
1. Gloss	150.00	200.00	300.00
2. Matt	175.00	250.00	375.00

Note: This model was approved by the Breed Society.

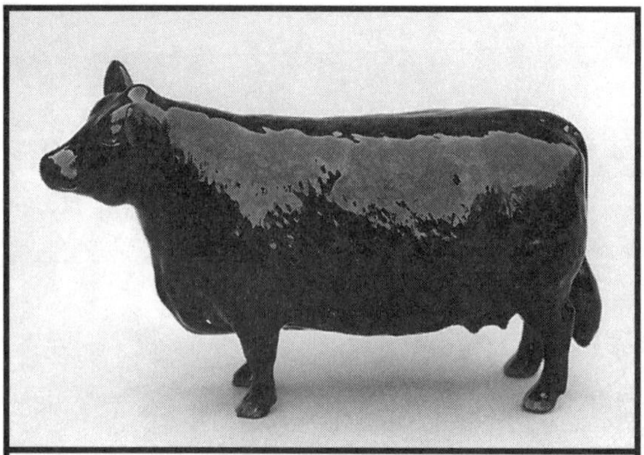

Model No. 1563
ABERDEEN ANGUS COW

Designer: Arthur Gredington
Height: 4 ¼", 10.8 cm
Colour: Black - gloss or matt
Issued: 1. Gloss - 1959-1989
2. Matt - 1985-1989

Description	U.K. £	U.S. $	Can. $
1. Gloss	200.00	300.00	450.00
2. Matt	250.00	350.00	525.00

Note: This model was approved by the Breed Society.

Model No. 1740
HIGHLAND COW

Designer: Arthur Gredington
Height: 5 ¼", 3.3 cm
Colour: Tan and brown - gloss or matt
Issued: 1. Gloss - 1961-1990
2. Matt - 1985-1989

Description	U.K. £	U.S. $	Can. $
1. Gloss	150.00	200.00	300.00
2. Matt	150.00	200.00	300.00

Model No. 1746A
GALLOWAY BULL

Designer: Arthur Gredington
Height: 4 ½", 11.9 cm
Colour: Black - gloss
Modelled: 1961
Issued: 1962-1969
Varieties: 1746B, 1746C

Colourway	U.K. £	U.S. $	Can. $
Black	*2,000.00*	*3,000.00*	*4,000.00*

Model No. 1746B
GALLOWAY BULL - BELTED

Designer: Arthur Gredington
Height: 4 ½", 11.9 cm
Colour: Black and white - gloss
Modelled: 1961
Issued: 1963-1969
Varieties: 1746A, 1746C

Colourway	U.K. £	U.S. $	Can. $
Black/white	1,450.00	2,000.00	3,000.00

Model No. 1746C
GALLOWAY BULL - SILVER DUNN

Designer: Arthur Gredington
Height: 4 ½", 11.9 cm
Colour: Fawn and brown - gloss
Modelled: 1961
Issued: 1962-1969
Varieties: 1746A, 1746B

Colourway	U.K. £	U.S. $	Can. $
Fawn/brown	1,000.00	1,400.00	2,100.00

Model No. 1827A
ABERDEEN ANGUS CALF

Designer: Arthur Gredington
Height: 3", 7.6 cm
Colour: Black - gloss or matt
Issued: 1. Gloss - 1985-1989
2. Matt - 1987-1989

Description	U.K. £	U.S. $	Can. $
1. Gloss	175.00	250.00	375.00
2. Matt	175.00	250.00	375.00

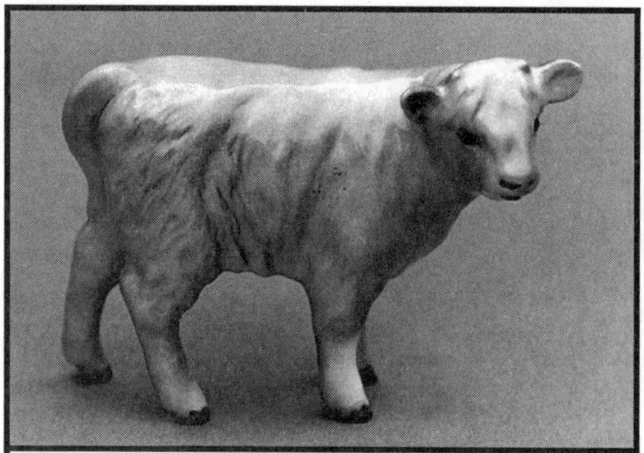

Model No. 1827B
CHAROLAIS CALF

Designer: Arthur Gredington
Height: 3", 7.6 cm
Colour: Cream - gloss or matt
Issued: 1. Gloss - 1985-1997
2. Matt - 1987-1989

Description	U.K. £	U.S. $	Can. $
1. Gloss	50.00	70.00	100.00
2. Matt	30.00	45.00	65.00

Model No. 1827C
HEREFORD CALF

Designer: Arthur Gredington
Height: 3", 7.6 cm
Colour: Brown and white - gloss or matt
Issued: 1. Gloss - 1985-1997
2. Matt - 1987-1989

Description	U.K. £	U.S. $	Can. $
1. Gloss	50.00	70.00	100.00
2. Matt	30.00	45.00	65.00

Model No. 1827D
HIGHLAND CALF

Designer: Arthur Gredington
Height: 3", 7.6 cm
Colour: Tan and brown - gloss or matt
Issued: 1. Gloss - 1962-1990
2. Matt - 1987-1989

Description	U.K. £	U.S. $	Can. $
1. Gloss	50.00	70.00	100.00
2. Matt	35.00	50.00	75.00

Model No. 1827E
LIMOUSIN CALF

Designer: Arthur Gredington
Height: 3", 7.6 cm
Colour: Brown and white - gloss
Issued: 1998 in a limited edition of 711

Colourway	U.K. £	U.S. $	Can. $
Brown/white	75.00	110.00	165.00

Note: Special colourway produced for The Beswick Collectors Club. The B.C.C. backstamp appears in addition to the normal Beswick backstamp.

FARM ANIMALS
BULLS

Model 949
Hereford Bull

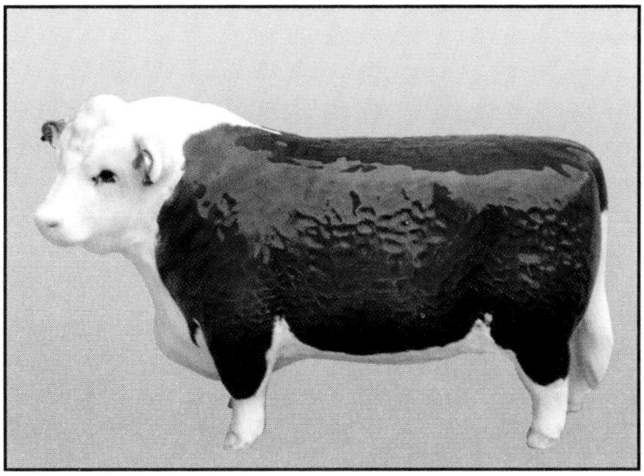

Model 1363
Hereford Bull

Model 1422
Jersey Bull

Model 1439A
Friesian Bull

Model 1439C
Red Friesian Bull

Model 1451
Guernsey Bull

FARM ANIMALS
BULLS

Model 1454B
Ayrshire Bull

Model 1504
Dairy Shorthorn Bull

Model 1562
Aberdeen Angus Bull

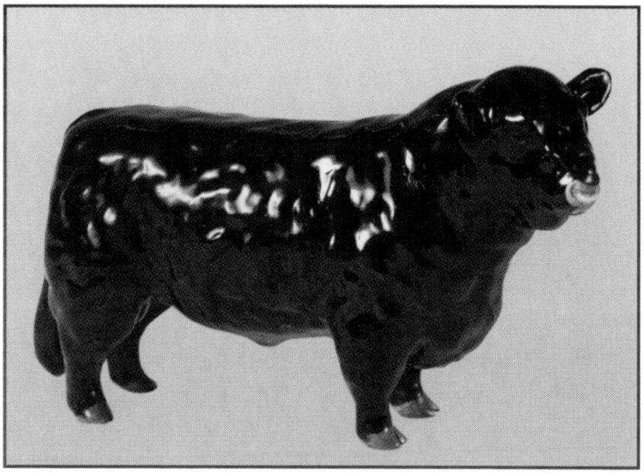

Model 1746A
Galloway Bull

Model 1746B
Galloway Bull – belted

Model 1746C
Galloway Bull – silver dunn

FARM ANIMALS
BULLS

Model 2008
Highland Bull

Model 2463A
Charolais Bull

Model 2463B
Limousin Bull

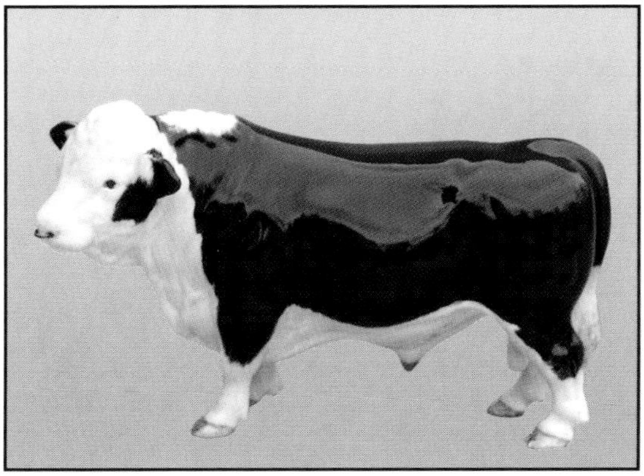

Model 2549A
Polled Hereford Bull

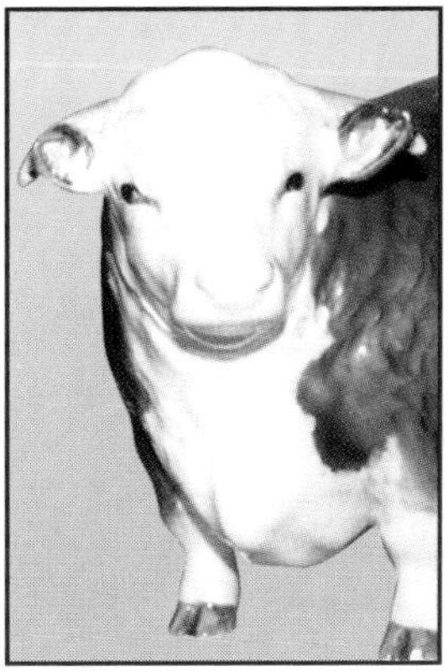

Model 1363A
Hereford Bull, first version

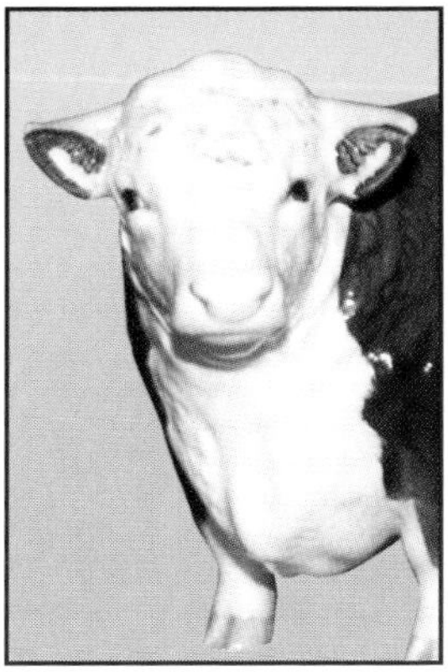

Model 1363B
Hereford Bull, second version

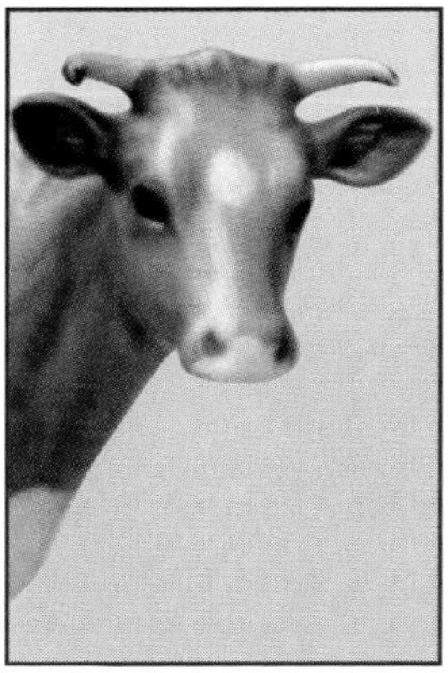

Model 1248A
Guernsey Cow, first version

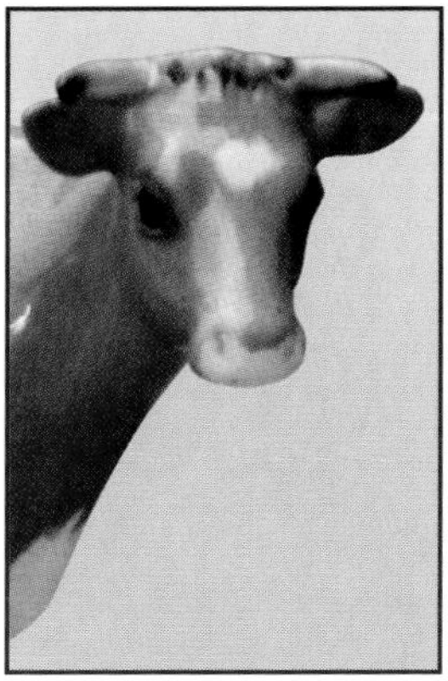

Model 1248B
Guernsey Cow, second version

FARM ANIMALS
COWS

Model 899
Hereford Cow, first version

Model 1248A
Guernsey Cow, first version

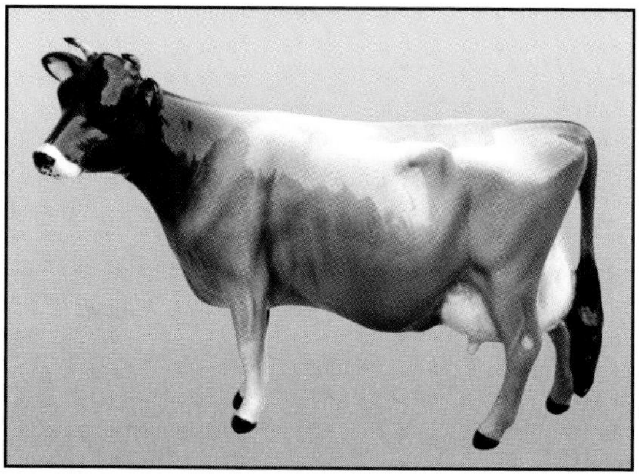

Model 1345
Jersey Cow

Model 1350
Ayrshire Cow

Model 1360
Hereford Cow

Model 1510
Dairy Shorthorn Cow

FARM ANIMALS
COWS

Model 1362A
Friesian Cow

Model 1362B
Red Friesian Cow

Model 1563
Aberdeen Angus Cow

Model 1740
Highland Cow

Model 3075A
Charolais Cow

Model 3075B
Limousin Cow

FARM ANIMALS
CALVES

Model 854
Hereford Calf

Model 901A
Hereford Calf

Model 901B
Hereford Calf

Model 1249A
Guernsey Calf

Model 1249B
Ayrshire Calf

Model 1249C
Friesian Calf

FARM ANIMALS
CALVES

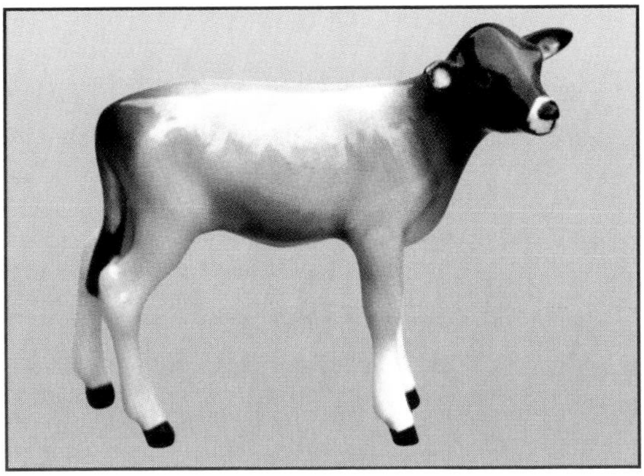

Model 1249D
Jersey Calf

Model 1249E
Hereford Calf

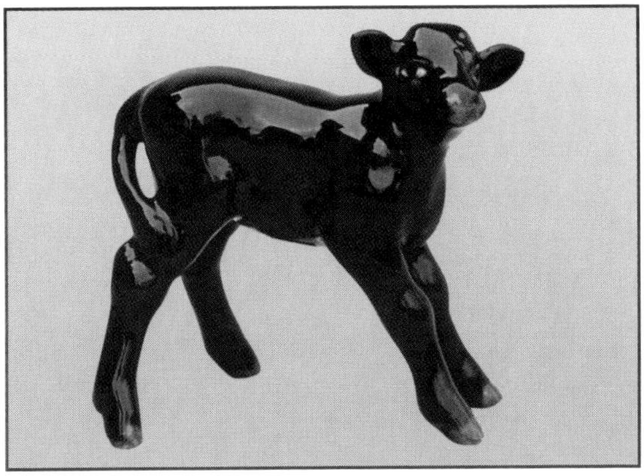

Model 1406A
Aberdeen Angus Calf

Model 1406B
Hereford Calf

Model 1406C
Dairy Shorthorn Calf

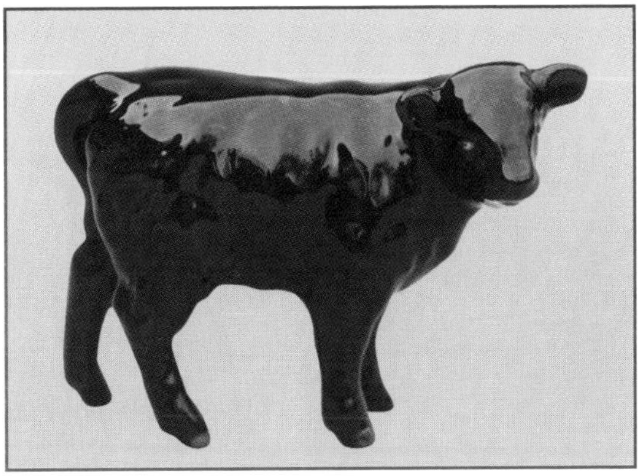

Model 1827A
Aberdeen Angus Calf

FARM ANIMALS
CALVES

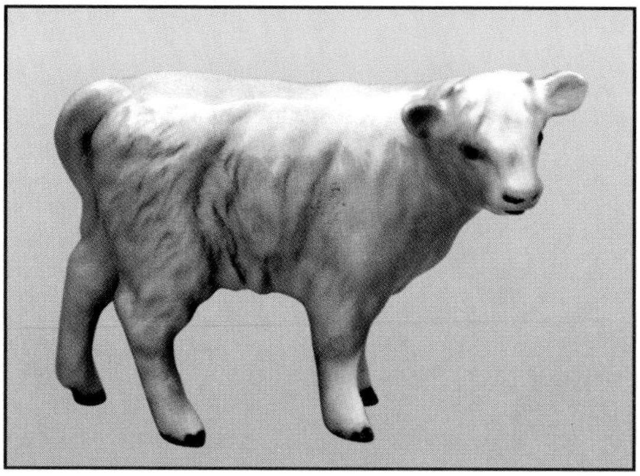

Model 1827B
Charolais Calf

Model 1827C
Hereford Calf

Model 1827D
Highland Calf

Model 1827E
Limousin Calf

Model 1827E
Limousin Calves - colour variations

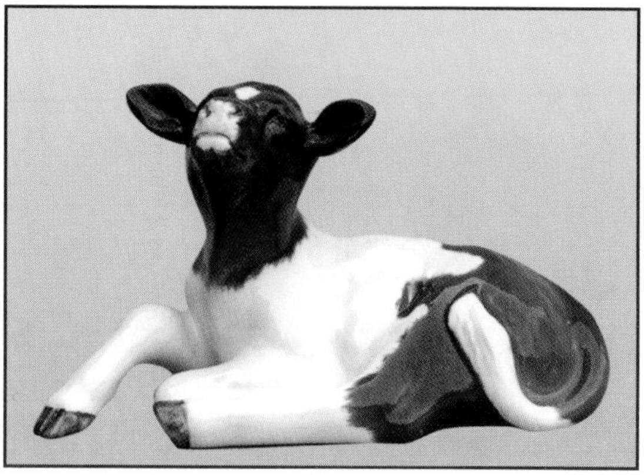

Model 2690
Red Friesian Calf

Model No. 2008
HIGHLAND BULL

Designer: Arthur Gredington
Height: 5", 12.7 cm
Colour: Tan/brown - gloss or matt
Issued: 1. Gloss - 1965-1990
2. Matt - 1985-1989

Description	U.K. £	U.S. $	Can. $
1. Gloss	150.00	200.00	300.00
2. Matt	135.00	175.00	275.00

Model No. 2463A
CHAROLAIS BULL

Designer: Alan Maslankowski
Height: 5", 12.7 cm
Colour: Cream - gloss or matt
Modelled: 1973
Issued: 1. Gloss - 1979-1997
2. Matt - 1985-1989

Description	U.K. £	U.S. $	Can. $
1. Gloss	60.00	85.00	125.00
2. Matt	65.00	90.00	135.00

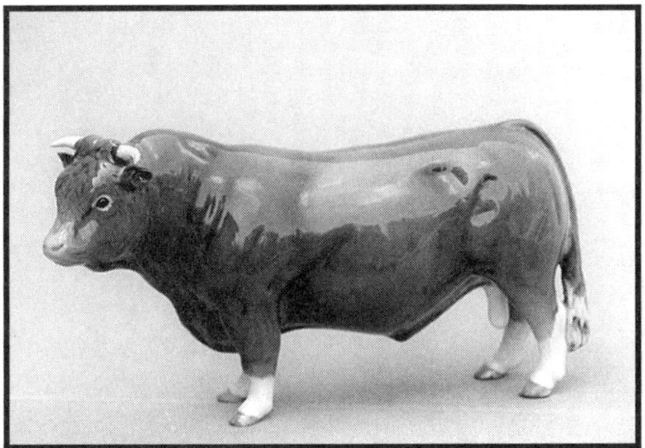

Model No. 2463B
LIMOUSIN BULL

Designer: Alan Maslankowski
Height: 5", 12.7 cm
Colour: Brown and white - gloss
Issued: 1998 in a limited edition of 653

Description	U.K. £	U.S. $	Can. $
Gloss	150.00	225.00	350.00

Note: Special colourway produced for The Beswick Collectors Club. The B.C.C. backstamp appears in addition to the normal Beswick backstamp.

Model No. A2463A
CHAROLAIS BULL - on wooden plinth

Designer: Alan Maslankowski
Height: 5 ½", 14.0 cm
Colour: Cream - satin matt
Modelled: 1973
Issued: 1975-1979
Series: Connoisseur Cattle

Description	U.K. £	U.S. $	Can. $
Satin matt	175.00	250.00	375.00

Model No. A2542A
HEREFORD BULL - on wooden plinth

Designer: Graham Tongue
Height: 7 ½", 19.1 cm
Colour: Brown and white - satin matt
Modelled: 1975
Issued: a. Beswick – 1976-1989
b. Doulton (DA19) – 1989-1996
Series: Connoisseur Cattle

Description	U.K. £	U.S. $	Can. $
a. Beswick	150.00	225.00	350.00
b. Doulton (DA19)	175.00	250.00	375.00

Model No. A2542B
HEREFORD BULL - on ceramic base

Designer: Graham Tongue
Height: 7 ½", 19.1 cm
Colour: Bronze, black shading - satin
Modelled: 1975
Issued: 1989-1992
Series: Britannia Collection

Colourway	U.K.£	U.S.$	Can.$
Bronze/black	150.00	225.00	350.00

Model No. 2549A
POLLED HEREFORD BULL

Designer: Graham Tongue
Height: 5", 12.7 cm
Colour: Brown, white ringed nose - gloss or matt
Modelled: 1975
Issued: 1. Gloss – 1977-1997
2. Matt – 1985-1989

Description	U.K. £	U.S. $	Can. $
1. Gloss	100.00	150.00	225.00
2. Matt	100.00	150.00	225.00

Photograph not available at press time

Model 2549B
POLLED HEREFORD BULL- on ceramic base

Designer: Graham Tongue
Height: 5", 12.7 cm
Colour: Bronze, black shading - satin
Modelled: 1975
Issued: 1989-1992
Series: Britannia Collection

Colourway	U.K.£	U.S.$	Can.$
Bronze/black	125.00	175.00	275.00

Model No. A2574
POLLED HEREFORD BULL - on wooden plinth

Designer: Graham Tongue
Height: 7 ½", 19.1 cm
Colour: Brown and white - satin matt
Modelled: 1976
Issued: a. Beswick – 1977-1989
b. Doulton (DA21) – 1989-1996
Series: Connoisseur Cattle

Description	U.K. £	U.S. $	Can. $
a. Beswick	125.00	175.00	275.00
b. Doulton (DA21)	150.00	225.00	350.00

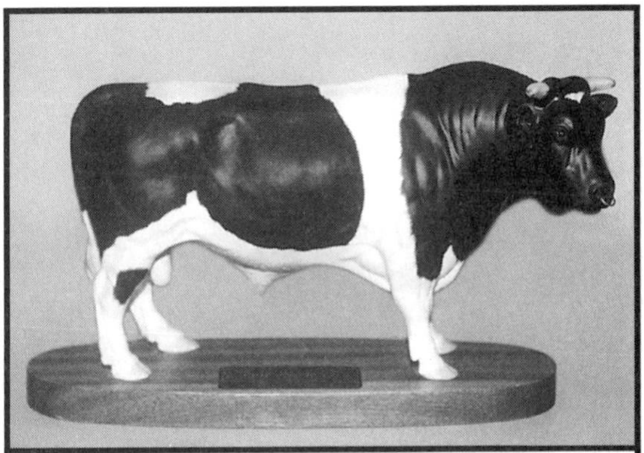

Model No. A2580
FRIESIAN BULL - on wooden plinth

Designer: Graham Tongue
Height: 7 ½", 19.1 cm
Colour: Black and white - satin matt
Modelled: 1976
Issued: a. Beswick – 1978-1989
b. Doulton (DA23) – 1989-1997
Series: Connoisseur Cattle

Description	U.K. £	U.S. $	Can. $
a. Beswick	125.00	175.00	275.00
b. Doulton (DA23)	150.00	225.00	350.00

Model No. A2600
CHAROLAIS BULL - on wooden plinth

Designer: Graham Tongue
Height: 7 ½", 19.1 cm
Colour: Cream - satin matt
Issued: a. Beswick – 1971-1979
b. Doulton (DA27) – 1989-1996
Series: Connoisseur Cattle

Description	U.K. £	U.S. $	Can. $
a. Beswick	135.00	200.00	300.00
b. Doulton (DA27)	175.00	250.00	375.00

Model No. A2607
FRIESIAN COW - on wooden plinth

Designer: Graham Tongue
Height: 7 ½", 19.1 cm
Colour: Black and white - satin matt
Modelled: 1977
Issued: a. Beswick – 1979-1989
b. Doulton (DA29) – 1989-1997
Series: Connoisseur Cattle

Description	U.K. £	U.S. $	Can. $
a. Beswick	135.00	200.00	300.00
b. Doulton (DA29)	150.00	225.00	350.00

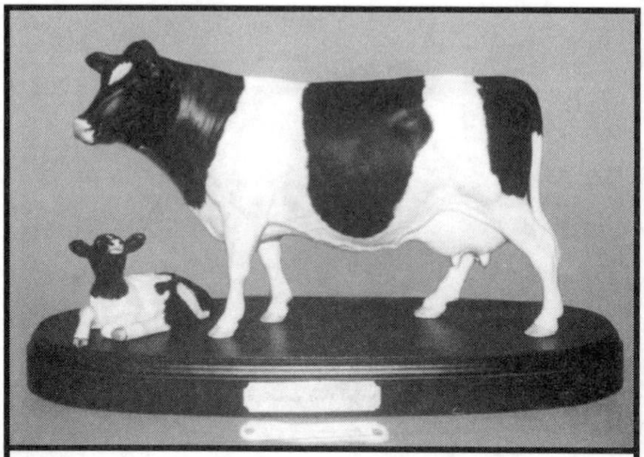

Model No. A2607/2690
FRIESIAN COW AND CALF - on wooden plinth

Designer:	Graham Tongue
Height:	6 ½", 16.5 cm
Colour:	Black and white - satin matt
Modelled:	Cow - 1977; Calf - 1982
Issued:	a. Beswick – 1982-1989
	b. Doulton (DA30) – 1989-1997
Series:	Connoisseur Cattle

Description	U.K. £	U.S. $	Can. $
a. Beswick	150.00	200.00	300.00
b. Doulton (DA30)	175.00	250.00	375.00

Note: Cow is no. A2607; Calf is no. 2690.

Model No. A2648/2652
CHAROLAIS COW AND CALF - on wooden plinth

Designer:	Graham Tongue
Height:	7 ¼", 18.4 cm
Colour:	Cream - satin matt
Modelled:	1979
Issued:	See below
Series:	Connoisseur

Description	U.K. £	U.S. $	Can. $
a. Beswick 1981/89	175.00	250.00	375.00
b. Doulton (DA33) 1989/96	175.00	250.00	375.00

Note: Cow is no. A2648; Calf is no. 2652 which was never issued individually.

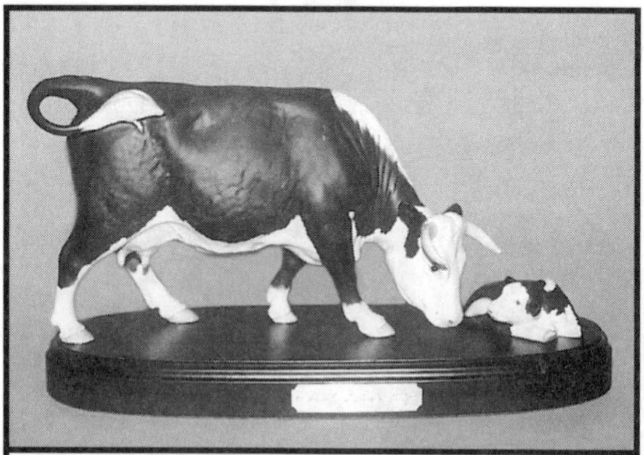

Model No. A2667/2669
HEREFORD COW AND CALF - on wooden plinth

Designer:	Graham Tongue
Height:	7", 17.8 cm
Colour:	Brown and white - satin matt
Modelled:	1980
Issued:	See below
Series:	Connoisseur

Description	U.K. £	U.S. $	Can. $
a. Beswick 1981/89	175.00	250.00	375.00
b. Doulton (DA34) 1989/96	175.00	250.00	375.00

Note: Cow is no. A2667; Calf is no. 2669, which was never issued individually.

Model No. 2690
RED FRIESIAN CALF

Designer:	Graham Tongue
Height:	2 ¼", 5.7 cm
Colour:	Brown and white - gloss
Modelled:	1980
Issued:	1992 in a special edition of 132

Colourway	U.K. £	U.S. $	Can. $
Brown/white	*375.00*	*525.00*	*800.00*

Note: Produced as a free standing model, in this special colourway for The Beswick Collectors Circle. The B.C.C. backstamp appears in addition to the normal Beswick Backstamp.

Model No. 3075A
CHAROLAIS COW

Designer: Unknown
Height: 5", 12.7 cm
Colour: Cream - gloss or matt
Modelled: 1987
Issued: 1. Gloss - 1988-1997
2. Matt - 1988-1989

Description	U.K. £	U.S. $	Can. $
1. Gloss	60.00	85.00	125.00
2. Matt	65.00	95.00	135.00

Model No. 3075B
LIMOUSIN COW

Designer: Unknown
Height: 5", 12.7 cm
Colour: Brown and white - gloss
Issued: 1998 in a limited edition of 656

Description	U.K. £	U.S. $	Can. $
Brown/white	150.00	225.00	350.00

Note: Special colourway produced for The Beswick Collectors Club.The B.C.C. backstamp appears in in addition to the normal Beswick backstamp.

Model No. 3075A/1827B
CHAROLAIS COW AND CALF - on wooden plinth

Designer: 3075 - Unknown
1827B - Arthur Gredington
Height: 6", 15.0 cm
Colour: Cream - gloss
Issued: 1993-1996

Description	U.K. £	U.S. $	Can. $
Cream	60.00	85.00	125.00

Note: Cow is no. 3075; Calf is no. 1827B.

Model No. 4111
RED POLL COW

Designer: Robert Donaldson
Length: 6 ¼", 15.9 cm
Colour: Red - gloss
Issued: 2001 to the present
Series: Rare Breeds

Description	U.K. £	U.S. $	Can. $
Red	75.00	N/A	N/A

Model No. 4112
SHETLAND COW

Designer: Robert Donaldson
Length: 5 ¼", 13.3 cm
Colour: Black and white - gloss
Issued: 2001 to the present
Series: Rare Breeds

Description	U.K. £	U.S. $	Can. $
Black and white	75.00	N/A	N/A

Model No. 4113
BELTED GALLOWAY COW

Designer: Robert Donaldson
Length: 5 ¼", 13.3 cm
Colour: Black and white - gloss
Issued: 2001 to the present
Series: Rare Breeds

Description	U.K. £	U.S. $	Can. $
Black and white	75.00	N/A	N/A

FARM ANIMALS OTHERS

With the exception of the earlier models, the majority of the animals in this group are realistically portrayed. Examples of this are the goat and kid, which make a delightful pair, and the donkeys, as popular now as they ever were.

In 2001, Beswick finally introduced a Rare Breeds Series for other animals usually found on a farm besides cattle. Seven new models were introduced.

INDEX BY MODEL NUMBER

Model No. 323
LAMB ON BASE

Designer: Miss Greaves
Height: 7 ½", 19.1 cm
Colour: 1. Blue - gloss
2. Cream - satin matt
3. Natural - satin matt
Issued: c.1935-by 1954

Colourway	U.K. £	U.S. $	Can. $
1. Blue	125.00	175.00	275.00
2. Cream	75.00	100.00	150.00
3. Natural	150.00	200.00	300.00

Note: Modelled in Deco style.

Model No. 369
DONKEY

Designer: Miss Greaves
Height: 8", 20.3 cm
Colour: 1. Blue - gloss
2. Cream - satin matt
3. Natural - satin matt
Issued: 1936-by 1954

Colourway	U.K. £	U.S. $	Can. $
1. Blue	125.00	175.00	275.00
2. Cream	75.00	100.00	150.00
3. Natural	150.00	200.00	300.00

Note: Modelled in Deco style.

Model No. 398
GOAT

Designer: Mr. Owen
Height: 4 ½", 11.9 cm
Colour: 1. Blue - gloss
2. Green - satin matt
3. White - satin matt
Issued: 1936-by 1954

Colourway	U.K. £	U.S. $	Can. $
1. Blue	30.00	45.00	70.00
2. Green	30.00	45.00	70.00
3. White	25.00	40.00	60.00

Model No. 832
PIG

Designer: Arthur Gredington
Height: 3 ¾", 9.5 cm
Colour: White and pink with grey patches - gloss
Issued: 1940-1971
Set: 833, 834

Colourway	U.K. £	U.S. $	Can. $
White	30.00	45.00	70.00

Model No. 833
PIGLET - Running

Designer:	Arthur Gredington
Height:	1 ¾", 4.5 cm
Colour:	White and pink with grey patches - gloss
Issued:	1940-1971
Set:	832, 834

Colourway	U.K. £	U.S. $	Can. $
White	25.00	35.00	50.00

Model No. 834
PIGLET - Trotting

Designer:	Arthur Gredington
Height:	1 ½", 3.8 cm
Colour:	White and pink with grey patches - gloss
Issued:	1940-1971
Set:	832, 833

Colourway	U.K. £	U.S. $	Can. $
White	25.00	35.00	50.00

Photograph not available.
Model number 897 possibly
not put into production.

Model No. 897
DONKEY FOAL

Designer:	Arthur Gredington
Height:	Unknown
Colour:	Natural - gloss
Issued:	1941-Unknown

Description	U.K. £	U.S. $	Can. $
Gloss		Extremely Rare	

Note: Probably not put into production under this number, see no. 950.

Model No. 935
SHEEP

Designer:	Arthur Gredington
Height:	3 ½", 8.9 cm
Colour:	White - gloss
Issued:	1941-1971
Set:	936, 937, 938

Colourway	U.K. £	U.S. $	Can. $
White	30.00	45.00	70.00

Model No. 936
LAMB

Designer: Arthur Gredington
Height: 3 ¼″, 8.3 cm
Colour: White - gloss
Issued: 1941-1971
Set: 935, 937, 938

Colourway	U.K. £	U.S. $	Can. $
White	18.00	25.00	40.00

Model No. 937
LAMB

Designer: Arthur Gredington
Height: 2″, 5.0 cm
Colour: White - gloss
Issued: 1941-1971
Set: 935, 936, 938

Colourway	U.K. £	U.S. $	Can. $
White	18.00	25.00	40.00

Model No. 938
LAMB

Designer: Arthur Gredington
Height: 2″, 5.0 cm
Colour: White - gloss
Issued: 1941-1971
Set: 935, 936, 937

Colourway	U.K. £	U.S. $	Can. $
White	18.00	25.00	40.00

Model No. 950
DONKEY FOAL

Designer: Arthur Gredington
Height: 5″, 12.7 cm
Colour: Grey-brown - gloss
Issued: 1941-1962

Colourway	U.K. £	U.S. $	Can. $
Grey-brown	95.00	135.00	200.00

Model No. 1035
GOAT

Designer: Arthur Gredington
Height: 5 ½", 14.0 cm
Colour: Tan - gloss
Issued: 1945-1971
Set: 1036

Colourway	U.K. £	U.S. $	Can. $
Tan	175.00	250.00	375.00

Model No. 1036
KID

Designer: Arthur Gredington
Height: 2 ½", 6.4 cm
Colour: Tan - gloss
Issued: 1945-1971
Set: 1035

Colourway	U.K. £	U.S. $	Can. $
Tan	125.00	175.00	275.00

Model No. 1364A
DONKEY
First Version - Tail free from hind leg

Designer: Mr. Orwell
Height: 4 ½", 11.9 cm
Colour: Natural brown - gloss
Issued: Jan. 1955- Oct. 1955

Colourway	U.K. £	U.S. $	Can. $
Brown		Extremely Rare	

Note: Probably not put into prodution.

Model No. 1364B
DONKEY
Second Version - Tail attached to hind leg

Designer: Mr. Orwell
Height: 4 ½", 11.9 cm
Colour: Natural - gloss or matt
Issued: 1. Gloss - Oct. 1955 to the present
2. Matt - 1987-1989

Description	U.K. £	U.S. $	Can. $
1. Gloss	26.00	N/A	N/A
2. Matt	30.00	45.00	65.00

Model No. 1452A
SOW CH "WALL QUEEN 40th"

Designer: Arthur Gredington
Height: 2 ¾", 7.0 cm
Colour: White - gloss or matt
Issued: 1. Gloss - 1956-1998
2. Matt - 1987-1989

Description	U.K. £	U.S. $	Can. $
1. Gloss	20.00	30.00	45.00
2. Matt	25.00	40.00	60.00

Photograph not available at press time

Model No. 1452B
SOW - on wooden plinth

Designer: Arthur Gredington
Height: 3 ¾", 9.5 cm
Colour: White - gloss
Issued: 1993-1995

Colourway	U.K. £	U.S. $	Can. $
White	30.00	45.00	65.00

Model No. 1453A
BOAR Ch. "WALL CHAMPION BOY 53rd"

Designer: Arthur Gredington
Height: 2 ¾", 7.0 cm
Colour: White - gloss or matt
Issued: 1. Gloss - 1956-1998
2. Matt - 1987-1989

Description	U.K. £	U.S. $	Can. $
1. Gloss	20.00	30.00	45.00
2. Matt	25.00	40.00	60.00

Photograph not available at press time

Model No. 1453B
BOAR - on wooden plinth

Designer: Arthur Gredington
Height: 3 ¾", 9.5 cm
Colour: White - gloss
Issued: 1993 -1995

Colourway	U.K. £	U.S. $	Can. $
White	30.00	45.00	65.00

Model No. 1511
WESSEX SADDLEBACK SOW
"MERRYWOOD SILVER WINGS 56th"

Designer: Colin Melbourne
Height: 2 ¾", 7.0 cm
Colour: Black and white - gloss
Issued: 1957-1969
Set: 1512

Colourway	U.K. £	U.S. $	Can. $
Black/white	400.00	550.00	850.00

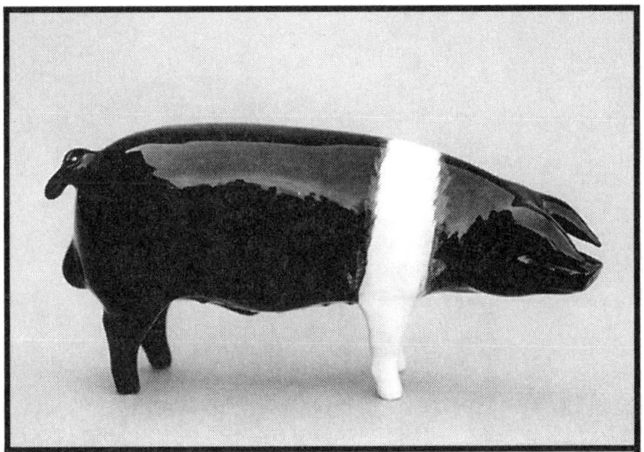

Model No. 1512
WESSEX SADDLEBACK BOAR
"FARACRE VISCOUNT 3rd"

Designer: Colin Melbourne
Height: 2 ¾", 7.0 cm
Colour: Black and white - gloss
Issued: 1957-1969
Set: 1511

Colourway	U.K. £	U.S. $	Can. $
Black/white	400.00	550.00	850.00

Model No. 1765
BLACK-FACED SHEEP

Designer: Mr. Garbet
Height: 3 ¼", 8.3 cm
Colour: Black and white - gloss or matt
Modelled: 1961
Issued: 1. Gloss - 1963 to the present
2. Matt - 1987-1989
Set: 1828

Description	U.K. £	U.S. $	Can. $
1. Gloss	23.00	N/A	N/A
2. Matt	20.00	30.00	45.00

Model No. 1765/1828
BLACK-FACED SHEEP AND LAMB
- on wooden plinth

Designer: Mr. Garbet and Arthur Gredington
Height: 3 ¾", 9.5 cm
Colour: Black and white - gloss
Issued: 1993-1996

Colourway	U.K. £	U.S. $	Can. $
Black/white	30.00	45.00	70.00

Note: Sheep is no. 1765; Lamb is no. 1828.

Model No. 1828
BLACK-FACED LAMB

Designer:	Arthur Gredington
Height:	2 ½", 6.4 cm
Colour:	Black and white - gloss or matt
Modelled:	1962
Issued:	1. Gloss - 1963 to the present 2. Matt - 1987-1989
Set:	1765

Description	U.K. £	U.S. $	Can. $
1. Gloss	15.00	N/A	N/A
2. Matt	15.00	25.00	35.00

Model No. 1917
MERINO RAM

Designer:	Arthur Gredington
Height:	4 ¼", 10.8 cm
Colour:	Grey with white face - gloss
Modelled:	1963
Issued:	1964-1967

Colourway	U.K. £	U.S. $	Can. $
Grey	1,200.00	1,650.00	2,475.00

Model No. 2110
DONKEY FOAL

Designer:	Graham Tongue
Height:	4 ½", 11.9 cm
Colour:	Grey-brown - gloss or matt
Modelled:	1967
Issued:	1. Gloss - 1968 to the present 2. Matt - 1987-1989

Description	U.K. £	U.S. $	Can. $
1. Gloss	23.00	N/A	N/A
2. Matt	25.00	35.00	50.00

Model No. 2267
DONKEY

Designer:	Albert Hallam and Graham Tongue
Height:	5 ½", 14.0 cm
Colour:	Grey-brown - gloss or matt
Modelled:	1969
Issued:	1. Gloss - 1970 to the present 2. Matt - 1987-1989

Description	U.K. £	U.S. $	Can. $
1. Gloss	31.00	N/A	N/A
2. Matt	35.00	50.00	75.00

Model No. 2746
PIG AND PIGLET "Piggy Back"

Designer: Graham Tongue
Length: 6 ½", 16.5 cm
Colour: Pink and white - gloss
Modelled: 1981
Issued: 1983-1994
Series: Fun Models

Colourway	U.K. £	U.S. $	Can. $
Pink/white	50.00	70.00	100.00

Model No. 3071
BLACK-FACED RAM

Designer: Mr. Chawner
Height: 3 ¼", 8.3 cm
Colour: Black and white - gloss or matt
Modelled: 1987
Issued: 1. Gloss - 1988 to the present
2. Matt - 1988-1989

Description	U.K. £	U.S. $	Can. $
1. Gloss	24.00	N/A	N/A
2. Matt	30.00	45.00	65.00

Model No. 3071/1765
"EWE AND I" - on ceramic plinth

Designer: Unknown
Height: 4 ½", 11.9 cm
Base: 7 ½", 19.1 cm
Colour: Black and white - gloss
Issued: Unknown

Colourway	U.K. £	U.S. $	Can. $
Black/white	65.00	90.00	135.00

Note: Ram is no. 3071; Sheep is no. 1765.
Produced as a special commission.

Model No. 4114
TAMWORTH SOW

Designer: Robert Donaldson
Length: 4 ¼, 10.8 cm
Colour: Tan - gloss
Issued: 2001 to the present
Series: Rare Breeds

Colourway	U.K. £	U.S. $	Can. $
Tan	45.00	N/A	N/A

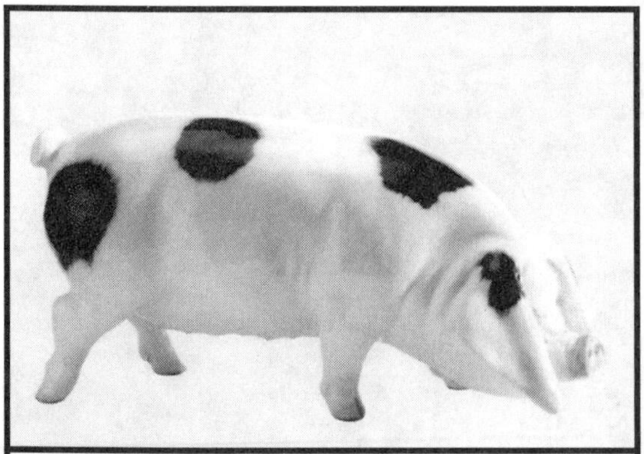

Model No. 4116
GLOUCESTERSHIRE OLD SPOT

Designer: Robert Donaldson
Length: 3 ¼", 8.7 cm
Colour: White with black markings - gloss
Issued: 2001 to the present
Series: Rare Breeds

Colourway	U.K. £	U.S. $	Can. $
White/black	45.00	N/A	N/A

Model No. 4117
MIDDLEWHITE BOAR

Designer: Robert Donaldson
Length: 4", 10.1 cm
Colour: White - gloss
Issued: 2001 to the present
Series: Rare Breeds

Colourway	U.K. £	U.S. $	Can. $
White	45.00	N/A	N/A

Model No. 4118
BERKSHIRE BOAR

Designer: Robert Donaldson
Length: 3 ¼", 8.2 cm
Colour: Black and grey - gloss
Issued: 2001 to the present
Series: Rare Breeds

Colourway	U.K. £	U.S. $	Can. $
Black/grey	45.00	N/A	N/A

Model No. 4122
COTSWOLD SHEEP

Designer: Robert Donaldson
Length: 4 ¼", 10.8 cm
Colour: White - gloss
Issued: 2001 to the present
Series: Rare Breeds

Colourway	U.K. £	U.S. $	Can. $
White	45.00	N/A	N/A

Model No. 4123
WENSLEYDALE SHEEP

Designer: Robert Donaldson
Length: 4 ¼", 10.8 cm
Colout: White with black markings - gloss
Issued: 2001 to the present
Series: Rare Breeds

Colourway	U.K. £	U.S. $	Can. $
White/black	45.00	N/A	N/A

Model No. 4124
BORERAY SHEEP

Designer: Robert Donaldson
Length: 4 ¼", 10.8 cm
Colout: White with black markings - gloss
Issued: 2001 to the present
Series: Rare Breeds

Colourway	U.K. £	U.S. $	Can. $
White/black	45.00	N/A	N/A

Model No. G189
VIETNAMESE POT-BELLIED PIG

Designer: Amanda Hughes-Lubeck
Length: 6", 15.2 cm
Colour: Dark brown - gloss
Issued: a. Doulton (DA189) – 1992-1999
b. Beswick – 1999 to the present

Description	U.K. £	U.S. $	Can. $
a. Doulton (DA189)	30.00	45.00	65.00
b.. Beswick	31.00	N/A	N/A

Model No. G213
VIETNAMESE POT-BELLIED PIGLET

Designer: Warren Platt
Length: 3", 7.6 cm
Colour: Grey - gloss
Issued: a. Doulton (DA213) – 1993-1999
b. Beswick – 1999 to the present

Description	U.K. £	U.S. $	Can. $
a. Doulton (DA213)	15.00	20.00	30.00
b. Beswick	14.50	N/A	50.00

Model G215
TAMWORTH PIG

Designer: Amanda Hughes-Lubeck
Length: 6", 15.2 cm
Colour: Brown - gloss
Issued: a. Doulton (DA215) – 1994-1999
b. Beswick – 1999 to the present

Description	U.K. £	U.S. $	Can. $
a. Doulton (DA215)	30.00	45.00	65.00
b. Beswick	31.00	N/A	110.00

Model No. G223
NYGERIAN POT-BELLIED PYGMY GOAT

Designer: Amanda Hughes-Lubeck
Height: 5 ¼", 14.0 cm
Colour: White with black markings - gloss
Issued: a. Doulton (DA223) – 1993-1999
b. Beswick – 1999 to the present

Description	U.K. £	U.S. $	Can. $
a. Doulton (DA223)	30.00	45.00	65.00
b. Beswick	31.00	N/A	N/A

Model No. G230
GLOUCESTER OLD SPOT PIG

Designer: Amanda Hughes-Lubeck
Height: 3", 7.6 cm
Colour: Pink with black markings - gloss
Issued: a. Doulton (DA230) – 1995-1999
b. Beswick – 1999 to the present

Description	U.K. £	U.S. $	Can. $
a. Doulton (DA230)	30.00	450.00	65.00
b. Beswick	31.00	N/A	110.00

Chapter Six

FISH

All but one of these fish models are realistically portrayed. The detail on many of them is amazing, for example the Golden Trout. So many colours were used, and the result is simply stunning.

The only stylized version of a fish is one from the Moda series. All the rest are supported on bases, although their fins are still vulnerable to damage. Very few, therefore, have survived intact to the present, and as a result they are particularly hard to find in mint condition, although restored ones do appear.

INDEX BY MODEL NUMBER

MODEL TRANSFERRED TO *THE CHARLTON STANDARD CATALOGUE OF BESWICK COLLECTABLES*

Model No.	Desription
1304	Fish Tray / Trinket Dish

Model No. 1032
TROUT

Designer: Arthur Gredington
Height: 6 ¼", 15.9 cm
Colour: Brown and dark green - gloss
Issued: 1945-1975

Description	U.K. £	U.S. $	Can. $
Gloss	75.00	125.00	175.00

Model No. 1047
ANGEL FISH

Designer: Arthur Gredington
Height: 7 ¼", 18.4 cm
Colour: Silver, red and green-brown - gloss
Issued: 1946-1967

Description	U.K. £	U.S. $	Can. $
Gloss	325.00	450.00	675.00

Model No. 1232
OCEANIC BONITO

Designer: Arthur Gredington
Height: 7 ¼", 18.4 cm
Colour: Blue, silver and green - gloss
Issued: 1952-1968

Description	U.K. £	U.S. $	Can. $
Gloss	300.00	450.00	675.00

Model No. 1233
ATLANTIC SALMON

Designer: Arthur Gredington
Height: 6 ½", 16.5 cm
Colour: Blue, silver and green - gloss
Issued: 1952-1970

Description	U.K. £	U.S. $	Can. $
Gloss	225.00	325.00	500.00

Model No. 1235
BARRACUDA

Designer: Arthur Gredington
Height: 4 ¾", 12.1 cm
Colour: Blue and silver
Issued: 1952-1968

Description	U.K. £	U.S. $	Can. $
Gloss	350.00	500.00	750.00

Model No. 1243
MARLIN

Designer: Arthur Gredington
Height: 5 ½", 14.0 cm
Colour: Blue, grey and green
Issued: 1952-1970

Description	U.K. £	U.S. $	Can. $
Gloss	550.00	775.00	1,150.00

Model No. 1246
GOLDEN TROUT

Designer: Arthur Gredington
Height: 6", 15.0 cm
Colour: Blue, yellow and green
Issued: 1952-1970

Description	U.K. £	U.S. $	Can. $
Gloss	150.00	225.00	350.00

Model No. 1266
LARGE-MOUTHED BLACK BASS

Designer: Arthur Gredington
Height: 5", 12.7 cm
Colour: Yellow, black, beige and blue
Issued: 1952-1968

Description	U.K. £	U.S. $	Can. $
Gloss	300.00	450.00	675.00

Model No. 1390
TROUT

Designer: Arthur Gredington
Colour: Brown and dark green - gloss
Height: 4", 10.1 cm
Issued: 1955-1975

Description.	U.K. £	U.S. $	Can. $
Gloss	50.00	75.00	125.00

Model No. 1485
BLACK BASS

Designer: Colin Melbourne
Height: 6", 15.0 cm
Colour: Brown and dark green - gloss
Issued: 1957-1968

Description	U.K. £	U.S. $	Can. $
Gloss	650.00	1,000.00	1,500.00

Model No. 1874
ROACH

Designer: Arthur Gredington
Height: 6 ¼", 15.9 cm
Colour: Turquoise and browns
Issued: 1963-1971

Description	U.K. £	U.S. $	Can. $
Gloss	350.00	500.00	750.00

Model No. 1875
PERCH

Designer: Arthur Gredington
Height: 6 ¼", 15.9 cm
Colour: Greens and browns
Issued: 1963-1971

Description	U.K. £	U.S. $	Can. $
Gloss	350.00	500.00	750.00

Model No. 2066
SALMON

Designer: Graham Tongue
Height: 8", 20.3 cm
Colour: Browns and silver - gloss
Issued: 1966-1975

Description	U.K. £	U.S. $	Can. $
Gloss	225.00	325.00	500.00

Model No. 2087
TROUT

Designer: Graham Tongue
Height: 6", 15.0 cm
Colour: Brown with red-brown spots - gloss
Issued: 1967-1975

Description	U.K. £	U.S. $	Can. $
Gloss	200.00	300.00	450.00

Model No 2254
FISH (Stylized Model)

Designer: Harry Sales
Height: 4 ½", 11.9 cm
Colour: Dark and light blue
Issued: 1968-1971
Series: Moda

Description	U.K. £	U.S. $	Can. $
Gloss	125.00	175.00	275.00

Chapter Seven

HORSES

Beswick is most readily associated with the production of accurately modelled horses. Indeed horses form the largest section by far of all the Beswick range. From 1939 to 1989, Beswick produced over 150 different horse models, the vast majority available in several colourways and in gloss or matt finishes. Although each model had a shape number, many were only listed in price lists and catalogues as horse, mare or foal, which left less knowledgeable collectors and dealers with a considerable identification problem! Some horses do have their names incorporated into their backstamp (for example, the Mountain and Moorland ponies) or numbers imprinted into their base (such as the lying down foal, 915), and of course those with riders are easy to sort out. But those that remain need careful examination to determine exactly which models they are.

A further consideration is colour. Initially Beswick produced horses in dark chestnut, light brown, dark brown, rocking horse grey and even in blue gloss. Later brown, painted white, opaque, palomino, chestnut and light grey glosses were added to the range, and most of the initial colourways were dropped. Special colours were also used for specific models, such as on the 2282 Fjord. From 1970 onwards, matt finishes were introduced in various colours: brown, grey, palomino, white and black. Within each colour there can be considerable variations, from a light tone with shading to an all-over, solid, one-tone version of the same colour. Avid collectors will value the former, which usually indicates an earlier example, painted when more attention was paid to details like well-painted eyes and pink mouths.

The Beswick stable comprises the full spectrum of the equine world, from children's ponies, specific breeds, famous racehorses, to the giant Shires, whilst the *Colin Melbourne* series adds a contemporary touch to the collection.

Arthur Gredington modelled Beswick's first realistic horse in 1939 when he produced the first version of the 1938 Derby winner, *Bois Roussel*. Although a handful of other modellers made contributions to the horse models it was Arthur Gredington who was responsible for the vast majority until he retired in 1968. Graham Tongue then took over, adding many more horses to the range, including a new bronze finish for the Britannia Series. In August 1989 all except three Beswick horses became Doulton Animals and so from that date, although they continued to be produced in the Beswick factory, they were backstamped with the name of the parent company, Royal Doulton. In 1994 to mark the Beswick Centenary it was a horse model that was chosen as a special piece to represent Beswick. This was the large rearing model of *Downland Cancara*. Graham Tongue modelled this magnificent horse. In 1995 Cancara was issued with a Royal Doulton backstamp and the three remaining Beswick horses were completely withdrawn.

1996 saw the revival of the Beswick backstamp on horses when the 1642 Dartmoor pony stallion was commissioned by Doug Middleweek in bright bay gloss as "Warlord." Warlord was followed at the end of 1997 with a brand new model of a Dartmoor Mare "Another Bunch." The set was completed in 1998 with the "birth" of their foal *Another Star*. Doug was planning to continue the Native ponies theme but unfortunately this has not been possible.

At the time of writing there is still ONE horse shape, known to have been in general production, which has not come to light. This is the action foal 766. Why this remains elusive is something of a mystery. It was illustrated in the 1940 Overseas brochure/price list which stated it as being available on or off a ceramic base in Dark Chestnut and Light Brown colourways. The model was priced at 14 shillings per dozen in "Dark Chestnut" and 13 shillings per dozen in "Light Brown off stand"! Surely out of these "dozens" some have survived?!

There remain a handful of horse models which reached various stages of production and it is a possibility that there are the odd examples *somewhere*! These include 2451, a mounted piece given the title of "The Outlaw" which was to be part of a "Riders of the World" collection. Unfortunately this was not pursued further than a prototype. "The Outlaw" was modelled by Graham Tongue in March 1973.

At least three other horse models are recorded in the shape book which did not get as far as being generally released by Beswick. All were designed during the late 1970s. They are 2468 *Icelandic Pony* and 2626 *Haflinger Pony* both by Graham Tongue; 2577 *Racehorse* by David Littleton. The 2548 Small Shire, also referred to as the "Whitbread" Shire as it was intended as a souvenir for visitors to the Whitbread Shire Horse Farm in Kent to purchase, does exist as there were a small number actually produced. Examples, in grey gloss and matt, are now in the hands of a few extremely lucky collectors and are illustrated in this book. Although no examples of the Haflinger have come to my attention I do know that they exist as I saw them in Graham Tongue's studio several years ago. This was at least ten years following the Haflinger's original modelling and suggest that Doulton were perhaps reconsidering issuing it. They were obviously trial pieces, being in various colourways and were attractive action models. It is a great pity that once more the model was rejected. There could be an Icelandic Pony model in existence but the racehorse was not illustrated in the shape book and so probably did not get to the stage where models could exist.

In 2000 the *Beswick Collectors Club* commissioned the Welsh Champion Pony in grey (white) gloss as a companion piece to the previous BCC version in black gloss.

Following the return to the Beswick backstamp as from October 1999 the range of Beswick horses was extended during 2000 and 2001 by several new models in the Connoisseur and Spirit series. All these newer models are in matt finish and mounted on either a wooden or slate effect base.

Prices for many of the equine pieces have continued to "level off" and in some cases have fallen. Rarer shapes and colourways, particularly concerning Shires and mounted pieces, obviously still command premium prices. However some models and colourways which were considered "rare" in the past have now been located in sufficient numbers to satisfy the more ardent collectors. Hence although there have been some spectacular auction prices realised recently they are for very rarely found items. The internet auction site eBay always has a number of Beswick horses, both relatively common and rare, available amongst the thousand or so pieces of Beswick continually listed.

The 818 Shire continues to be the most commonly seen Beswick equine at Collectors Fairs, invariably in brown gloss. The 818 has the distinction of not only being Beswick's longest produced unaltered horse shape but also the one found in the most range of production colours. Fifteen colourways have now been located, including blue gloss and there could be a few more!

Note: DA numbers are given for easy cross-reference with *The Charlton Standard Catalogue of Royal Doulton Animals.*

INDEX BY MODEL NUMBER

Model No. 701 / H701

BOIS ROUSSEL
RACEHORSE

There are two varieties of Bois Roussell. The first version was introduced in 1939 and is rarely backstamped.

FIRST VERSION : The tail is attached to the hind legs all the way down and the legs are long and thick.

Designer: Arthur Gredington
Height: 8", 20.3 cm

Colourway	Finish	Intro.	Disc.	U.K. £	U.S. $	Can. $
Blue	Gloss	1939	1947		Extremely Rare	
Light brown	Gloss	1940	1947	250.00	350.00	525.00
Dark brown	Gloss	1940	1947	275.00	385.00	575.00
Dark chestnut	Gloss	1939	1947	350.00	500.00	750.00
Rocking horse grey	Gloss	c.1940	1947	600.00	850.00	1,275.00

SECOND VERSION: In 1947 Bois Roussel was remodelled with only the tail-end attached to the leg.

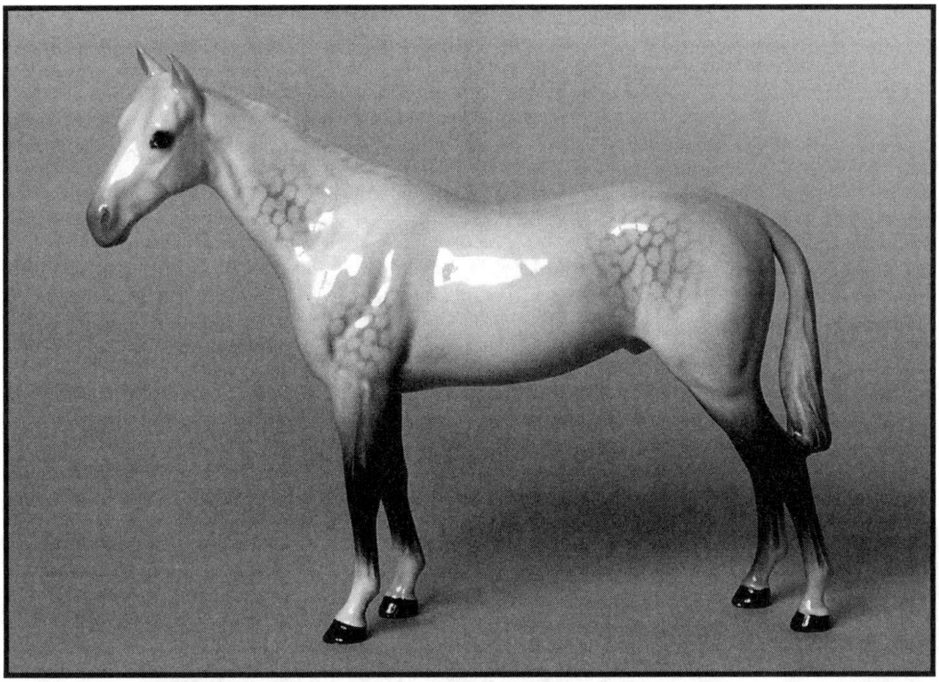

Colourway	Finish	Model	Intro.	Disc.	U.K. £	U.S. $	Can. $
Brown							
a. Beswick	Gloss	701	1947	1989	50.00	75.00	100.00
b. Royal Doulton	Gloss	DA42	1989	1999	50.00	75.00	100.00
c. Beswick	Gloss	H701	1999	Current	49.00	N/A	115.00
Brown							
a. Beswick	Matt	701	1979	1989	55.00	80.00	125.00
b. Royal Doulton	Matt	DA42	1989	1999	55.00	80.00	125.00
c. Beswick	Matt	H701	1999	Current	52.00	N/A	145.00
Chestnut	Gloss	701	1958	1967	400.00	550.00	825.00
Grey							
a. Beswick	Gloss	701	1960	1989	80.00	120.00	175.00
b. Royal Doulton	Gloss	DA42	1989	1995	80.00	120.00	175.00
Grey	Matt	701	1970	1989	80.00	120.00	175.00
Opaque	Gloss	701	1960	1967	225.00	325.00	500.00
Painted white	Gloss	701	1952	1967	325.00	450.00	675.00
Palomino	Gloss	701	1960	1989	80.00	120.00	175.00
Palomino	Matt	701	1970	1983	80.00	120.00	175.00
Rocking horse grey	Gloss	701	1947	1962	425.00	600.00	900.00
White	Matt	701	1970	1982	100.00	150.00	225.00

SERIES: On ceramic stand or wooden plinths

The stand was shape no. 1809, modelled by Albert Hallam in 1963.

Colourway/stand/finish	Intro.	Disc.	U.K. £	U.S. $	Can. $
Brown/brown ceramic/gloss	c.1963	Unknown	165.00	250.00	375.00
Brown/copper lustre ceramic/gloss	c.1963	Unknown	135.00	200.00	300.00
Chestnut/ceramic/gloss	c.1963	Unknown	400.00	650.00	975.00
Brown/wooden plinth/matt	c.1989	c.1989	80.00	120.00	175.00

Model No. 728

FOAL
(Comical Type)

Designer: Arthur Gredington
Height: 5", 12.7 cm

Colourway	Finish	Intro.	Disc.	U.K. £	U.S. $	Can. $
Black	Satin	Unknown	Unknown		Rare	
Blue	Gloss	1939	1954	300.00	425.00	650.00
Brown	Gloss	1940	1971	35.00	50.00	75.00
Chestnut	Gloss	1958	1966	225.00	325.00	500.00
Dark chestnut	Gloss	1939	1954	175.00	250.00	375.00
Grey	Gloss	1961	1971	100.00	150.00	225.00
Opaque	Gloss	1961	1971	135.00	200.00	300.00
Painted white	Gloss	1961	1966	200.00	300.00	450.00
Palomino	Gloss	1961	1971	100.00	150.00	225.00
Rocking horse grey	Gloss	c.1940	1962	250.00	350.00	525.00
Stone/ivory	Satin	Unknown	1954	100.00	150.00	225.00
White	Matt	1970	1970	75.00	115.00	165.00

Model No. 763/1421

FOAL
(Small, Stretched, Upright)

First Version: Long ears

Second Version: Short ears

Designer: Arthur Gredington
Height: 3 ½", 8.9 cm

***FIRST VERSION:** Long ears, thick legs. Outline of mane more wavy. When viewed from the back legs almost touch.*

Colourway	Finish	Intro.	Disc.	U.K. £	U.S. $	Can. $
Blue	Gloss	1940	Unknown	450.00	650.00	975.00
Brown	Gloss	1940	Unknown	30.00	45.00	65.00
Rocking horse grey	Gloss	c.1940	Unknown	225.00	325.00	500.00

***SECOND VERSION:** Short ears, thick legs. Outline of mane less wavy.*

Colourway	Finish	Intro.	Disc.	U.K. £	U.S. $	Can. $
Blue	Gloss	Unknown	1956	450.00	650.00	975.00
Brown	Gloss	Unknown	1956	30.00	45.00	65.00
Painted white	Gloss	Unknown	1956	150.00	225.00	300.00
Rocking horse grey	Gloss	Unknown	1956	225.00	325.00	500.00

*THIRD VERSION: Very thin legs with off hind stretched out well behind the near hind.
Tail is slightly bent.*

In 1956 model no. 763 was completely remodelled by Arthur Gredington, but the model no. 763 was retained.

Colourway	Finish	Intro.	Disc.	U.K. £	U.S. $	Can. $
Brown	Gloss	1956	1976	25.00	40.00	55.00
Chestnut	Gloss	1958	1967	175.00	250.00	375.00
Grey	Gloss	1961	1976	60.00	85.00	125.00
Opaque	Gloss	1961	1973	85.00	125.00	200.00
Painted white	Gloss	1962	1967	150.00	225.00	350.00
Palomino	Gloss	1956	1976	55.00	75.00	100.00
Rocking horse grey	Gloss	1956	1961	225.00	325.00	500.00
White	Matt	1970	1976	50.00	75.00	100.00

Model No. 766

FOAL - TROTTING
(With Or Without Base)

Designer: Arthur Gredington
Height: 3 ¾", 9.5 cm

VARIATION No. 1. Free standing

Colourway	Finish	Intro.	Disc.	U.K. £	U.S. $	Can. $
Blue	Gloss	*1940*	*By 1954*			
Light brown	Gloss	*1940*	*By 1954*			
Dark brown	Gloss	*1940*	*By 1954*	All colourways are		
Dark chestnut	Gloss	*1940*	*By 1954*	extremely rare		
Rocking horse grey	Gloss	1940	By 1954			

VARIATION No. 2. On ceramic base

Colourway	Finish	Intro.	Disc.	U.K. £	U.S. $	Can. $
Blue	Gloss	1940	By 1954			
Light brown	Gloss	1940	By 1954	All colourways are		
Dark brown	Gloss	1940	By 1954	extremely rare		
Dark chestnut	Gloss	1940	By 1954			

Model No. 815 / F815

FOAL
(Small, Stretched, Facing Right)

Designer: Arthur Gredington
Height: 3 ¼", 8.3 cm

Colourway	Finsh	Model	Intro.	Disc.	U.K. £	U.S. $	Can. $
Blue	Gloss	815	1940	1954	425.00	600.00	900.00
Brown							
a. Beswick	Gloss	815	1940	1989	25.00	35.00	55.00
b. Royal Doulton	Gloss	DA74	1989	1999	25.00	35.00	55.00
c. Beswick	Gloss	F815	1999	1999	25.00	35.00	55.00
Brown							
a. Beswick	Matt	815	1979	1989	25.00	35.00	55.00
b. Royal Doulton	Matt	DA74	1989	1996	25.00	35.00	55.00
Chestnut	Gloss	815	1958	1967	200.00	300.00	450.00
Dark chestnut	Gloss	815	1940	1954		Extremely Rare	
Grey							
a. Beswick	Gloss	815	*1961*	1989	30.00	45.00	65.00
b. Royal Doulton	Gloss	DA74	1989	1995	30.00	45.00	65.00
Opaque	Gloss	815	*1961*	1973	85.00	125.00	185.00
Painted white	Gloss	815	1962	1967	150.00	225.00	350.00
Palomino	Gloss	815	*1961*	1989	25.00	35.00	55.00
Pink	Gloss	815	1940	1954		Extremely Rare	
Rocking horse grey	Gloss	815	c.1940	1962	225.00	325.00	500.00
White	Matt	815	1970	1982	40.00	60.00	90.00

Model No. 818 / H818

SHIRE MARE

In recognition of 50 years of production of model number 818 a black gloss shire mare was commissioned by the Beswick Collectors Circle in 1990. Approximately 135 of these were issued with a gold backstamp for Circle Members.

Designer: Arthur Gredington
Height: 8 ½", 21.6 cm

FIRST VERSION: Without Harness

Colourway	Finish	Model	Intro.	Disc.	U.K. £	U.S. $	Can. $
Black	Gloss	818	Unknown	Unknown	675.00	950.00	1,500.00
Black (BCC90)	Gloss	818	1990	1990	675.00	950.00	1,500.00
Blue	Gloss	818	*c.1940*	*1954*		Extremely Rare	
Brown							
a. Beswick	Gloss	818	1940	1989	50.00	75.00	100.00
b. Royal Doulton	Gloss	DA43	1989	1999	50.00	75.00	100.00
c. Beswick	Gloss	H818	1999	1999	50.00	75.00	100.00
Brown							
a. Beswick	Matt	818	1979	1989	75.00	115.00	165.00
b. Royal Doulton	Matt	DA43	1989	1996	75.00	115.00	165.00
Chestnut	Gloss	818	1958	1967	800.00	1,100.00	1,700.00
Grey	Gloss	818	*1961*	1989	95.00	135.00	200.00
Iron Grey	Gloss	818	1952	Unknown		Very Rare	
Opaque	Gloss	818	*1961*	1973	500.00	700.00	1,000.00
Painted white	Gloss	818	*1961*	1970	900.00	1,250.00	1,850.00
Palomino	Gloss	818	*1961*	1973	900.00	1,250.00	1,850.00
Piebald	Gloss	818	Unknown	Unknown	1,000.00	1,450.00	2,150.00
Pink	Gloss	818	1952	Unknown		Very Rare	
Rocking horse grey	Gloss	818	*c.1940*	1962	350.00	500.00	750.00
Skewbald	Gloss	818	Unknown	Unknown	2,000.00	2,750.00	4,000.00
White	Matt	818	1970	1982	150.00	225.00	350.00

Note: Other than the BCC Special which has a blue and yellow ribbon, all models of No.818 have yellow ribbons.

SECOND VERSION: Dressed; Series — Harnessed Horses

Colourway	Finish	Intro.	Disc.	U.K. £	U.S. $	Can. $
Brown	Gloss	1974	1982	135.00	200.00	300.00
Grey	Gloss	1974	1982	150.00	225.00	350.00

Model No. 836

FOAL
(Large, Stretched)

First Version: Parallel fore legs

Second Version: Splayed fore legs

Designer: Arthur Gredington
Height: 5", 12.7 cm

FIRST VERSION: Parallel fore legs.

Colourway	Finish	Intro.	Disc.	U.K. £	U.S. $	Can. $
Blue	Gloss	Unknown	Unknown	300.00	450.00	675.00
Brown	Gloss	1940	Unknown	35.00	50.00	75.00
Light Brown	Gloss	c.1940-50	Unknown	50.00	75.00	115.00
Brown	Matt	1979	Unknown	35.00	50.00	75.00
Chestnut	Gloss	*1961*	Unknown	225.00	350.00	525.00
Grey	Gloss	*1961*	Unknown	50.00	75.00	115.00
Opaque	Gloss	*1961*	Unknown	85.00	125.00	185.00
Painted white	Gloss	*1961*	Unknown	175.00	250.00	375.00
Palomino	Gloss	*1961*	Unknown	50.00	75.00	115.00
Pink	Gloss	Unknown	Unknown		Extremely Rare	
Rocking horse grey	Gloss	*1961*	Unknown	275.00	400.00	600.00
White	Matt	1970	Unknown	40.00	60.00	90.00

SECOND VERSION: Splayed fore legs.

Colourway	Finish	Intro.	Disc.	U.K. £	U.S. $	Can. $
Brown	Gloss	Unknown	1984	35.00	50.00	75.00
Brown	Matt	Unknown	1984	35.00	50.00	75.00
Chestnut	Gloss	Unknown	1967	225.00	350.00	525.00
Grey	Gloss	Unknown	1983	50.00	75.00	115.00
Opaque	Gloss	Unknown	1973	100.00	150.00	225.00
Painted white	Gloss	Unknown	1967	175.00	250.00	375.00
Palomino	Gloss	Unknown	1984	50.00	75.00	115.00
White	Matt	Unknown	1982	45.00	65.00	100.00

Model No. 855/1090/H855

STOCKY JOGGING MARE

FIRST VERSION: Modelled September 1940. Near fore leg is raised off the ground, near hind leg is under the body. Tail attached to the leg all the way down. Legs rather crudely modelled.

Designer: Arthur Gredington
Height: 6", 5.0 cm

Colourway	Finish	Intro.	Disc.	U.K. £	U.S. $	Can. $
Blue	Gloss	1940	1941			
Dark brown	Gloss	1940	1941		All colourways are extremely rare	
Light brown	Gloss	1940	1941			
Dark chestnut	Gloss	1940	1941			
Rocking horse grey	Gloss	1940	1941			

Note: This model is rarely found with a backstamp.

SECOND VERSION: Modelled September 1941. Near fore leg is raised off the ground, near hind leg is under the body. Tail arched away from the leg. More shape to the joints of the legs.

Colourway	Finish	Intro.	Disc.	U.K. £	U.S. $	Can. $
Blue	Gloss	1941	1947	800.00	1,200.00	1,800.00
Brown	Gloss	1941	1947	300.00	450.00	675.00
Dark chestnut	Gloss	1941	1947	350.00	500.00	750.00
Rocking horse grey	Gloss	1941	1947	600.00	850.00	1,250.00

Note: This model is rarely found with a backstamp.

THIRD VERSION: *Shape no. 1090 was modelled in 1947 but retained the number 855. Off fore leg raised from the ground, off hind leg under the body. Tail more arched from the body. Head lowered. A chunkier model.*

Colourway	Finish	Model	Intro.	Disc.	U.K. £	U.S. $	Can. $
Blue	Gloss	855	1947	Unknown		Extremely Rare	
Brown							
a. Beswick	Gloss	855/1090	1947	1989	50.00	75.00	115.00
b. Royal Doulton	Gloss	DA44	1989	1999	50.00	75.00	115.00
c. Beswick	Gloss	H855	1999	Current	49.00	N/A	110.00
Chestnut	Gloss	855	1958	1967	300.00	450.00	700.00
Grey	Gloss	855	1961	1989	70.00	100.00	150.00
Opaque	Gloss	855	1961	1973	200.00	300.00	450.00
Painted white	Gloss	855	1961	1967	275.00	400.00	600.00
Palomino	Gloss	855	1961	1989	70.00	100.00	150.00
Rocking horse grey	Gloss	855	c.1947	1962	350.00	500.00	750.00
White	Matt	855	1970	1982	100.00	150.00	225.00

Model No. 868

HUNTSMAN (On Rearing Horse)

Designer: Arthur Gredington
Height: 10", 25.4 cm

Style One

Style Two

STYLE ONE: On rearing horse

FIRST VERSION: Huntsman is sitting straight up and his lower legs are also vertical. His coat is cut away at the waist. He is riding a common headed horse.

COLOURWAY No. 1. Orangey red coat, cream breeches.

Colourway	Finish	Intro.	Disc.	U.K. £	U.S. $	Can. $
Brown	Gloss	1940	1952	350.00	525.00	750.00
Dark chestnut	Gloss	1940	1952	500.00	700.00	1,100.00
Rocking horse grey	Gloss	c.1940	1952	1,000.00	1,500.00	2,250.00

COLOURWAY No. 2. Scarlet coat and white breeches.

Colourway	Finish	Intro.	Disc.	U.K. £	U.S. $	Can. $
Brown	Gloss	1940	1952	325.00	500.00	750.00
Rocking horse grey	Gloss	c.1948	1952	1,000.00	1,500.00	2,250.00

SECOND VERSION: Huntsman is leaning back slightly. His coat is not cut away at the waist. The horse's head has an Arab appearance (dished profile).

Colourway	Finish	Intro.	Disc.	U.K. £	U.S. $	Can. $
Brown	Gloss	1952	1995	200.00	300.00	450.00
Chestnut	Gloss	1958	1967	775.00	1,100.00	1,600.00
Grey	Gloss	1962	1972	600.00	900.00	1,350.00
Opaque	Gloss	1971	1973	350.00	500.00	750.00
Painted white	Gloss	1965	1971	450.00	650.00	975.00
Palomino	Gloss	*1961*	1972	775.00	1,100.00	1,600.00
Rocking horse grey	Gloss	*1952*	*1962*	1,000.00	1,500.00	2,250.00
White	Matt	1971	1981	250.00	350.00	525.00

SERIES: Britannia Collection

Colourway	Finish	Intro.	Disc.	U.K. £	U.S. $	Can. $
Bronze	Satin	1989	1993	150.00	250.00	375.00

Model No. 915 / F915

FOAL (Lying)

Designer: Arthur Gredington
Height: 3 ¼", 8.3 cm

Colourway	Finish	Model	Intro.	Disc.	U.K. £	U.S. $	Can. $
Brown							
a. Beswick	Gloss	915	1941	1989	20.00	30.00	45.00
b. Royal Doulton	Gloss	DA75	1989	1999	20.00	30.00	45.00
c. Beswick	Gloss	F915	1999	Current	16.50	N/A	65.00
Brown							
a. Beswick	Matt	915	1979	1989	25.00	35.00	55.00
b. Royal Doulton	Matt	DA75	1989	1996	25.00	35.00	55.00
Chestnut	Gloss	915	1958	1967	200.00	300.00	450.00
Grey							
a. Beswick	Gloss	915	*1961*	1989	40.00	60.00	90.00
b. Royal Doulton	Glass	DA75	1989	1995	30.00	45.00	65.00
Opaque	Gloss	915	*1961*	1973	80.00	120.00	175.00
Painted white	Gloss	915	1962	1967	175.00	250.00	375.00
Palomino	Gloss	915	*1961*	1989	40.00	60.00	90.00
Rocking horse grey	Gloss	915	c.1942	*1962*	225.00	400.00	525.00
White	Matt	915	1970	1982	45.00	65.00	100.00

Model No. 939

GIRL ON JUMPING HORSE

The horse used for model 939 is also that used for model 982 "Huntswoman."

Designer: Arthur Gredington
Height: 9 ¾", 24.7 cm
Colour: Brown - gloss
Issued: 1941-1965

Colourway	U.K. £	U.S. $	Can. $
Brown	325.00	475.00	700.00

Model No. 946 / F946

FOAL
(Grazing)

First Version: Off-side hooves almost touch

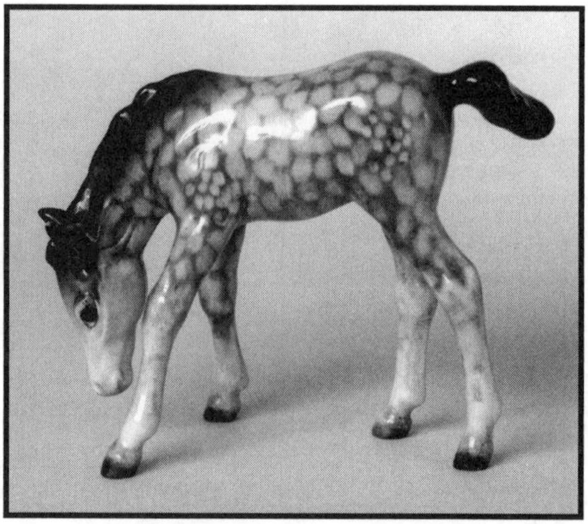

Second Version: Legs well separated

Designer: Arthur Gredington
Height: 3 ¼", 8.3 cm

FIRST VERSION: Has common head and the off-side hooves almost touch.

Colourway	Finish	Model	Intro.	Disc.	U.K. £	U.S. $	Can. $
Brown	Gloss	946	1941	1955	40.00	60.00	90.00
Dark Chestnut	Gloss	946	Unknown	Unknown	100.00	150.00	225.00
Rocking horse grey	Gloss	946	1941	1955	300.00	450.00	675.00

SECOND VERSION: Much finer head with the legs being well separated.

Colourway	Finish	Model	Intro.	Disc.	U.K. £	U.S. $	Can. $
Brown							
a. Beswick	Gloss	946	1955	1989	20.00	30.00	45.00
b. Royal Doulton	Gloss	DA76	1989	1999	20.00	30.00	45.00
c. Beswick	Gloss	F946	1999	Current	18.50	N/A	60.00
Brown							
a. Beswick	Matt	946	1979	1989	25.00	35.00	50.00
b. Royal Doulton	Matt	DA76	1989	1996	25.00	35.00	50.00
Chestnut	Gloss	946	1958	1967	200.00	300.00	450.00
Grey							
a. Beswick	Gloss	946	*1961*	1989	35.00	50.00	75.00
b. Royal Doulton	Gloss	DA76	1989	1996	35.00	50.00	75.00
Opaque	Gloss	946	*1961*	1967	100.00	150.00	225.00
Painted white	Gloss	946	*1961*	1967	175.00	250.00	375.00
Palomino							
a. Beswick	Gloss	946	*1961*	1989	30.00	45.00	70.00
b. Royal Doulton	Gloss	DA76	1989	1996	30.00	45.00	70.00
Rocking horse grey	Gloss	946	1955	1962	300.00	450.00	700.00
White	Matt	946	1970	1982	45.00	65.00	100.00

Model No. 947 / F947

FOAL
(Large, Head Down)

This model in the dun colourway, along with the Mare (976), was the 1997 Beswick Collectors Club Special. They show both the "Beswick" and BCC97 backstamps. The Foal (in the dun colourway) was issued in a limited edition of 730.

Designer: Arthur Gredington
Height: 4 ½", 11.9 cm

Colourway	Finish	Model	Intro.	Disc.	U.K. £	U.S. $	Can. $
Brown							
a. Beswick	Gloss	947	1941	1989	30.00	45.00	65.00
b. Royal Doulton	Gloss	DA77	1989	1999	30.00	45.00	65.00
c. Beswick	Gloss	F947	1999	Current	26.00	N/A	75.00
Brown							
a. Beswick	Matt	947	1979	1989	30.00	45.00	60.00
b. Royal Doulton	Matt	DA77	1989	1996	30.00	45.00	60.00
Chestnut	Gloss	947	1958	1967	200.00	300.00	450.00
Dun (BCC97)	Gloss	947	1997	1997	75.00	115.00	165.00
Grey	Gloss	947	*1961*	1983	40.00	60.00	90.00
Opaque	Gloss	947	*1961*	1973	75.00	115.00	165.00
Painted white	Gloss	947	1962	1967	200.00	300.00	450.00
Palomino	Gloss	947	*1961*	1983	35.00	50.00	70.00
Rocking horse grey	Gloss	947	c.1942	1962	275.00	400.00	600.00
White	Matt	947	1970	1982	50.00	75.00	110.00

Model No. 951

SHIRE FOAL
(Large)

Designer: Arthur Gredington
Height: 6 ¼", 15.9 cm

Colourway	Finish	Intro.	Disc.	U.K. £	U.S. $	Can. $
Blue	Gloss	1941	Unknown	350.00	500.00	750.00
Brown	Gloss	1941	1971	50.00	75.00	125.00
Chestnut	Gloss	1958	1967	350.00	500.00	750.00
Grey	Gloss	*1961*	1971	150.00	225.00	350.00
Opaque	Gloss	*1961*	1971	125.00	200.00	300.00
Painted white	Gloss	1962	1967	300.00	425.00	650.00
Palomino	Gloss	*1961*	1971	200.00	300.00	450.00
Rocking horse grey	Gloss	1941	1962	450.00	625.00	950.00
White	Matt	1970	1970	100.00	150.00	225.00

Model No. 953

MARE AND FOAL ON BASE

The mare is a modern 976 with the foal and the base varying.

*FIRST VERSION: The foal has its tail and near fore leg slightly raised.
The base is rectangular.*

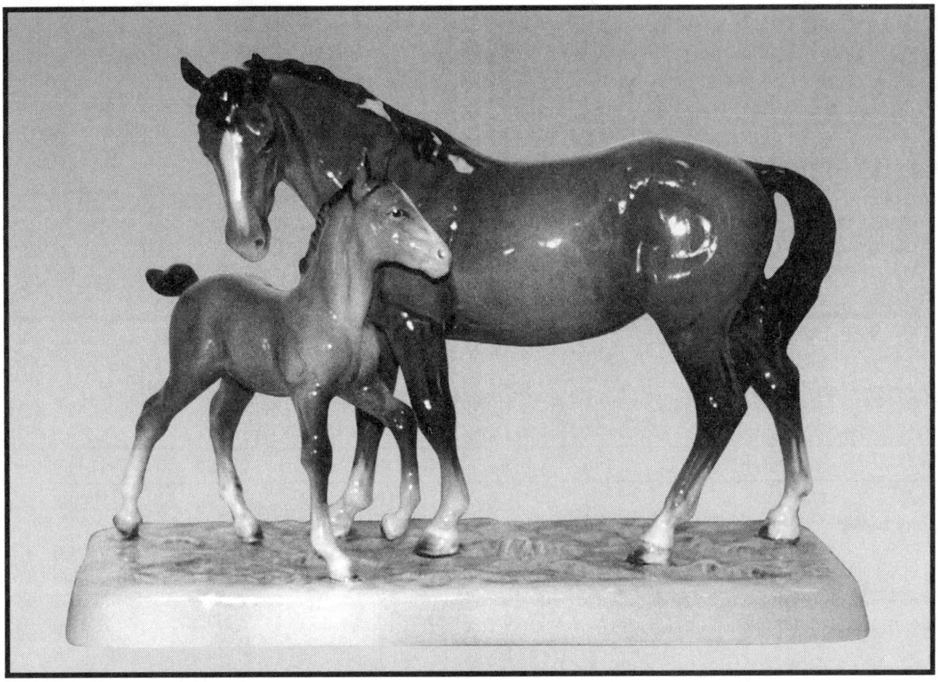

Designer: Arthur Gredington
Height: 7 ¾", 19.7 cm

Colourway	Finish	Intro.	Disc.	U.K. £	U.S. $	Can. $
Brown	Gloss	1941	1949	675.00	950.00	1,425.00
Rocking horse grey	Gloss	1941	1949	1,000.00	1,500.00	2,250.00

Model 953, Second Version

Model 953, Third Version

SECOND VERSION: *Foal has all four legs attached to an irregularly shaped base and the tail hangs straight down.*

Colourway	Finish	Intro.	Disc.	U.K. £	U.S. $	Can. $
Brown mare / orangey bay foal	Gloss	1949	1983	125.00	200.00	300.00
Chestnut	Gloss	1958	1967	600.00	900.00	1,350.00
Grey	Gloss	1958	1972	500.00	750.00	1,100.00
Opaque	Gloss	1971	1973	250.00	375.00	550.00
Painted white mare / brown foal	Gloss	1962	1967	450.00	675.00	1,000.00
Painted white mare / painted white foal	Gloss	1962	1967	450.00	675.00	1,000.00
Palomino	Gloss	*1958*	1972	425.00	650.00	975.00
Rocking horse grey	Gloss	*1950*	1962	750.00	1,100.00	1,600.00
White	Matt	1971	1981	150.00	225.00	350.00

THIRD VERSION: *Foal is model no. 1813, second version, on an irregularly shaped base.*

Colourway	Finish	Intro.	Disc.	U.K. £	U.S. $	Can. $
Brown mare with an orangey bay foal	Gloss	1981	1983	100.00	150.00	225.00
Brown mare and foal, green matt base	Matt	*1981*	*1983*	125.00	175.00	250.00

Model No. 975 / H975

CANTERING SHIRE

This model in the black colourway was the 1996 Beswick Collectors Club Special.

Designer: Arthur Gredington
Height: 8 ¾", 22.2 cm

Colourway	Finish	DA #	Intro.	Disc.	U.K. £	U.S. $	Can. $
Black (BCC96)	Gloss	975	1996	1996	150.00	225.00	350.00
Brown							
a. Beswick	Gloss	975	1943	1989	60.00	85.00	125.00
b. Royal Doulton	Gloss	DA45	1989	1999	60.00	85.00	125.00
Brown	Matt	—	1980	1989	70.00	100.00	150.00
Chestnut	Gloss	—	1958	1967	800.00	1,150.00	1,700.00
Grey	Gloss	—	*1961*	1989	100.00	150.00	225.00
Opaque	Gloss	—	1966	1967	200.00	300.00	450.00
Painted white	Gloss	—	1962	1967	500.00	700.00	1,050.00
Palomino	Gloss	—	*1961*	1970	475.00	675.00	1,000.00
Rocking horse grey	Gloss	—	*c.1944*	*1962*	450.00	650.00	975.00
White	Matt	—	1971	1982	100.00	150.00	225.00

Note: An example has been found in flambé.

Model No. 976

MARE
(Facing Left)

This model and the foal (947) in dun gloss were the 1997 Beswick Collectors Club Special. They have both the "Beswick" and BCC97 backstamps. The Mare (in the dun colourway) was issued in a limited edition of 710.

Designer: Arthur Gredington
Height: 6 ¾", 17.2 cm

Colourway	Finish	Model	Intro.	Disc.	U.K. £	U.S. $	Can. $
Brown							
a. Beswick	Gloss	976	1941	1989	45.00	65.00	95.00
b. Royal Doulton	Gloss	DA46	1989	1997	45.00	65.00	95.00
Brown							
a. Beswick	Matt	976	1979	1989	55.00	80.00	125.00
b. Royal Doulton	Matt	DA46	1989	1997	50.00	75.00	115.00
Chestnut	Gloss	976	1958	1967	400.00	575.00	875.00
Dun (BCC97)	Gloss	976	1997	1997	150.00	225.00	350.00
Grey							
a. Beswick	Gloss	976	1962	1989	75.00	115.00	165.00
b. Royal Doulton	Gloss	DA46	1989	1997	70.00	100.00	150.00
Opaque	Gloss	976	*1961*	1973	175.00	250.00	375.00
Painted white	Gloss	976	*1961*	1967	375.00	525.00	800.00
Palomino	Gloss	976	*1961*	1983	85.00	125.00	185.00
Rocking horse grey	Gloss	976	*c.1942*	*1962*	425.00	600.00	900.00
White	Matt	976	1970	1982	75.00	115.00	165.00

Model No. 982

HUNTSWOMAN

The horse used for model 982 is the same as that used for model 939 "Girl on Jumping Horse."

STYLE ONE: Rider and Horse Jumping

Designer: Arthur Gredington
Height: 10", 25.4 cm

Colourway	Finish	Intro.	Disc.	U.K. £	U.S. $	Can. $
Brown	Gloss	1942	1967	300.00	450.00	675.00

Model No. 996

FOAL
(Small, Gambolling left)

Designer: Arthur Gredington
Height: 3 ¼", 8.3 cm

Colourway	Finish	Intro.	Disc.	U.K. £	U.S. $	Can. $
Brown	Gloss	1943	1976	30.00	45.00	70.00
Chestnut	Gloss	1958	1967	175.00	250.00	375.00
Grey	Gloss	*1961*	1976	40.00	55.00	80.00
Opaque	Gloss	*1961*	1973	75.00	115.00	165.00
Painted white	Gloss	*1961*	1967	200.00	300.00	450.00
Palomino	Gloss	*1961*	1976	45.00	65.00	95.00
Rocking horse grey	Gloss	*c.1944*	*1962*	225.00	325.00	475.00
White	Matt	1970	1976	45.00	65.00	95.00

Model No. 997 / F997

FOAL
(Small, Stretched, Facing Left)

Designer: Arthur Gredington
Height: 3 ¼", 8.3 cm

Colourway	Finish	Model	Intro.	Disc.	U.K. £	U.S. $	Can. $
Brown							
a. Beswick	Gloss	997	1943	1989	20.00	30.00	45.00
b. Royal Doulton	Gloss	DA78	1989	1999	20.00	30.00	45.00
c. Beswick	Gloss	F997	1999	Current	16.50	N/A	45.00
Brown							
a. Beswick	Matt	997	1979	1989	30.00	45.00	70.00
b. Royal Doulton	Matt	DA78	1989	1996	30.00	45.00	70.00
Chestnut	Gloss	997	1958	1967	175.00	275.00	400.00
Grey							
a. Beswick	Gloss	997	*1961*	1989	40.00	60.00	85.00
b. Royal Doulton	Gloss	DA78	1989	1999	35.00	50.00	75.00
Opaque	Gloss	997	*1961*	1973	80.00	120.00	175.00
Painted white	Gloss	997	*1961*	1967	185.00	250.00	375.00
Palomino	Gloss	997	*1961*	1989	40.00	60.00	85.00
Rocking horse grey	Gloss	997	*c.1944*	1962	200.00	300.00	450.00
White	Matt	997	1970	1982	40.00	60.00	85.00

Model No. 1014

WELSH COB
(Rearing)

Designer: Arthur Gredington   Height: 10 ¼", 26.0 cm

First Version: Tail attached to base

Second Version: Tail hangs loose

FIRST VERSION: The tail is attached to the ceramic base.

Colourway	Finish	Intro.	Disc.	U.K. £	U.S. $	Can. $
Black	Gloss	Unknown	Unknown	175.00	250.00	375.00
Brown	Gloss	1944	Unknown	75.00	115.00	165.00
Chestnut	Gloss	1958	Unknown	500.00	750.00	1,100.00
Grey	Gloss	*1961*	Unknown	375.00	525.00	800.00
Opaque	Gloss	*1961*	Unknown	225.00	350.00	525.00
Painted white	Gloss	*1962*	Unknown	400.00	575.00	875.00
Palomino	Gloss	*1961*	Unknown	300.00	450.00	675.00
Piebald	Gloss	Unknown	Unknown		Extremely Rare	
Rocking horse grey	Gloss	*c.1945*	Unknown	800.00	1,150.00	1,750.00
White	Matt	1970	Unknown	150.00	225.00	350.00

SECOND VERSION: Tail hangs loose.

Colourway	Finish	Model	Intro.	Disc.	U.K. £	U.S. $	Can. $
Black							
a. Beswick	Gloss	1014	*c.1990*	*c.1990*	175.00	250.00	375.00
b. Royal Doulton	Gloss	DA41	1994	1994	175.00	250.00	375.00
c. Royal Doulton	Matt	DA41	1994	1994	175.00	250.00	375.00
Brown							
a. Beswick	Gloss	1014	Unknown	1989	100.00	150.00	225.00
b. Royal Doulton	Gloss	DA41	1989	1990	100.00	150.00	225.00
Chestnut	Gloss	1014	Unknown	1967	475.00	675.00	1,000.00
Grey	Gloss	1014	Unknown	1973	400.00	550.00	775.00
Grey	Matt	1014	Unknown	1983	175.00	250.00	375.00
Opaque	Gloss	1014	Unknown	1973	225.00	325.00	500.00
Painted white	Gloss	1014	Unknown	1967	400.00	550.00	775.00
Palomino	Gloss	1014	Unknown	1973	325.00	450.00	675.00
White	Matt	1014	Unknown	1983	125.00	175.00	250.00

Note: An example is known in a black satin matt colourway.

Model No. 1033 / H1033
SHETLAND PONY
(Woolly Shetland Mare)

Designer: Arthur Gredington
Height: 5 ¾", 14.6 cm

Colourway	Finish	Model	Intro.	Disc.	U.K. £	U.S. $	Can. $
Brown							
a. Beswick	Gloss	1033	1945	1989	35.00	50.00	75.00
b. Royal Doulton	Gloss	DA47	1989	1999	35.00	50.00	75.00
c. Beswick	Gloss	H1033	1999	Current	31.00	N/A	N/A
Brown	Matt	1033	Unknown	Unknown	250.00	350.00	525.00
Chestnut	Gloss	1033	Unknown	Unknown	600.00	850.00	1,275.00
Dapple grey	Gloss	1033	Unknown	Unknown	600.00	850.00	1,275.00
Palomino	Gloss	1033	Unknown	Unknown	600.00	850.00	1,275.00
White	Matt	1033	1973	1982	75.00	115.00	165.00

Model No. 1034 / F1034
SHETLAND FOAL

Designer: Arthur Gredington
Height: 3 ¾", 9.5 cm

Colourway	Finish	Model	Intro.	Disc.	U.K. £	U.S. $	Can. $
Brown							
a. Beswick	Gloss	1034	1945	1989	20.00	30.00	45.00
b. Royal Doulton	Gloss	DA79	1989	1999	20.00	30.00	45.00
c. Beswick	Gloss	F1034	1999	Current	16.50	N/A	50.00
Brown							
a. Beswick	Matt	1034	1979	1989	30.00	45.00	65.00
b. Royal Doulton	Matt	DA79	1989	1996	30.00	45.00	65.00
White	Matt	1034	1973	1982	45.00	65.00	95.00

Model No. 1037

RACEHORSE AND JOCKEY
(Walking Racehorse)

The jockey's silks, for an extra payment, could be decorated as the purchaser wished. A great many colourways and number cloths could exist.

Colourway No. 1 - Stripes on saddlecloth

Colourway No. 2 - Number on saddlecloth

Designer: Arthur Gredington
Height: 8 ½", 21.6 cm

STYLE ONE: Walking Racehorse

Colourway No. 1. Stripes on saddlecloth

Colourway	Finish	Intro.	Disc.	U.K. £	U.S. $	Can. $
Brown	Gloss	1945	Unknown	325.00	475.00	725.00

Colourway No. 2. Number on saddlecloth

Colourway	Finish	Intro.	Disc.	U.K. £	U.S. $	Can. $
Brown	Gloss	Unknown	1976	325.00	475.00	725.00
Chestnut	Gloss	Unknown	Unknown	Sold October, 2001 Bonhams, Chelsea, £750.00		

Model No. 1050
GRAZING SHIRE

Designer: Arthur Gredington
Height: 5 ½", 14.0 cm

Colourway	Finish	Intro.	Disc.	U.K. £	U.S. $	Can. $
Brown	Gloss	1946	1970	85.00	125.00	185.00
Chestnut	Gloss	1958	1967	700.00	1,000.00	1,500.00
Grey	Gloss	1962	1970	600.00	850.00	1,275.00
Opaque	Gloss	*1961*	1970	300.00	425.00	625.00
Painted white	Gloss	1962	1967	700.00	1,000.00	1,500.00
Palomino	Gloss	*1961*	1970	700.00	1,000.00	1,500.00
Rocking horse grey	Gloss	*c.1947*	1962	850.00	1,200.00	1,750.00

Note: A copper lustre model is known to exist.

Model No. 1053
SHIRE FOAL
(Small)

Designer: Arthur Gredington
Height: 5", 12.7 cm

Colourway	Finish	Intro.	Disc.	U.K. £	U.S. $	Can. $
Brown	Gloss	1946	1984	40.00	55.00	80.00
Brown	Matt	1979	1984	35.00	50.00	75.00
Chestnut	Gloss	1958	1967	350.00	550.00	825.00
Grey	Gloss	*1961*	1973	175.00	250.00	375.00
Opaque	Gloss	*1961*	1973	125.00	175.00	250.00
Painted white	Gloss	1962	1967	275.00	400.00	600.00
Palomino	Gloss	*1961*	1973	150.00	200.00	300.00
Rocking horse grey	Gloss	*c.1947*	1962	425.00	600.00	900.00
White	Matt	1970	1982	80.00	120.00	175.00

Model No. 1084
FOAL
(Medium, Almost Stood Square)

Designer: Arthur Gredington
Height: 4 ½", 11.9 cm

Colourway	Finish	Intro.	Disc.	U.K. £	U.S. $	Can. $
Brown	Gloss	1947	1984	30.00	45.00	65.00
Brown	Matt	1979	1983	25.00	35.00	50.00
Chestnut	Gloss	1958	1967	275.00	400.00	625.00
Grey	Gloss	*1961*	1973	85.00	125.00	185.00
Opaque	Gloss	*1961*	1973	80.00	120.00	175.00
Painted white	Gloss	*1961*	1967	200.00	300.00	450.00
Palomino	Gloss	*1961*	1973	70.00	100.00	150.00
Rocking horse grey	Gloss	*c.1948*	1962	325.00	450.00	675.00
White	Matt	1970	1982	60.00	85.00	125.00

Model No. 1085
FOAL
(Medium, Head Down)

Designer: Arthur Gredington
Height: 3 ½", 8.9 cm

Colourway	Finish	Intro.	Disc.	U.K. £	U.S. $	Can. $
Brown	Gloss	1947	1971	40.00	55.00	80.00
Chestnut	Gloss	1958	1967	300.00	425.00	625.00
Grey	Gloss	*1961*	1971	125.00	175.00	250.00
Opaque	Gloss	*1961*	1971	100.00	150.00	225.00
Painted white	Gloss	*1961*	1967	175.00	250.00	375.00
Palomino	Gloss	*1961*	1971	100.00	150.00	225.00
Rocking horse grey	Gloss	*c.1948*	1962	350.00	500.00	750.00
White	Matt	1970	1970	75.00	100.00	150.00

Model No. 1145

KNIGHT IN ARMOUR
(The Earl of Warwick)

Designer: Arthur Gredington
Height: 10 ¾", 27.8 cm

Colourway	Finish	Intro.	Disc.	U.K. £	U.S. $	Can. $
Grey	Gloss	1949	1973	1,000.00	1,500.00	2,250.00

Model No. 1182

SWISH TAIL HORSE

First Version: The tail is attached to the quarter almost parallel to the ground

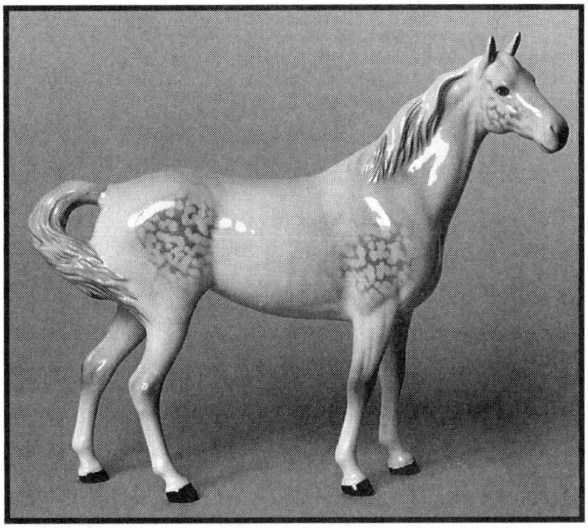

Second Version: The tail is slightly lower down and only to the edge of the quarter

Designer: Arthur Gredington
Height: 8 ¾", 22.2 cm

FIRST VERSION: The tail is attached to the quarters almost parallel to the ground.

Colourway	Finish	Intro.	Disc.	U.K. £	U.S. $	Can. $
Brown	Gloss	1950	c.1982	75.00	115.00	165.00
Brown	Matt	1970	c.1982	65.00	95.00	150.00
Chestnut	Gloss	1958	1967	350.00	500.00	750.00
Grey	Gloss	1961	c.1982	100.00	150.00	225.00
Grey	Matt	1970	c.1982	85.00	125.00	185.00
Opaque	Gloss	*1961*	1973	225.00	325.00	500.00
Painted white	Gloss	*1961*	1967	350.00	500.00	750.00
Palomino	Gloss	*1961*	c.1982	85.00	125.00	185.00
Palomino	Matt	1970	c.1982	85.00	125.00	185.00
Rocking horse grey	Gloss	*c.1951*	1962	450.00	650.00	975.00
White	Matt	1970	c.1982	85.00	125.00	185.00

SECOND VERSION: The tail is attached slightly lower down and only to the edge of the quarters.

Colourway	Finish	Model	Intro.	Disc.	U.K. £	U.S. $	Can. $
Brown							
a. Beswick	Gloss	1182	c.1982	1989	50.00	75.00	125.00
b. Royal Doulton	Gloss	DA48	1989	1999	50.00	75.00	125.00
Brown							
a. Beswick	Matt	1182	c.1982	1989	50.00	75.00	125.00
b. Royal Doulton	Matt	DA48	1989	1997	50.00	75.00	125.00
Grey	Gloss	1182	c.1982	1989	60.00	90.00	135.00
Grey	Matt	1182	c.1982	1989	60.00	90.00	135.00
Palomino	Gloss	1182	c.1982	1983	60.00	90.00	135.00
Palomino	Matt	1182	c.1982	1983	60.00	90.00	135.00
White	Matt	1182	c.1982	1982	65.00	95.00	145.00

Model No. 1197

PONY
(Head Up)

Designer: Arthur Gredington
Height: 5 ½", 14.0 cm

Colourway	Finish	Intro.	Disc.	U.K. £	U.S. $	Can. $
Brown	Gloss	1950	1975	65.00	95.00	145.00
Chestnut	Gloss	1958	1967	350.00	500.00	750.00
Grey	Gloss	1962	1975	95.00	135.00	200.00
Opaque	Gloss	*1961*	1973	150.00	225.00	350.00
Painted white	Gloss	*1961*	1967	300.00	425.00	625.00
Palomino	Gloss	*1961*	1975	85.00	125.00	185.00
Piebald	Gloss	Unknown	Unknown		Extremely Rare	
Rocking horse grey	Gloss	*c.1951*	1962	375.00	525.00	800.00
White	Matt	1970	1975	85.00	125.00	185.00

Model No. 1261 / H1261

PALOMINO
(Prancing Arab Type)

Designer: Arthur Gredington
Height: 6 ¾", 17.2 cm

Model No. 1261 First Version

First Version - Thicker tail

Second Version - Thinner tail

FIRST VERSION: Thicker tail with more definition.

Colourway	Finish	Intro.	Disc.	U.K. £	U.S. $	Can. $
Brown	Gloss	*1961*	Unknown	60.00	85.00	125.00
Brown	Matt	1970	Unknown	55.00	80.00	120.00
Chestnut	Gloss	*1958*	1967	450.00	650.00	975 00
Grey	Gloss	*1961*	Unknown	75.00	115.00	165.00
Grey	Matt	1970	Unknown	70.00	100.00	150.00
Opaque	Gloss	*1961*	1973	150.00	200.00	300.00
Painted white	Gloss	*1961*	1967	225.00	325.00	475.00
Palomino	Gloss	1952	Unknown	70.00	100.00	150.00
Palomino	Matt	1970	Unknown	60.00	85.00	125.00
Rocking horse grey	Gloss	*c.1956*	1962	350.00	500.00	750.00
White	Matt	1970	Unknown	75.00	115.00	165.00

SECOND VERSION: Thinner tail with little definition.

Colourway	Finish	Model	Intro.	Disc.	U.K. £	U.S. $	Can. $
Brown							
a. Beswick	Gloss	1261	Unknown	1989	50.00	75.00	110.00
b. Royal Doulton	Gloss	DA49	1989	1999	50.00	75.00	110.00
c. Beswick	Gloss	H1261	1999	Current	49.00	N/A	110.00
Brown							
a. Beswick	Matt	1261	Unknown	1989	50.00	75.00	110.00
b. Royal Doulton	Matt	DA49	1989	1998	50.00	75.00	110.00
Grey							
a. Beswick	Gloss	1261	Unknown	1989	50.00	75.00	110.00
b. Royal Doulton	Gloss	DA49	1989	1999	50.00	75.00	110.00
c. Beswick	Gloss	H1261	1999	Current	49.00	N/A	120.00
Grey	Matt	—	Unknown	1989	55.00	80.00	120.00
Palomino							
a. Beswick	Gloss	1261	Unknown	1989	50.00	70.00	110.00
b. Royal Doulton	Gloss	DA49	1989	1999	50.00	70.00	110.00
c. Beswick	Gloss	H1261	1999	Current	49.00	N/A	110.00
Palomino	Matt	—	Unknown	1989	55.00	80.00	120.00
White	Matt	—	Unknown	1982	60.00	85.00	125.00

Model No. 1265

ARAB "XAYAL"

The charcoal grey colourway with four white socks is the authentic colouring for " Xayal. " The charcoal grey colourway varies from black to charcoal grey.

Arab " Xayal "

Arab " Xayal " Connoisseur Horse

Designer: Arthur Gredington
Height: 6 ¼", 15.9 cm

Colourway	Finish	Model	Intro.	Disc.	U.K. £	U.S. $	Can. $
Brown							
a. Beswick	Gloss	1265	1952	1989	50.00	80.00	125.00
b. Royal Doulton	Gloss	DA50	1989	1996	50.00	80.00	125.00
Charcoal grey	Gloss	1265	*1952*	*1984*	100.00	150.00	225.00
Chestnut	Gloss	1265	1958	1967	275.00	400.00	600.00
Grey							
a. Beswick	Gloss	1265	*1961*	1989	85.00	125.00	185.00
b. Royal Doulton	Gloss	DA50	1989	1997	75.00	115.00	165.00
Opaque	Gloss	1265	*1961*	1973	165.00	250.00	375.00
Painted white	Gloss	1265	*1961*	1967	250.00	375.00	550.00
Palomino							
a. Beswick	Gloss	1265	*1961*	1989	75.00	115.00	165.00
b. Royal Doulton	Gloss	DA50	1989	1997	75.00	115.00	165.00
Rocking horse grey	Gloss	1265	c.1953	1962	375.00	550.00	825.00
White	Matt	1265	*1961*	1984	80.00	115.00	175.00

SERIES: Connoisseur Horses

Height: 7 ¼", 18.4 cm

Colourway	Finish	Model	Intro.	Disc.	U.K. £	U.S. $	Can. $
Dark brown							
a. Beswick	Matt	1265	1970	1989	100.00	150.00	225.00
b. Doulton	Matt	DA14	1989	1990	125.00	175.00	275.00

Note: A black gloss model is know to exist.

Model No. 1359

SUFFOLK PUNCH
CHAMPION "HASSE DAINTY"

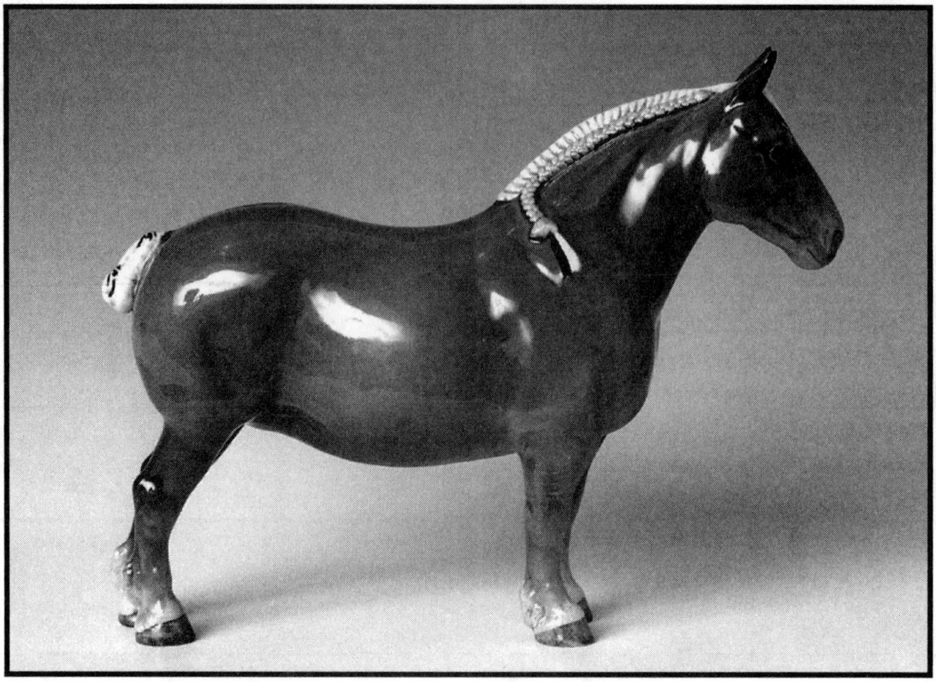

Designer: Mr. Orwell
Height: 8", 20.3 cm

Colourway	Finish	Intro.	Disc.	U.K. £	U.S. $	Can. $
Light chestnut	Gloss	1954	Unknown	325.00	450.00	675.00
Dark chestnut	Gloss	Unknown	1971	325.00	450.00	675.00
Grey	Gloss	1965	1965	800.00	1,150.00	1,700.00
Palomino	Gloss	Unknown	Unknown	800.00	1,150.00	1,700.00

COLOURWAY DESCRIPTIONS

Light Chestnut: Light chestnut horse with much lighter chestnut hooves. Blended thin stripe down the front of the head. Mane and tail are cream with yellow ribbon braided through the mane ending with cream and maroon. Two maroon bows on the tail.

Dark Chestnut: Much darker chestnut horse with dark chestnust mane and tail. Definite white blaze extending over muzzle, and four short white socks. The mane ribbon is lemon with pink at the end and the tail bows are lemon and pink and indistinct.

Model No. 1361

HACKNEY

The black colourway is the authentic colouring of "Black Magic of Nork" and has white patches on the flanks.

Designer: Mr. Orwell
Height: 7 ¾", 19.7 cm

Colourway	Finish	Intro.	Disc.	U.K. £	U.S. $	Can. $
Black	Gloss	1955	1983	185.00	250.00	375.00
Black	Matt	1980	1983	165.00	225.00	350.00
Brown	Gloss	1955	1982	100.00	150.00	225.00
Chestnut	Gloss	1958	1967	400.00	550.00	825.00
Grey	Gloss	*1961*	1975	350.00	500.00	750.00
Opaque	Gloss	*1961*	1973	225.00	300.00	450.00
Painted white	Gloss	*1961*	1967	350.00	500.00	750.00
Palomino	Gloss	*1961*	1970	275.00	400.00	600.00
Rocking horse grey	Gloss	*c.1956*	1962	425.00	600.00	900.00
White	Matt	1970	1982	90.00	130.00	200.00

Model No. 1373

PINTO PONY

First Version: Tail attached to hind leg from hock down

Second Version: Tail hangs loose

Designer: Arthur Gredington
Height: 6 ½", 16.5 cm

FIRST VERSION: Tail is attached to the hind leg from the hock down.

Colourway	Finish	Intro.	Disc.	U.K. £	U.S. $	Can. $
Chestnut	Gloss	1958	1967	425.00	600.00	900.00
Grey	Gloss	1962	1970	475.00	675.00	1,000.00
Palomino	Gloss	*1961*	1970	475.00	675.00	1,000.00
Piebald (black and white)	Gloss	1972	Unknown	110.00	165.00	250.00
Skewbald (brown and white)	Gloss	1955	Unknown	110.00	165.00	250.00

SECOND VERSION: Tail hangs loose.

Colourway	Finish	Model	Intro.	Disc.	U.K. £	U.S. $	Can. $
Piebald (black/white)							
a. Beswick	Gloss	1373	Unknown	1989	90.00	135.00	225.00
b. Royal Doulton	Gloss	DA67	1989	1990	80.00	125.00	200.00
Piebald (black/white)							
a. Beswick	Matt	1373	Unknown	1989	80.00	125.00	200.00
b. Royal Doulton	Matt	DA67	1989	1990	80.00	125.00	200.00
Skewbald (brown/white)							
a. Beswick	Gloss	1373	Unknown	1989	80.00	125.00	200.00
b. Royal Doulton	Gloss	DA67	1989	1990	80.00	125.00	200.00
Skewbald (brown/white)							
a. Beswick	Matt	1373	Unknown	1989	80.00	125.00	200.00
b. Royal Doulton	Matt	DA67	1989	1990	80.00	125.00	200.00

00

Model No. 1374

GALLOPING HORSE

Model no. 1374 was the horse used for no. 1377 Canadian Mounted Cowboy. However no. 1374 has only three hooves attached to the base compared to four hooves attached in the ridden variety.

Designer: Mr. Orwell
Height: 7 ½", 19.1 cm

Colourway	Finish	Intro.	Disc.	U.K. £	U.S. $	Can. $
Brown	Gloss	1955	1975	200.00	300.00	450.00
Chestnut	Gloss	1958	1967	425.00	600.00	900.00
Grey	Gloss	1962	1973	250.00	350.00	525.00
Palomino	Gloss	*1961*	1973	175.00	250.00	375.00

Model No. 1375

CANADIAN MOUNTIE

Designer: Arthur Gredington
Height: 8 ¼", 21.0 cm

Colourway	Finish	Intro.	Disc.	U.K. £	U.S. $	Can. $
Black	Gloss	1955	1976	475.00	675.00	1,000.00

Model No. 1377

CANADIAN MOUNTED COWBOY

The horse used for model 1377 was also that used for model 1374.

Designer: Mr. Orwell
Height: 8 ¾", 22.2 cm

Colourway	Finish	Intro.	Disc.	U.K. £	U.S. $	Can. $
Palomino	Gloss	1955	1973	700.00	1,000.00	1,500.00

Model No. 1391

MOUNTED INDIAN

Designer: Mr. Orwell
Height: 8 ½", 21.6 cm

Colourway	Finish	Intro.	Disc.	U.K. £	U.S. $	Can. $
Skewbald	Gloss	1955	1990	400.00	575.00	850.00

Model No. 1407 / F1407

ARAB FOAL

Designer: Arthur Gredington
Height: 4 ½", 11.9 cm

Colourway	Finish	Model	Intro.	Disc.	U.K. £	U.S. $	Can. $
Brown							
a. Beswick	Gloss	1407	1956	1989	20.00	30.00	45.00
b. Royal Doulton	Gloss	DA80	1989	1999	20.00	30.00	45.00
b. Reissued	Gloss	F1407	1999	Current	16.50	N/A	60.00
Brown							
a. Beswick	Matt	1407	1979	1989	35.00	50.00	75.00
b. Royal Doulton	Matt	DA80	1989	1996	30.00	45.00	70.00
Chestnut	Gloss	1407	1958	1967	275.00	400.00	600.00
Grey							
a. Beswick	Gloss	1407	*1961*	1989	50.00	70.00	100.00
b. Royal Doulton	Gloss	DA80	1989	1999	45.00	65.00	95.00
Opaque	Gloss	1407	*1961*	1973	70.00	100.00	150.00
Painted white	Gloss	1407	*1961*	1967	250.00	350.00	525.00
Palomino							
a. Beswick	Gloss	1407	*1961*	1989	35.00	50.00	75.00
b. Royal Doulton	Gloss	DA80	1989	1995	35.00	50.00	75.00
Rocking horse grey	Gloss	—	*c.1957*	1962	325.00	450.00	675.00
White	Matt	—	1970	1982	50.00	70.00	100.00

Model No. 1480

PONY
(Boy's Pony)

Designer: Arthur Gredington
Height: 3 ¾", 9.5 cm
Issued: Brown gloss, 1957-1967
Chestnut gloss, 1958-1967
Grey gloss, 1957-1967
Opaque, 1957-1967
Painted white, 1957-1957
Palomino gloss, 1957-1967
Rocking horse grey, 1957-1962

Colourway	U.K. £	U.S. $	Can. $
Brown	90.00	135.00	200.00
Chestnut	475.00	675.00	1,000.00
Grey	375.00	525.00	875.00
Opaque	150.00	200.00	300.00
Painted white	400.00	575.00	875.00
Palomino	90.00	135.00	200.00
Rocking horse grey	550.00	775.00	1,100.00

Model No. 1483

PONY
(Girl's Pony)

Designer: Arthur Gredington
Height: 5", 12.7 cm
Issued:
1. Brown, gloss – 1957-1967
2. Chestnut, gloss, –1958-1967
3. Grey, gloss – 1957-1967
4. Opaque, gloss – 1957-1967
5. Painted white, gloss – 1957-1967
6. Rocking horse grey – 1957-1962
7. Skewbald, gloss – 1957-1967 (brown/white)

Colourway	U.K. £	U.S. $	Can. $
Brown	100.00	150.00	225.00
Chestnut	500.00	700.00	1,050.00
Grey	375.00	525.00	800.00
Opaque	150.00	200.00	300.00
Painted white	375.00	525.00	800.00
Palomino	300.00	425.00	650.00
Rocking horse grey	550.00	775.00	1,175.00
Skewbald	150.00	200.00	300.00

Model No. 1484

HUNTSMAN'S HORSE

This model was used as the horse in model no. 1501 "The Huntsman."

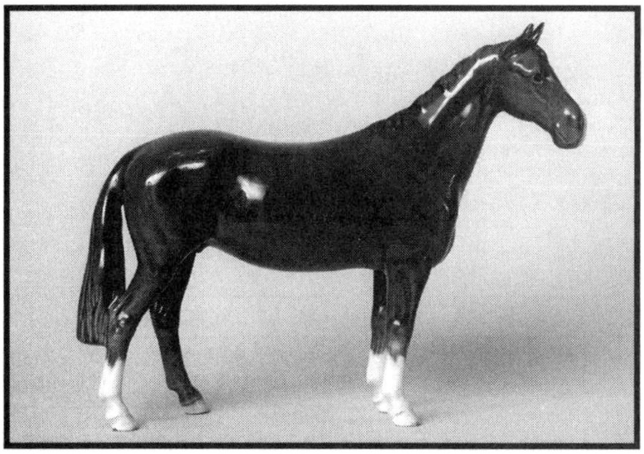

Designer: Arthur Gredington
Height: 6 ¾", 17.2 cm
Issued:
1. Brown, gloss – 1957-1982
2. Chestnut, gloss – 1958-1967
3. Grey, gloss – 1957-1982
4. Opaque, gloss – 1957-1973
5. Painted white, gloss – 1957-1967
6. Palomino, gloss – 1957-1982
7. Rocking horse grey, gloss – 1957-1962
8. White, matt – 1970-1982

Colourway	U.K. £	U.S. $	Can. $
Brown	60.00	85.00	125.00
Chestnut	300.00	425.00	650.00
Grey	90.00	125.00	175.00
Opaque	165.00	225.00	350.00
Painted white	400.00	575.00	875.00
Palomino	65.00	90.00	135.00
Rocking horse grey	500.00	700.00	1,050.00
White	75.00	100.00	150.00

Model No. 1499

GIRL ON PONY

The pony used for model no. 1499 was also available separately as model no. 1483 "Girl's Pony." The Girl on Pony is available in two variations, one with the girl looking straight ahead and the other has the girl looking down at the pony's neck. There is no price difference between the two variations. Examples have been found with a red jacket.

Designer: Arthur Gredington
Height: 5 ½", 14.0 cm

Colourway	Finish	Intro.	Disc.	U.K. £	U.S. $	Can. $
Brown	Gloss	1957	1965	650.00	900.00	1,350.00
Light dapple grey	Gloss	c.1961	1965	1,000.00	1,400.00	2,100.00
Palomino	Gloss	c.1957	1965	750.00	1,050.00	1,600.00
Rocking horse grey	Gloss	c.1961	1962	1,225.00	1,725.00	2,600.00
Skewbald	Gloss	1957	1965	160.00	225.00	350.00

Model No. 1500

BOY ON PONY

The pony used for model number 1500 was also available separately as model number 1480 "Boy's Pony. " The Boy on Pony is available in two variations, one with the boy looking straight ahead and the other has the boy looking down at the pony's neck. There is no price difference between the two variations. Examples have been found with the boy wearing a red jacket.

Designer: Arthur Gredington
Height: 5 ½", 14.0 cm
Issued: Brown, gloss – c.1961-1976
Chestnut, gloss – c.1961-1967
Light dapple grey, gloss –c.1961-1976
Palomino, gloss – 1957-1976
Rocking horse grey, gloss – c.1961-1962
Skewbald, gloss – Unknown

Colourway	U.K. £	U.S. $	Can. $
Brown	600.00	850.00	1,275.00
Chestnut	1,000.00	1,400.00	2,100.00
Light dapple grey	1,000.00	1,400.00	2,100.00
Palomino	150.00	200.00	300.00
Rocking horse grey	1,000.00	1,400.00	2,100.00
Skewbald	1,000.00	1,400.00	2,100.00

Model No. 1501

HUNTSMAN

STYLE TWO: Standing

The horse used for model 1501 was also available separately as model number 1484 "Huntsman's Horse."

Designer: Arthur Gredington
Height: 8 ¼", 21.0 cm
Issued: Brown, gloss – 1957-1995
Chestnut, gloss – 1965-1967
Grey, gloss – 1962-1975
Opaque, gloss – 1971-1973
Painted white, gloss – 1958-1971
Palomino, gloss – 1965-1971
Rocking horse grey, gloss – *c.1958*-1962
White, matt – 1971-1981

Colourway	U.K. £	U.S. $	Can. $
Brown	175.00	250.00	375.00
Chestnut	650.00	900.00	1,350.00
Grey	300.00	425.00	650.00
Opaque	200.00	300.00	450.00
Painted white	350.00	500.00	750.00
Palomino	600.00	850.00	1,275.00
Rocking horse grey	1,000.00	1,400.00	2,100.00
White	150.00	200.00	300.00

Note: Model with Huntsman wearing a green jacket is known.

Model No. 1516

APPALOOSA
(Spotted Walking Pony)

Designer: Arthur Gredington
Height: 5 ¼", 13.3 cm

Colourway	Finish	Intro.	Disc.	U.K. £	U.S. $	Can. $
Brown	Gloss	*1958*	*1967*	200.00	300.00	450.00
Chestnut	Gloss	*1958*	1967	600.00	850.00	1,275.00
Grey	Gloss	*1958*	1967	450.00	625.00	950.00
Opaque	Gloss	*1958*	1967	200.00	300.00	450.00
Painted white	Gloss	*1958*	1967	500.00	700.00	1,050.00
Palomino	Gloss	*1958*	1967	375.00	550.00	825.00
Rocking Horse Grey	Gloss	*1958*	1962	750.00	1,050.00	1,575.00
Spotted (British)	Gloss	1957	1966	300.00	425.00	650.00

Model No. 1546

H.M. QUEEN ELIZABETH II
ON IMPERIAL

The horse "Imperial' was also available separately as model number 1557.

Designer: Mr. Folkard
Height: 10 ½", 26.7 cm

Colourway	Finish	Intro.	Disc.	U.K. £	U.S. $	Can. $
Chestnut	Gloss	1958	1981	350.00	500.00	750.00

Model No. 1549

HORSE
(Head Tucked, Leg Up)

There are two version of model no. 1549, the first has the tail angled towards the off-hind hock, the second has the tail straight down. At the present time the dates cannot be determined as to when the mould was changed.

Model 1549 - First Version

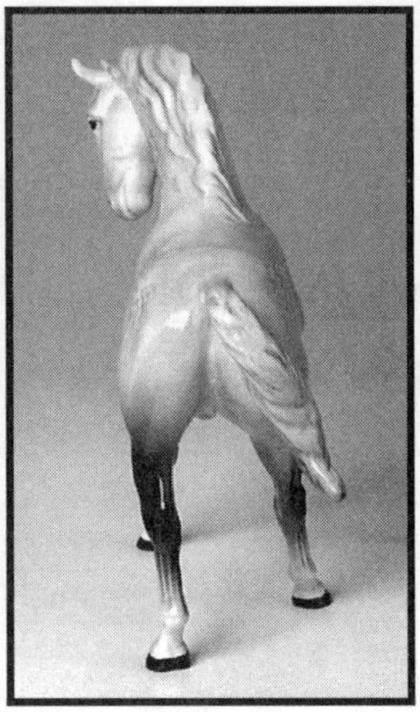

First Version - Tail angled toward off-hind hock

Second Version - Tail straight down

Designer: Pal Zalmen
Height: 7 ½", 19.1 cm

FIRST VERSION: Tail angled towards the off-hind hock

Colourway	Finish	Intro.	Disc.	U.K. £	U.S. $	Can. $
Brown	Gloss	1958	Unknown	70.00	100.00	150.00
Chestnut	Gloss	1958	1967	300.00	425.00	650.00
Grey	Gloss	*1961*	Unknown	90.00	135.00	200.00
Grey	Matt	1981	Unknown	80.00	120.00	175.00
Opaque	Gloss	1964	1973	150.00	200.00	300.00
Painted white	Gloss	*1961*	1967	250.00	350.00	525.00
Palomino	Gloss	*1961*	Unknown	80.00	120.00	175.00
Palomino	Matt	1981	Unknown	70.00	100.00	150.00
Rocking horse grey	Gloss	*c.1959*	*1962*	375.00	525.00	800.00
White	Matt	1970	Unknown	90.00	135.00	200.00

SECOND VERSION: Tail is straight down

Colourway	Finish	Model	Intro.	Disc.	U.K. £	U.S. $	Can. $
Brown							
a. Beswick	Gloss	1549	Unknown	1989	55.00	80.00	120.00
b. Royal Doulton	Gloss	DA51	1989	1999	55.00	80.00	120.00
c. Beswick	Gloss	H1549	1999	Current	52.00	N/A	110.00
Grey	Gloss	—	Unknown	1989	65.00	95.00	145.00
Grey	Matt	—	Unknown	1989	55.00	80.00	120.00
Palomino	Gloss	—	Unknown	1989	55.00	80.00	120.00
Palomino	Matt	—	Unknown	1989	45.00	65.00	100.00
White	Matt	—	Unknown	1982	75.00	110.00	165.00

Model No. 1557

"IMPERIAL"

This horse was used in model no. 1546 with Queen Elizabeth as rider.

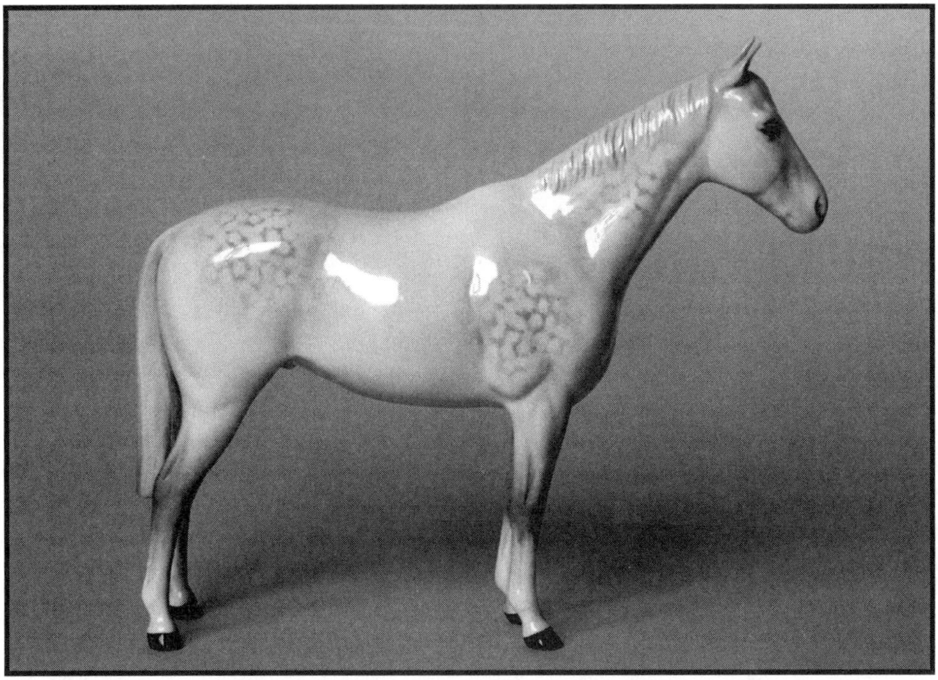

Designer: Albert Hallam and James Hayward
Height: 8 ¼", 21.0 cm

Colourway	Finish	Intro.	Disc.	U.K. £	U.S. $	Can. $
Brown	Gloss	1958	1982	70.00	100.00	150.00
Chestnut	Gloss	1958	1967	225.00	325.00	500.00
Grey	Gloss	1958	1982	90.00	135.00	200.00
Opaque	Gloss	1958	1973	175.00	250.00	375.00
Painted white	Gloss	1958	1967	350.00	500.00	750.00
Palomino	Gloss	1958	1982	80.00	120.00	175.00
Rocking horse grey	Gloss	1958	1962	425.00	650.00	975.00
White	Matt	1970	1982	100.00	150.00	225.00

Model No. 1564

LARGE RACEHORSE

This is the underlying model for the Connoisseur horse 1564 and the Harnessed version 1564.

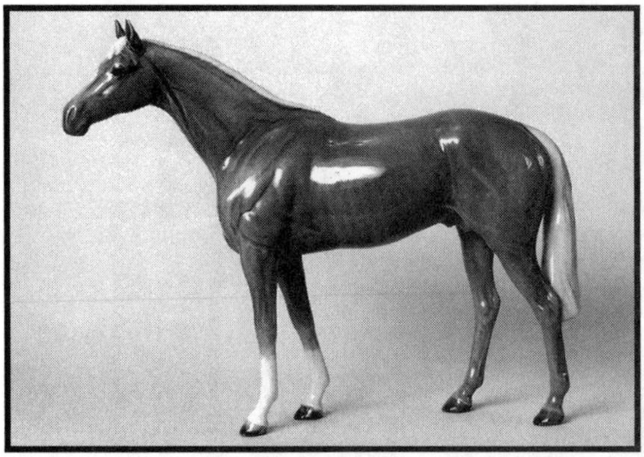

Model 1564 Large Racehorse

Model 1564 Connoisseur Horse

Designer: Arthur Gredington
Height: 11 ¼", 28.5 cm

Colourway	Finish	Intro.	Disc.	U.K. £	U.S. $	Can. $
Brown	Gloss	1959	1982	100.00	150.00	225.00
Chestnut	Gloss	1959	1967	450.00	625.00	950.00
Grey	Gloss	1959	1982	175.00	250.00	375.00
Opaque	Gloss	1959	1973	200.00	300.00	450.00
Painted white	Gloss	1959	1967	550.00	775.00	1,150.00
Palomino	Gloss	1959	1982	100.00	150.00	225.00
Rocking horse grey	Gloss	1959	1962	1,000.00	1,400.00	2,100.00
White	Matt	1970	1982	100.00	150.00	225.00

SERIES: Connoisseur Horse

Designer: Arthur Gredington
Height: 12 ¼", 31.1 cm

Colourway	Finish	Intro.	Disc.	U.K. £	U.S. $	Can. $
Brown	Matt	1970	1981	150.00	200.00	300.00

SERIES: Harnessed Horses

Height: 11 ¼", 28.5 cm

Colourway	Finish	Intro.	Disc.	U.K. £	U.S. $	Can. $
Brown	Gloss	1974	By 1981	150.00	200.00	300.00

Model No. 1588

H.R.H. DUKE OF EDINBURGH ON ALAMEIN

Designer: Mr. Folkard
Height: 10 ½", 26.7 cm

Colourway	Finish	Intro.	Disc.	U.K. £	U.S. $	Can. $
Light dapple grey	Gloss	1958	1981	400.00	550.00	800.00

Model No. 1624

LIFEGUARD

STYLE ONE: With trumpet

Designer: Arthur Gredington
Height: 9 ½" 24.0 cm

Colourway	Finish	Intro.	Disc.	U.K. £	U.S. $	Can. $
Light dapple grey	Gloss	1959	1977	425.00	600.00	1,000.00

Model No. 1641

CONNEMARA PONY
"TERESE OF LEAM"

SERIES: Mountain and Moorland Ponies

Designer: Arthur Gredington
Height: 7", 17.8 cm

Colourway	Finish	Intro.	Disc.	U.K. £	U.S. $	Can. $
Grey	Gloss	1961	1984	125.00	200.00	300.00

Model No. 1642

DARTMOOR PONY
"JENTYL" / "WARLORD"

Warlord was commissioned, in a limited edition of 1,500, by P. R. Middleweek & Co. as the first in a series of Dartmoor Ponies.

SERIES: Mountain and Moorland Ponies

Designer: Arthur Gredington
Height: 6 ¼", 15.9 cm

Name	Colourway/Finish	Intro.	Disc.	U.K. £	U.S. $	Can. $
"Jentyl"	Brown/Gloss	1961	1984	100.00	150.00	225.00
"Warlord"	Bay/Gloss	1996	1996	50.00	70.00	100.00

Note: See also The Dartmoor Family page 289.

Model No. 1643

WELSH MOUNTAIN PONY "COED COCH MADOG"

SERIES: Mountain and Moorland Ponies

First Version: Tail is attached to off-side hind leg

Second Version: Tail hangs loose

Designer: Arthur Gredington
Height: 6 ¼", 15.9 cm

FIRST VERSION: Tail is attached to off-side hind leg.

Colourway	Finish	Intro.	Disc.	U.K. £	U.S. $	Can. $
Grey	Gloss	1961	Unknown	125.00	175.00	275.00

SECOND VERSION: Tail hangs loose.

Colourway	Finish	Intro.	Disc.	U.K. £	U.S. $	Can. $
Grey	Gloss	Unknown	1989	175.00	250.00	375.00

Model No. 1644

HIGHLAND PONY "MACKIONNEACH"

SERIES: Mountain and Moorland Ponies

Designer: Arthur Gredington
Height: 7 ¼", 18.4 cm

Colourway	Finish	Intro.	Disc.	U.K. £	U.S. $	Can. $
Dun	Gloss	1961	1989	100.00	150.00	225.00
Dark Dun	Gloss	Unknown	Unknown	150.00	200.00	300.00
Light Grey	Gloss	Unknown	Unknown	500.00	700.00	1,050.00
Opaque	Gloss	Unknown	Unknown		Extremely Rare	

Model No. 1645

EXMOOR PONY "HEATHERMAN"

SERIES: Mountain and Moorland Ponies

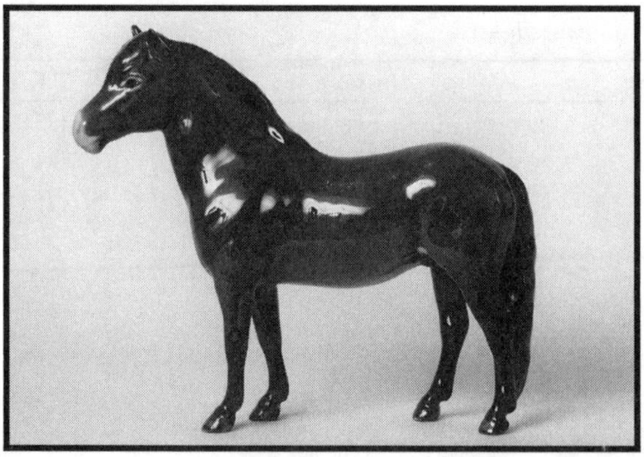

Designer: Arthur Gredington
Height: 6 ½", 16.5 cm

Colourway	Finish	Intro.	Disc.	U.K. £	U.S. $	Can. $
Bay	Gloss	1961	1983	150.00	225.00	350.00

Model No. 1646

NEW FOREST PONY "JONATHEN 3RD"

SERIES: Mountain and Moorland Ponies

First Version: Tail is attached to the near-side hock

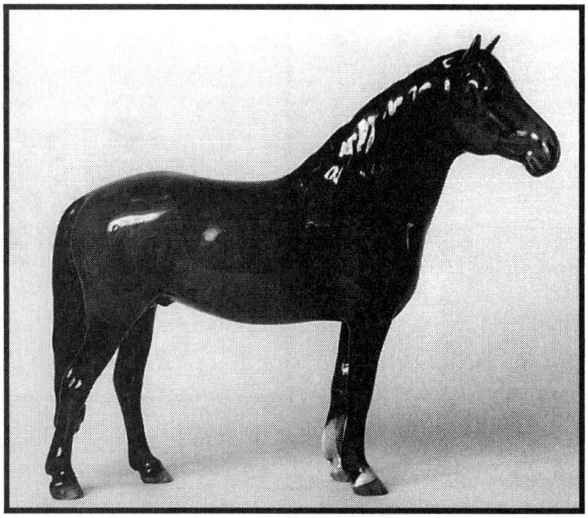

Second Version: Tail hangs loose

Designer: Arthur Gredington
Height: 7", 17.8 cm

FIRST VERSION: Tail is attached to the near-side hock.

Colourway	Finish	Intro.	Disc.	U.K. £	U.S. $	Can. $
Bay	Gloss	1961	Unknown	125.00	175.00	275.00

SECOND VERSION: Tail hangs loose.

Colourway	Finish	Intro.	Disc.	U.K. £	U.S. $	Can. $
Bay	Gloss	Unknown	1984	100.00	150.00	225.00

Model No. 1647

FELL PONY "DENE DAUNTLESS"

SERIES: Mountain and Moorland Ponies

Designer: Arthur Gredington
Height: 6 ¾", 17.2 cm

Colourway	Finish	Intro.	Disc.	U.K. £	U.S. $	Can. $
Black	Gloss	1961	1982	125.00	175.00	275.00

Model No. 1648

SHETLAND PONY "ESCHONCHAN RONAY"

SERIES: Mountain and Moorland Ponies

Designer: Arthur Gredington
Height: 4 ¾", 12.1 cm

Colourway	Finish	Intro.	Disc.	U.K. £	U.S. $	Can. $
Brown	Gloss	1961	1989	85.00	125.00	185.00

Note: An example in Opaque gloss is know to exist.

WORKING HORSES

Model 2309
Burnham Beauty – in working harness

Model 2465
Clydesdale – in working harness

Model 2464
Percheron – in show harness

Model 2578
Large Action Shire – brown, matt

Model 2578
Shire – grey, matt – in working harness

Model 2578
Large Action Shire – grey, gloss

HORSES

Model 1033
Shetland Pony – chestnut, gloss

Model 1642
Dartmoor Pony "Warlord" – bay, gloss

Model 1484
Huntsman's Horse – chestnut, gloss

Model 1197
Pony – rocking horse grey, gloss

Model 1050
Grazing Shire – opaque, gloss

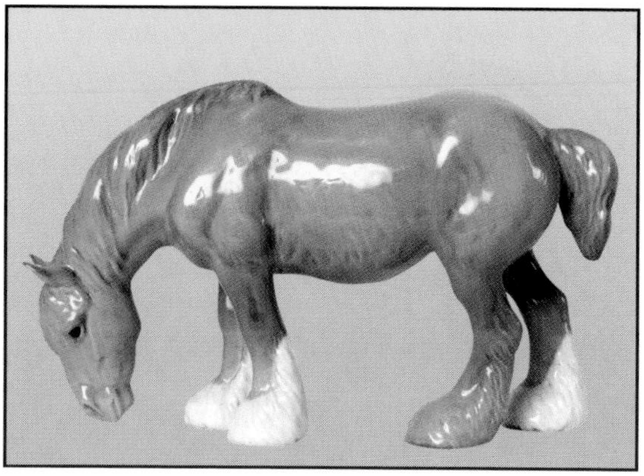

Model 1050
Grazing Shire – chestnut, gloss

FOALS – COLOURWAYS

Model 836
Foal, first version – rocking horse grey, gloss

Model 836
Foal, second version – grey, gloss

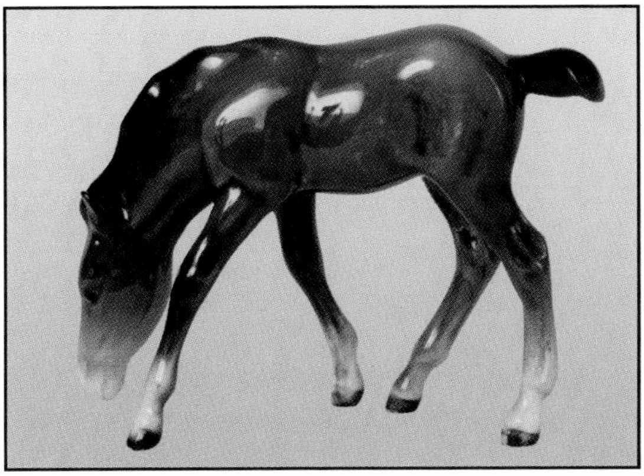

Model 946
Foal Grazing, first version – brown, gloss

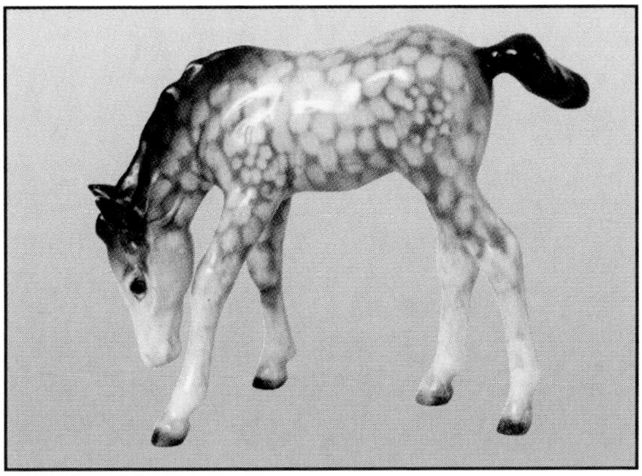

Model 946
Foal Grazing, second version – rocking horse grey, gloss

Model 763
Foal, first version – brown, gloss

Model 763
Foal, second version – rocking horse grey, gloss

Model 763
Foal, third version – palomino, gloss

HORSES

Model 1373
Pinto Pony, first version – skewbald, gloss

Model 1373
Pinto Pony, second version – skewbald, gloss

Model 1182
Swish tail, first version – grey, matt

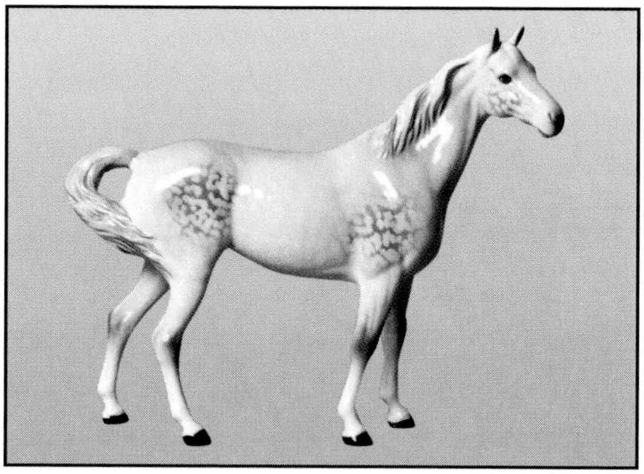

Model 1182
Swish tail, second version – grey, gloss

Model 1564
Large Racehorse – palomino, gloss

Model 1564
Large Racehorse – painted white, gloss

HORSES

Model 1772A
Appaloosa – early colour version

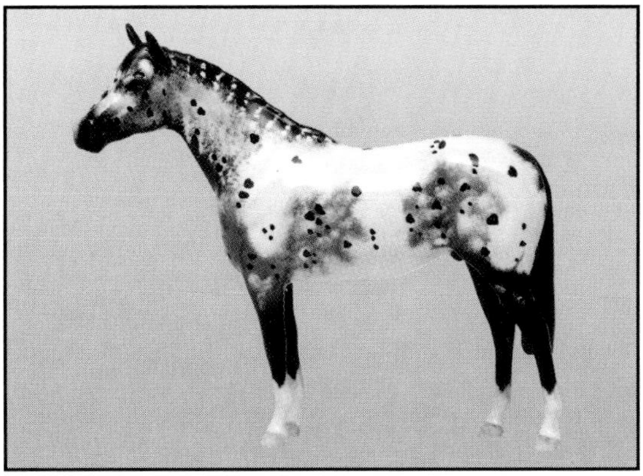

Model 1772A
Appaloosa – later colour version

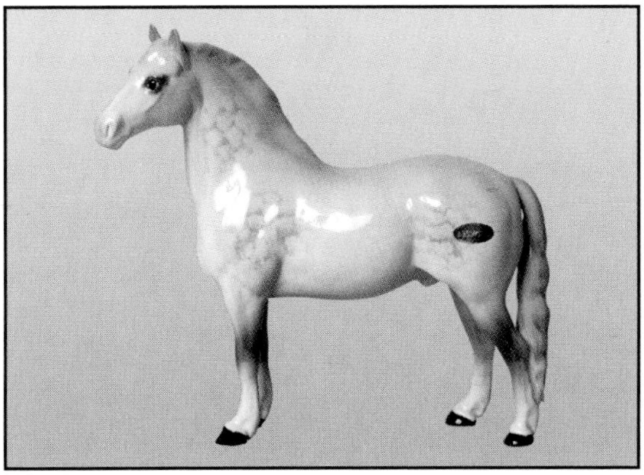

Model 1793
Welsh Cob, first version – grey, gloss

Model 1793
Welsh Cob, second version – brown, gloss

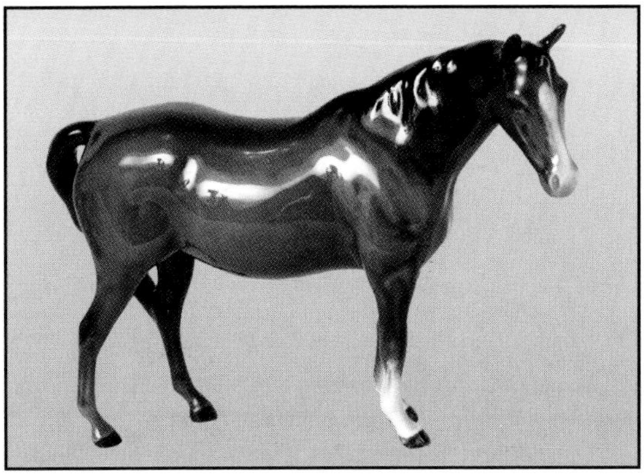

Model 1991
Mare, first version – brown, gloss

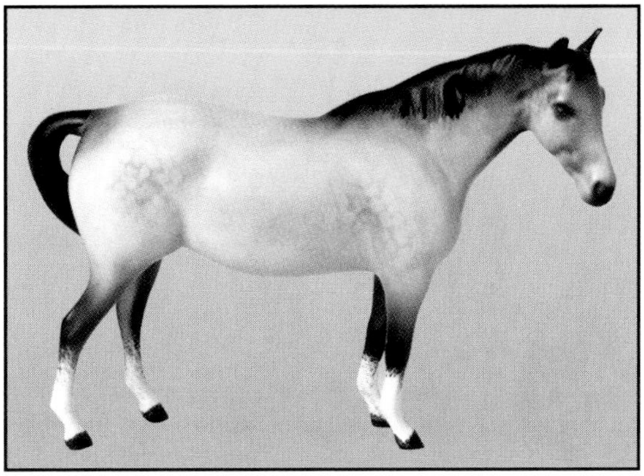

Model 1991
Mare, second version – grey, matt

RIDERS AND HORSES

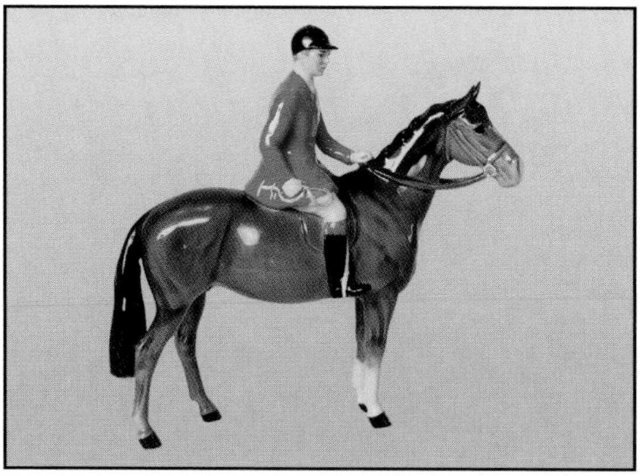

Model 1501
Huntsman, Style Two – brown, gloss

Model 1730
Huntswoman, Style Two – brown, gloss

Model 1499
Girl on Pony

Model 1500
Boy on Pony

Model 2352
Nijinsky – Lester Piggott Up

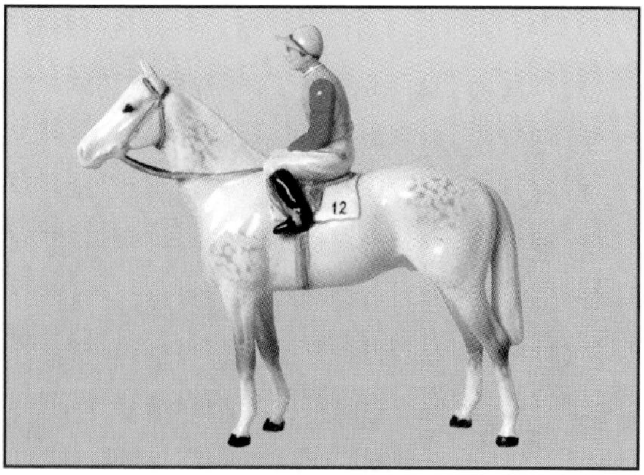

Model 1862
Horse and Jockey – light dapple grey

RIDERS AND HORSES

Huntsman, Style One
First version – orangey-red coat

Model 868
First version – scarlet coat

Huntsman, Style One
Second version – scarlet coat

Model 939
Girl on Jumping Horse

Model 982
Huntswoman, Style One

Model 1037
Racehorse and Jockey - stripes on saddlecloth

Model 1037
Racehorse and Jockey - number on saddlecloth

RIDERS AND HORSES

Model 2210
Highwayman

Model 2467
Lipizzaner with Rider, first version

Model 2467
Lipizzaner with Rider, second version

Model 2275
Bedouin Arab

Model 1145
Knight in Armour

Model 1377
Canadian Mounted Cowboy

Model 1391
Mounted Indian

Model No. 1671

DALES PONY "MAISIE"

SERIES: Mountain and Moorland Ponies

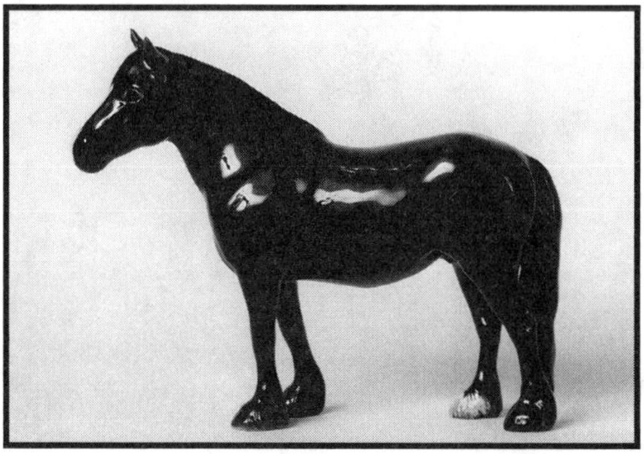

Designer: Arthur Gredington
Height: 6 ½", 16.5 cm

Colourway	Finish	Intro.	Disc.	U.K. £	U.S. $	Can. $
Black	Gloss	1961	1982	125.00	175.00	275.00

Model No. 1730

HUNTSWOMAN

STYLE TWO: Rider and horse stood still

Designer: Arthur Gredington
Height: 8 ¼", 21.0 cm

Colourway	Finish	Intro.	Disc.	U.K. £	U.S. $	Can. $
Brown	Gloss	1960	1975	300.00	435.00	650.00
Grey	Gloss	1960	1995	250.00	365.00	550.00
Opaque	Gloss	1971	1973	275.00	400.00	600.00
Painted white	Gloss	1960	1971	500.00	700.00	1,050.00
Rocking horse grey	Gloss	1960	1962	1,000.00	1,400.00	2,100.00
White	Matt	1971	1981	250.00	365.00	550.00

Note: An example is known in black gloss, with the rider wearing a green jacket.

Model No. 1734

LARGE HUNTER

FIRST VERSION: The tail hangs straight down, unattached to the leg

Designer: Arthur Gredington
Height: 11 ¼", 28.5 cm

Colourway	Finish	Intro.	Disc.	U.K. £	U.S. $	Can. $
Brown	Gloss	1961	1963	275.00	400.00	600.00
Chestnut	Gloss	1961	1963	750.00	1,050.00	1,500.00
Grey	Gloss	1961	1963	675.00	950.00	1,400.00
Opaque	Gloss	1961	1963	325.00	450.00	675.00
Painted white	Gloss	1961	1963	750.00	1,050.00	1,500.00
Palomino	Gloss	1961	1963	500.00	700.00	1,050.00
Rocking horse grey	Gloss	1961	1962	1,000.00	1,400.00	2,100.00

Second Version: Arched tail attached to off-side hock

Large Hunter - Connoisseur Horse

SECOND VERSION: The tail is slightly arched away from the body and is attached to the off-side hock.

Height: 11 ¾", 29.8 cm

Colourway	Finish	Intro.	Disc.	U.K. £	U.S. $	Can. $
Brown	Gloss	1963	1984	100.00	150.00	225.00
Chestnut	Gloss	1963	1967	550.00	775.00	1,150.00
Grey	Gloss	1963	1984	150.00	200.00	300.00
Opaque	Gloss	1963	1973	200.00	300.00	450.00
Painted white	Gloss	1963	1967	650.00	900.00	1,350.00
Palomino	Gloss	1963	1983	125.00	175.00	250.00
White	Matt	1970	1982	100.00	150.00	225.00

SERIES: Connoisseur Horses

Height: 12 ¼", 31.1 cm

Colourway	Finish	Intro.	Disc.	U.K. £	U.S. $	Can. $
Grey	Matt	1970	1982	125.00	185.00	275.00

Model No. 1771

ARAB "BAHRAM"

Arab "Bahram"

Arab "Bahram" Connoisseur Horse

Designer: Arthur Gredington
Height: 7 ½", 19.1 cm

Colourway	Finish	Model	Intro.	Disc.	U.K. £	U.S. $	Can. $
Brown							
a. Beswick	Gloss	1771	1961	1989	65.00	95.00	145.00
b. Royal Doulton	Gloss	DA52	1989	1997	65.00	95.00	145.00
Brown							
a. Beswick	Matt	1771	1980	1989	60.00	90.00	135.00
b. Royal Doulton	Matt	DA52	1989	1997	60.00	90.00	135.00
Chestnut	Gloss	1771	1961	1967	200.00	300.00	450.00
Grey	Gloss	1771	1961	1989	85.00	125.00	185.00
Grey	Matt	1771	1980	1989	85.00	125.00	185.00
Opaque	Gloss	1771	1961	1973	150.00	225.00	325.00
Painted white	Gloss	1771	1961	1967	400.00	600.00	875.00
Palomino	Gloss	1771	1961	1989	75.00	115.00	165.00
Palomino	Matt	1771	1980	1989	65.00	95.00	145.00
Rocking horse grey	Gloss	1771	1961	1962		Extremely Rare	
White	Matt	1771	1970	1982	65.00	95.00	145.00

Note: An example is known in a black satin colourway.

SERIES: Connoisseur Horses

Height: 8 ¼", 21.0 cm

Colourway	Finish	Intro.	Disc.	U.K. £	U.S. $	Can. $
Grey	Matt	1970	1989	160.00	235.00	350.00

Model No. 1772A / H1772

THOROUGHBRED STALLION
(Large)

Thoroughbred Stallion

Thoroughbred Stallion - Connoisseur Horse

Designer: Arthur Gredington
Height: 8", 20.3 cm

Colourway	Finish	Model	Intro.	Disc.	U.K. £	U.S. $	Can. $
Brown							
a. Beswick	Gloss	1772A	1961	1989	55.00	80.00	125.00
b. Royal Doulton	Gloss	DA53	1989	1999	55.00	80.00	125.00
c. Beswick	Gloss	H1772A	1999	Current	52.00	N/A	110.00
Chestnut	Gloss	1772A	1961	1967	350.00	500.00	750.00
Grey							
a. Beswick	Gloss	1772A	1961	1989	90.00	135.00	200.00
b. Royal Doulton	Gloss	DA53	1989	1998	80.00	120.00	185.00
Opaque	Gloss	1772A	1961	1973	150.00	200.00	300.00
Painted white	Gloss	1772A	1961	1967	450.00	650.00	975.00
Palomino	Gloss	1772A	1961	1983	100.00	150.00	225.00
Rocking horse grey	Gloss	1772A	1961	1962		Extremely Rare	
White	Matt	1772A	1970	1982	75.00	115.00	165.00

Note: An example is known in a grey matt colourway.

SERIES: Connoisseur Horses

Height: 8 ¾", 22.2 cm

Colourway	Finish	Intro.	Disc.	U.K. £	U.S. $	Can. $
Bay	Matt	1970	1989	100.00	150.00	225.00

Model No. 1772B / H1772

APPALOOSA STALLION

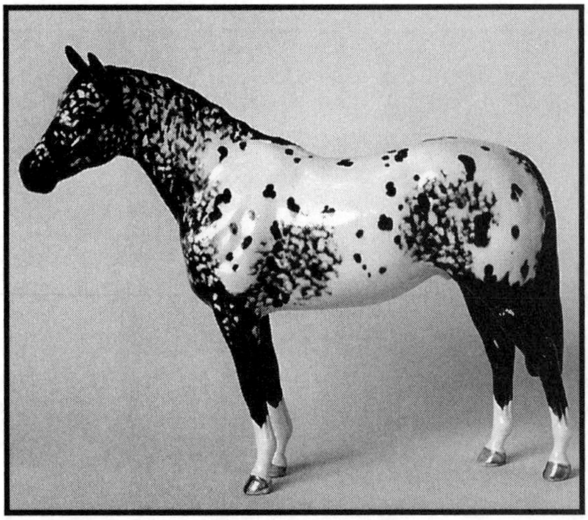

Colourway No. 1, More detailed paintwork, striped hooves

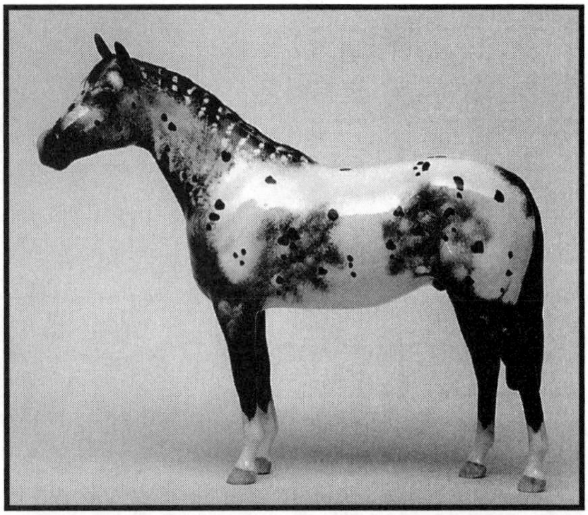

Colourway No. 2, Less distinct roan areas, cream hooves

Designer: Arthur Gredington
Height: 8", 20.3 cm

COLOURWAY No. 1. ***More detailed paintwork with the head and neck in particular more "mottled." Striped hooves.***

Colourway	Finish	Model	Intro.	Disc.	U.K. £	U.S. $	Can. $
Black and white	Gloss	1772B	c.1967	Unknown	150.00	200.00	300.00

COLOURWAY No. 2. ***Less distinct roan areas of black on head and neck and brown on lower body quarters. Cream hooves.***

Colourway	Finish	Model	Intro.	Disc.	U.K. £	U.S. $	Can. $
Black and white							
a. Beswick	Gloss	1772B	Unknown	1989	70.00	100.00	150.00
b. Royal Doulton	Gloss	DA68	1989	1999	70.00	100.00	150.00
c. Beswick	Gloss	H1772B	1999	Current	62.00	N/A	245.00

Model No. 1793

WELSH COB
(Standing)

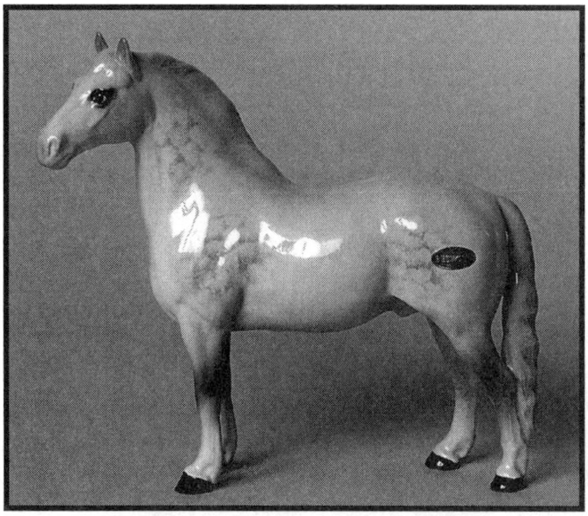

First Version: Tail hangs straight down

Second Version - Top part of tail arched away from body

Designer: Arthur Gredington
Height: 7 ½", 19.1 cm

FIRST VERSION: Tail hangs straight down.

Colourway	Finish	Intro.	Disc.	U.K. £	U.S. $	Can. $
Brown	Gloss	1962	c.1975/76	100.00	150.00	225.00
Chestnut	Gloss	1962	c.1975/76	500.00	700.00	1,050.00
Grey	Gloss	1962	c.1975/76	175.00	250.00	375.00
Opaque	Gloss	1962	c.1975/76	200.00	300.00	450.00
Painted white	Gloss	1962	c.1975/76	425.00	600.00	900.00
Palomino	Gloss	1962	1970	400.00	550.00	825.00
Piebald	Gloss	Unknown	Unknown		Very Rare	
White	Matt	1970	c.1975/76	100.00	150.00	225.00

SECOND VERSION: The tail was altered so that the top part (dock) arched away from the body.

Colourway	Finish	Intro.	Disc.	U.K. £	U.S. $	Can. $
Brown	Gloss	c.1975/76	1982	85.00	125.00	185.00
Grey	Gloss	c.1975/76	1982	150.00	225.00	350.00
White	Matt	c.1975/76	1982	85.00	125.00	185.00

Model No. 1811

MARE AND FOAL

The mare and foal are available separately as model nos. 1812 mare and 1813 foal.

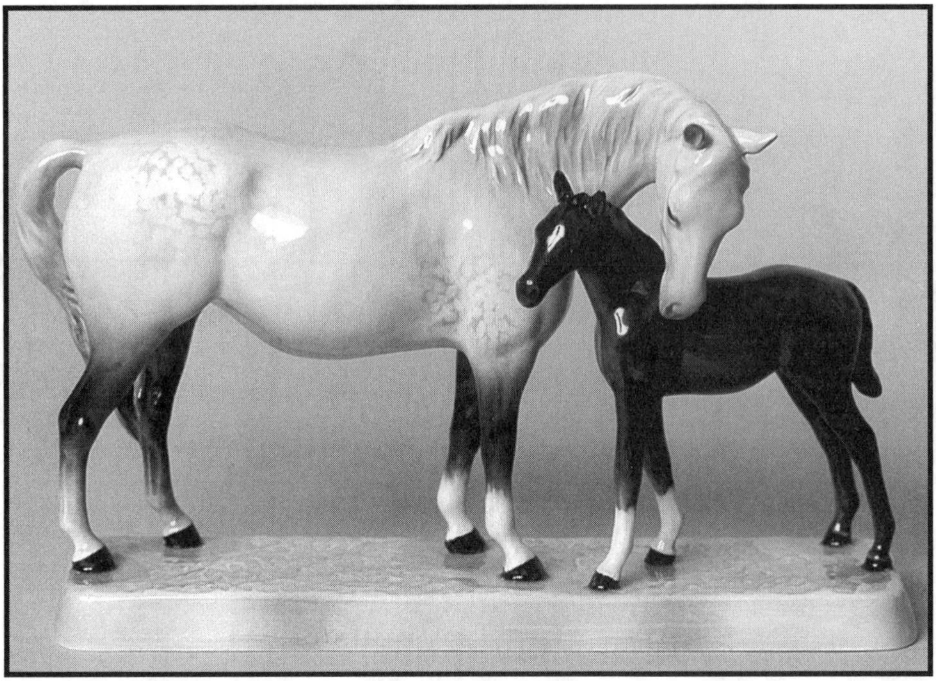

Designer: Arthur Gredington
Height: 6", 15.0 cm

Colourway	Finish	Intro.	Disc.	U.K. £	U.S. $	Can. $
Brown mare and chestnut foal	Gloss	1962	1975	300.00	425.00	650.00
Grey mare and black foal	Gloss	1962	1975	175.00	250.00	375.00

Model No. 1812

MARE
(Facing Right, Head Down)

Model no. 1811 was paired with foal model no. 1813 to make model no. 1811 "Mare and Foal."

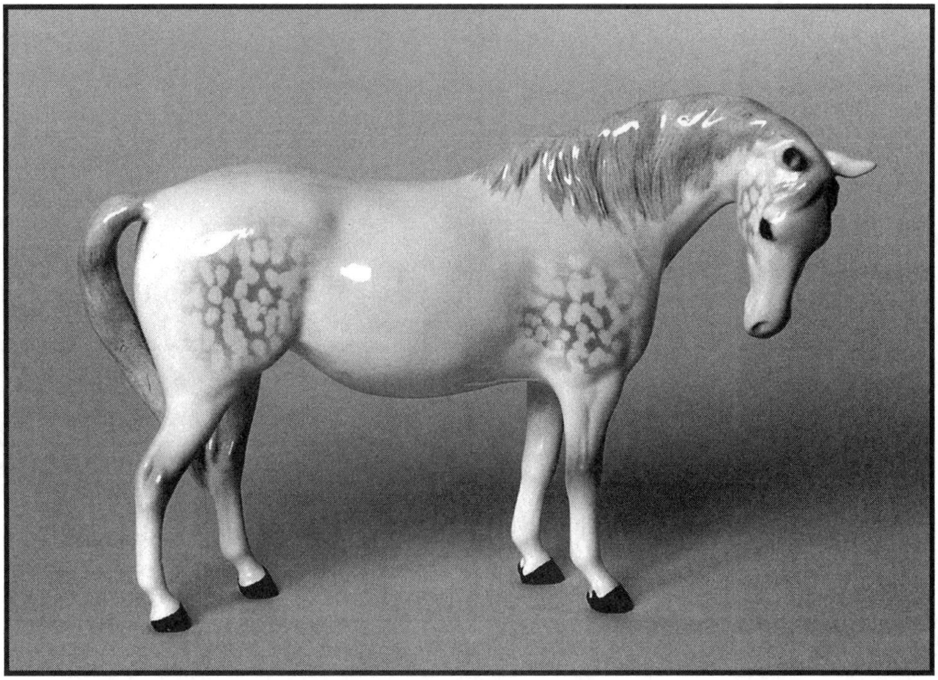

Designer: Arthur Gredington
Height: 5 ¾", 14.6 cm

Colourway	Finish	Model	Intro.	Disc.	U.K. £	U.S. $	Can. $
Brown							
a. Beswick	Gloss	1812	1962	1989	50.00	75.00	110.00
b. Royal Doulton	Gloss	DA54	1989	1989	50.00	75.00	110.00
Brown	Matt	1812	1970	1989	50.00	75.00	110.00
Chestnut	Gloss	1812	1962	1967	425.00	600.00	900.00
Grey	Gloss	1812	1962	1989	60.00	85.00	125.00
Grey	Matt	1812	1970	1989	55.00	80.00	120.00
Opaque	Gloss	1812	1962	1973	150.00	200.00	300.00
Painted white	Gloss	1812	1962	1967	300.00	425.00	675.00
Palomino	Gloss	1812	1962	1989	55.00	80.00	120.00
Palomino	Matt	1812	1970	1983	50.00	75.00	110.00
"Treacle"	Gloss	1812	1992	1992	75.00	100.00	150.00
"Treacle"	Matt	1812	1992	1992	75.00	100.00	150.00
White	Matt	1812	1970	1982	60.00	85.00	125.00

Note: "Treacle" (allover treacle brown gloss or matt finish, no other painted features) seems to have originated from Sinclairs, who offered this piece by mail order in 1992. The figures were supposed to be brown gloss, but a limited number of treacle ones surfaced.

Model No. 1813

FOAL
(Larger Thoroughbred Type)

First Version - Fine head and legs

Second Version - Plain head, thicker, less shapely legs

Designer: Arthur Gredington
Height: 4 ½", 11.9 cm

***FIRST VERSION:** Fine head and legs, off fore leg is placed well behind the near fore leg.*

Colourway	Finish	Intro.	Disc.	U.K. £	U.S. $	Can. $
Brown	Gloss	1962	1982	30.00	45.00	70.00
Brown	Matt	1979	1982	30.00	45.00	70.00
Chestnut	Gloss	1962	1967	250.00	350.00	525.00
Grey	Gloss	1962	1982	45.00	70.00	100.00
Opaque	Gloss	1962	1973	90.00	125.00	200.00
Painted white	Gloss	1963	1967	200.00	300.00	450.00
Palomino	Gloss	1962	1982	35.00	50.00	75.00
White	Matt	1970	c.1982	55.00	80.00	120.00

***SECOND VERSION:** Plain head, thicker legs with less shape, off fore leg almost parallel to near fore leg.*

Colourway	Finish	Model	Intro.	Disc.	U.K. £	U.S. $	Can. $
Brown							
a. Beswick	Gloss	1813	1982	1982	25.00	40.00	60.00
b. Royal Doulton	Gloss	DA81	1989	1999	25.00	40.00	60.00
c. Beswick	Gloss	F1813	1999	1999	25.00	40.00	60.00
Brown							
a. Beswick	Matt	1813	1982	1989	25.00	40.00	60.00
b. Royal Doulton	Matt	DA81	1989	1995	25.00	40.00	60.00
Grey	Gloss	1813	1982	1989	30.00	45.00	70.00
Palomino	Gloss	1813	1982	1989	25.00	40.00	60.00
Orange bay	Gloss	1813	1982	c.1984	55.00	80.00	120.00
White	Matt	1813	c.1982	1982	40.00	55.00	80.00

Model No. 1816

FOAL
(Smaller Thoroughbred Type, Facing Left)

First Version: Fine head, thin delicate legs

Second Version: Head and legs thicker

Designer: Arthur Gredington
Height: 3 ½", 8.9 cm

FIRST VERSION: Fine head and very thin delicate legs.

Colourway	Finish	Intro.	Disc.	U.K. £	U.S. $	Can. $
Brown	Gloss	1963	1975	30.00	45.00	70.00
Chestnut	Gloss	1963	1967	200.00	300.00	450.00
Grey	Gloss	1963	1975	45.00	65.00	100.00
Opaque	Gloss	1963	1973	75.00	120.00	175.00
Painted white	Gloss	1963	1967	175.00	250.00	375.00
Palomino	Gloss	1963	1975	40.00	55.00	80.00
White	Matt	1970	1975	40.00	55.00	80.00

SECOND VERSION: Head and legs made thicker and less shape to the legs.

Colourway	Finish	Model	Intro.	Disc.	U.K. £	U.S. $	Can. $
Brown							
a. Beswick	Gloss	1816	1975	1989	20.00	30.00	45.00
b. Royal Doulton	Gloss	DA82	1989	1999	20.00	30.00	45.00
Brown							
a. Beswick	Matt	1816	1979	1989	20.00	30.00	45.00
b. Royal Doulton	Matt	DA82	1989	1996	20.00	30.00	45.00
Grey	Gloss	1816	1975	1983	30.00	45.00	70.00
Palomino							
a. Beswick	Gloss	1816	1975	1989	30.00	45.00	70.00
b. Royal Doulton	Gloss	DA82	1989	1996	30.00	45.00	70.00
White	Matt	1816	1975	1982	30.00	45.00	70.00

Model No. 1817

FOAL
(Smaller Thoroughbred Type, Facing Right)

Designer: Arthur Gredington
Height: 3 ¼", 8.3 cm

Colourway	Finish	Intro.	Disc.	U.K. £	U.S. $	Can. $
Brown	Gloss	1963	1975	40.00	55.00	80.00
Chestnut	Gloss	1963	1967	200.00	300.00	450.00
Grey	Gloss	1963	1975	55.00	75.00	115.00
Opaque	Gloss	1963	1973	75.00	100.00	150.00
Painted white	Gloss	1963	1967	200.00	300.00	450.00
Palomino	Gloss	1963	1975	50.00	70.00	100.00
White	Matt	1970	1975	40.00	55.00	80.00

Model No. 1862

HORSE AND JOCKEY

STYLE TWO: Standing horse and jockey

Designer: Arthur Gredington
Height: 8", 20.3 cm

Colourway	Finish	Intro.	Disc.	U.K. £	U.S. $	Can. $
Brown	Gloss	1963	1984	350.00	500.00	750.00
Light dapple grey	Gloss	1963	1983	425.00	600.00	900.00
Painted white	Gloss	1963	by 1984	550.00	775.00	1,150.00

Model No. 1991 / H1991

MARE
(Facing Right, Head Up)

Designer: Arthur Gredington
Height: 5 ½", 14.0 cm

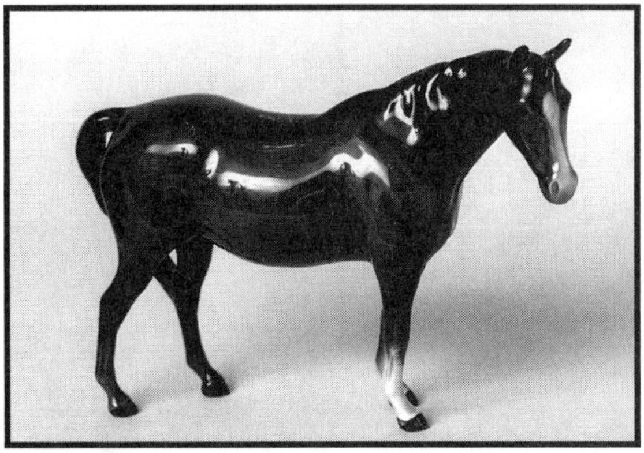

First Version – The end only of the tai attached to the hock

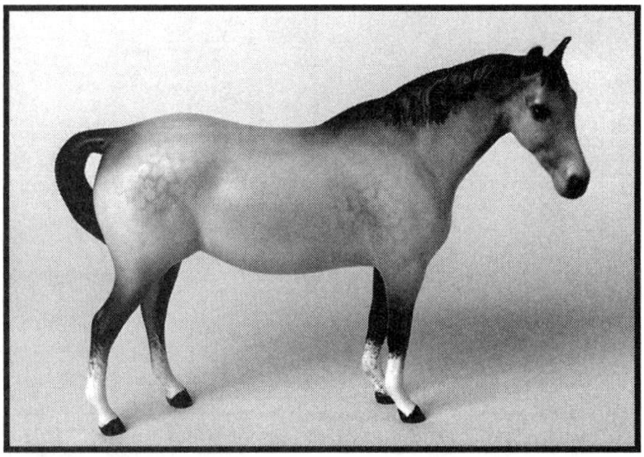

Second Version – Tail attached to the quarters and hock

FIRST VERSION: The end only of the tail is attached to the hock.

Colourway	Finish	Intro.	Disc.	U.K. £	U.S. $	Can. $
Brown	Gloss	1965	Unknown	50.00	70.00	105.00
Brown	Matt	1970	Unknown	45.00	65.00	100.00
Chestnut	Gloss	1965	Unknown	300.00	425.00	650.00
Grey	Gloss	1965	Unknown	65.00	95.00	145.00
Grey	Matt	1970	Unknown	55.00	80.00	120.00
Opaque	Gloss	1965	Unknown	125.00	175.00	275.00
Painted white	Gloss	1965	Unknown	275.00	400.00	600.00
Palomino	Gloss	1965	Unknown	55.00	80.00	120.00
Palomino	Matt	1970	Unknown	50.00	70.00	105.00
White	Matt	1970	Unknown	65.00	95.00	145.00

SECOND VERSION: The tail is attached to the quarters and the hock.

Colourway	Finish	Model	Intro.	Disc.	U.K. £	U.S. $	Can. $
Brown							
a. Beswick	Gloss	1991	Unknown	1989	35.00	50.00	75.00
b. Royal Doulton	Gloss	DA55	1989	1999	35.00	50.00	75.00
b. Beswick	Gloss	H1991	1999	Current	31.00	N/A	90.00
Brown							
a. Beswick	Matt	1991	Unknown	1989	35.00	50.00	75.00
b. Royal Doulton	Matt	DA55	1989	1995	35.00	50.00	75.00
Grey							
a. Beswick	Gloss	1991	Unknown	1989	45.00	65.00	100.00
b. Royal Doulton	Gloss	DA55	1989	1995	45.00	65.00	100.00
Grey	Matt	—	Unknown	1989	45.00	65.00	100.00
Palomino							
a. Beswick	Gloss	1991	Unknown	1989	45.00	65.00	100.00
b. Royal Doulton	Gloss	DA55	1989	1995	45.00	65.00	100.00
Palomino	Matt	—	Unknown	1989	35.00	50.00	75.00
White	Matt	—	Unknown	1982	45.00	65.00	100.00

Model No. 1992 / H1992

THOROUGHBRED STALLION
(Small)

Designer: Arthur Gredington   Height: 5 ½", 14.0.cm

Colourway	Finish	Model	Intro.	Disc.	U.K. £	U.S. $	Can. $
Brown							
a. Beswick	Gloss	1992	1965	1989	35.00	50.00	75.00
b. Royal Doulton	Gloss	DA56	1989	1999	35.00	50.00	75.00
c. Beswick	Gloss	H1992	1999	Current	31.00	N/A	N/A
Brown							
a. Beswick	Matt	1992	1970	1989	35.00	50.00	75.00
b. Royal Doulton	Matt	DA56	1989	1999	35.00	50.00	75.00
Chestnut	Gloss	1992	1965	1967	225.00	325.00	500.00
Grey							
a. Beswick	Gloss	1992	1965	1989	45.00	65.00	95.00
b. Royal Doulton	Gloss	DA56	1989	1998	45.00	65.00	95.00
Grey	Matt	1992	1970	1989	45.00	65.00	95.00
Opaque	Gloss	—	1965	1973	85.00	125.00	200.00
Painted white	Gloss	—	1965	1967	225.00	325.00	500.00
Palomino	Gloss	—	1965	1989	50.00	70.00	100.00
Palomino	Matt	—	1970	1989	40.00	55.00	80.00
White	Matt	—	1970	1982	50.00	70.00	100.00

Model No. 2065 / A2065

ARKLE

SERIES: Connoisseur Horses

Designer: Arthur Gredington
Height: 11 7/8", 30.1 cm
Colour: Bay, matt
Issued: a. Beswick – 1970-1989
b. Doulton (DA15) – 1989-1999
c. Beswick – 1999 to the present

Description	U.K. £	U.S. $	Can. $
a. Beswick - Original	175.00	250.00	375.00
b. Doulton (DA15)	175.00	250.00	375.00
c. Beswick - reissued	175.00	N/A	N/A

Model No. 2084

ARKLE
PAT TAAFFE UP

SERIES: Connoisseur Horses

Designer: Arthur Gredington
Height: 12 ½", 21.7 cm

Colourway	Finish	Intro.	Disc.	U.K. £	U.S. $	Can. $
Bay	Matt	1970	1982	350.00	500.00	750.00

Model No. 2186

QUARTER HORSE

Designer: Arthur Gredington
Height: 8 ¼", 21.0 cm

Colourway	Finish	Intro.	Disc.	U.K. £	U.S. $	Can. $
Brown	Gloss	1969	1982	100.00	150.00	225.00
Brown	Matt	1970	1982	100.00	150.00	225.00
Opaque	Gloss	1970	1982	275.00	400.00	600.00
White	Matt	1973	1982	80.00	125.00	175.00

Model No. 2210

HIGHWAYMAN

SERIES: Connoisseur Horses

Designer: Albert Hallam
Height: 13 ¾", 34.9 cm

Colourway	Finish	Intro.	Disc.	U.K. £	U.S. $	Can. $
Bay	Matt	1970	1975	850.00	1,200.00	1,800.00

Model No. 2242

ARAB STALLION

This is an authentic rendition of an Arab horse. It is on a pottery (base) stand.

Designer: Albert Hallam
Height: 8 ½", 21.6 cm

Colourway	Finish	Intro.	Disc.	U.K. £	U.S. $	Can. $
Brown	Gloss	1970	1975	375.00	525.00	800.00

Model No. 2269

ARAB STALLION WITH SADDLE

SERIES: Connoisseur Horses

Designer: Albert Hallam
Height: 9 ½", 24.0 cm

Colourway	Finish	Intro.	Disc.	U.K. £	U.S. $	Can.
Dappled grey	Matt	1970	1975	850.00	1,200.00	1,800.00

Model No. 2275

BEDOUIN ARAB

SERIES: Connoisseur Horses

Designer: Albert Hallam
Height: 11 ½", 29.2 cm

Colourway	Finish	Intro.	Disc.	U.K. £	U.S. $	Can. $
Chestnut	Matt	1970	1975	900.00	1,350.00	2,000.00

Model No. 2282

NORWEGIAN FJORD HORSE

Designer: Albert Hallam
Height: 6 ½", 16.5 cm

Colourway	Finish	Intro.	Disc.	U.K. £	U.S. $	Can. $
Dun	Gloss	1970	1975	375.00	550.00	825.00

Model No. 2309

BURNHAM BEAUTY

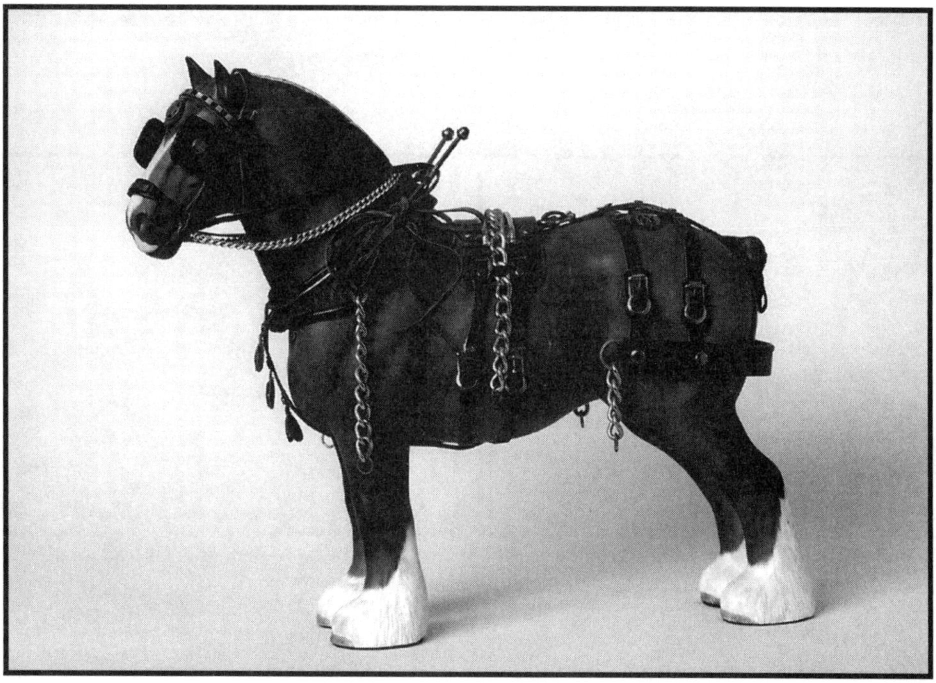

Designer: Albert Hallam
Height: 10 ¾", 27.8 cm

Colourway	Finish	Intro.	Disc.	U.K. £	U.S. $	Can. $
Brown	Gloss	1972	1982	100.00	150.00	225.00
White	Matt	1974	1982	100.00	150.00	225.00

SERIES: Connoisseur Horses

Height: 11 ¼", 28.5 cm

Colourway	Finish	Intro.	Disc.	U.K. £	U.S. $	Can. $
Bay	Matt	1971	1982	100.00	150.00	225.00

SERIES: Harnessed Horses

Height: 10 ¾", 27.8 cm

Colourway	Finish	Intro.	Disc.	U.K. £	U.S. $	Can. $
Brown	Matt	1979	1982	150.00	200.00	300.00

Model No. 2340

CARDIGAN BAY

Two versions of model no. 2340 exist. The first version has only two hooves attached to the base making it unstable and prone to breakage. The base was later redesigned to better support the model and has three legs attached to it.

Designer: Albert Hallam
Height: 9 ¼", 23.5 cm

First Version – Off hind leg is not attached to the base

Second Version – Off hind leg is attached to the base

SERIES: Connoisseur Horses

FIRST VERSION: Two legs attached to the base - off hind leg is not attached to the base.

Colourway	Finish	Intro.	Disc.	U.K. £	U.S. $	Can. $
Brown	Matt	1971	c.1972	650.00	900.00	1,350.00

SECOND VERSION: Three legs attached to the base - off hind leg is attached to the base.

Colourway	Finish	Intro.	Disc.	U.K. £	U.S. $	Can. $
Brown	Matt	c.1972	1976	450.00	650.00	975.00

Model No. 2345 / A2345

NIJINSKY

SERIES: Connoisseur Horses

Designer: Albert Hallam
Height: 11 ¼", 28.5 cm

Colourway	Finsh	Model	Intro.	Disc.	U.K. £	U.S. $	Can. $
Bay							
a. Beswick	Matt	2345	1971	1989	175.00	250.00	375.00
b. Royal Doulton	Matt	DA16	1989	1999	175.00	250.00	375.00
c. Beswick	Matt	A2345	1999	Current	175.00	N/A	N/A

Model No. 2352

NIJINSKY
LESTER PIGGOTT UP

SERIES: Connoisseur Horses

Designer: Albert Hallam
Height: 12 ½", 31.7 cm

Colourway	Finish	Intro.	Disc.	U.K. £	U.S. $	Can. $
Bay	Matt	1971	1982	350.00	500.00	750.00

Model No. 2421

THE WINNER

Designer: Albert Hallam
Height: 9 ½", 24.0 cm

Colourway	Finish	Intro.	Disc.	U.K. £	U.S. $	Can. $
Brown	Gloss	1973	1982	100.00	150.00	225.00
Brown	Matt	1973	1982	100.00	150.00	225.00
White	Matt	1973	1982	90.00	135.00	200.00

Model No. 2422

MILL REEF

The mahogany bay (gloss) variety was sold through Lawleys, Royal Doulton's retail shops, in the mid 1980s. When Mill Reef was withdrawn from the range at the end of 1989 a white matt variety was sold at the Beswick factory shop.

Designer: Albert Hallam
Height: 9", 22.9 cm

Colourway	Finish	Intro.	Disc.	U.K. £	U.S. $	Can. $
Mahogany bay	Gloss	1985	1988	150.00	200.00	300.00
White	Matt	1989	Unknown	125.00	175.00	275.00

SERIES: Connoisseur Horses

Colourway	Finish	Intro.	Disc.	U.K. £	U.S. $	Can. $
Brown/wooden plinth	Matt	1973	1989	175.00	250.00	375.00

Model No. 2431

MOUNTIE STALLION

SERIES: Connoisseur Horses

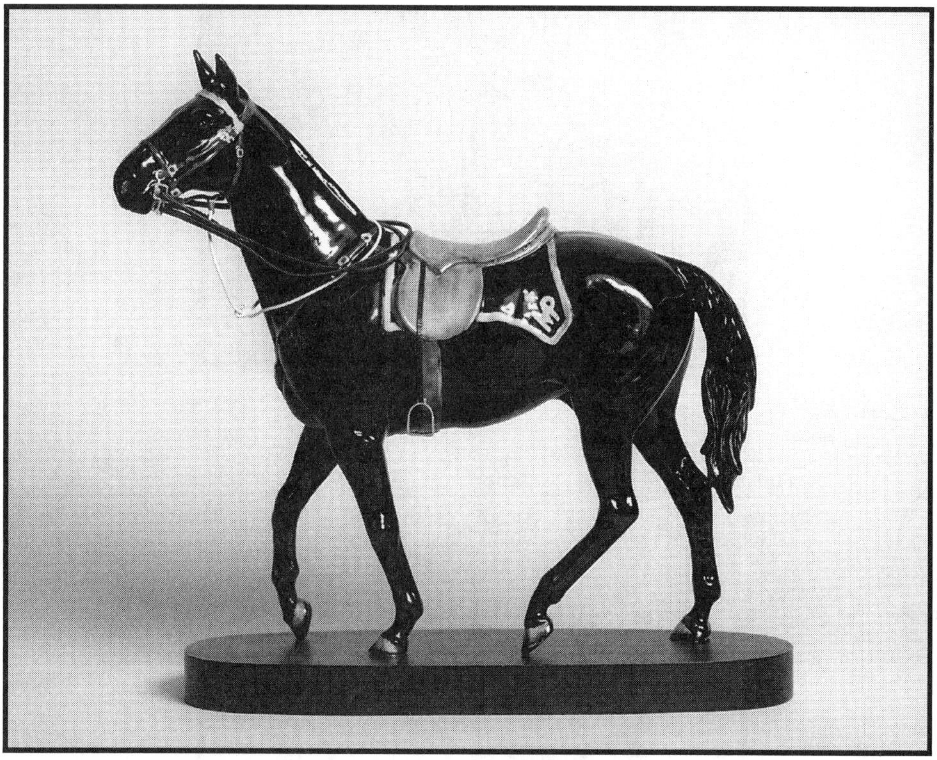

Designer: Graham Tongue
Height: 10", 25.4 cm

Colourway	Finish	Intro.	Disc.	U.K. £	U.S. $	Can. $
Black	Gloss	1973	1975	600.00	850.00	1,275.00

Model No. 2459

SHIRE MARE
(Lying)

Designer: Unknown
Height: 5", 12.7 cm

Colourways	Finish	Intro.	Disc.	U.K. £	U.S. $	Can. $
Brown	Gloss	1973	Unknown	350.00	500.00	750.00
Grey	Gloss	1973	1976	300.00	425.00	650.00

Model No. 2460

SHIRE FOAL
(Lying)

Designer: Unknown
Height: 3 ½", 8.9 cm

Colourway	Finish	Intro.	Disc.	U.K. £	U.S. $	Can. $
Dark brown	Gloss	1973	1976	135.00	200.00	300.00

Model No. 2464

PERCHERON

SERIES: Harnessed Horses

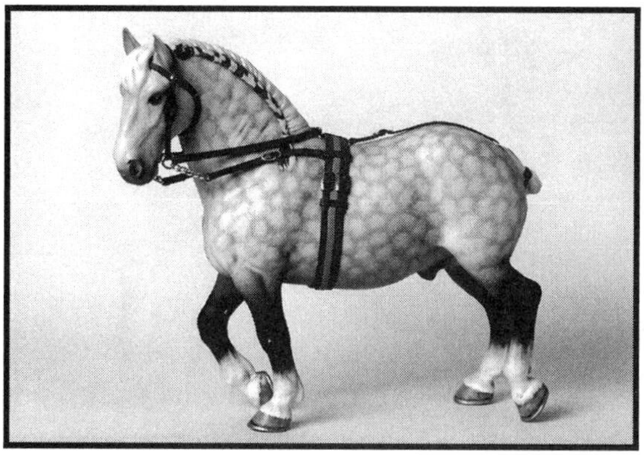

Designer: Unknown
Height: 9 ¾", 24.7 cm

Colourway	Finish	Intro.	Disc.	U.K. £	U.S. $	Can. $
Dappled grey	Matt	1974	1982	375.00	525.00	800.00

Model No. 2465

CLYDESDALE

SERIES: Harnessed Horses

Designer: Unknown
Height: 10 ¾", 27.8 cm

FIRST VERSION: Working Harness

Colourway	Finish	Intro.	Disc.	U.K. £	U.S. $	Can. $
Chocolate Brown	Matt	1974	1982	200.00	300.00	450.00

SECOND VERSION: Show Harness

Colourway	Finish	Intro.	Disc.	U.K. £	U.S. $	Can. $
Chocolate Brown	Matt	1974	1982	250.00	350.00	525.00

Model No. 2466 / H2466

BLACK BEAUTY

This model was used in model number 2466/2536 Black Beauty and Foal, and model number 2703 Spirit of Youth.

Designer: Graham Tongue
Height: 7 ¼", 18.4 cm

Colourway	Finish	Model	Intro.	Disc.	U.K. £	U.S. $	Can. $
Black							
a. Beswick	Matt	2466	1974	1989	55.00	80.00	120.00
b. Royal Doulton	Matt	DA65	1989	1999	55.00	80.00	120.00
c. Beswick	Matt	H2466	1999	Current	52.00	N/A	180.00

Model No. 2466/2536

BLACK BEAUTY AND FOAL

A special edition of this model was commissioned by Lawleys by Post to celebrate the centenary of Beswick's Gold Street factory.

Centenary Edition (1898 - 1998)

General Issue

Designer: Graham Tongue
Length: 13 ½", 34.3 cm
Height: 9 ½", 24.0 cm

Colourway	Finish	Model	Intro.	Disc.	U.K. £	U.S. $	Can. $
Black							
a. Royal Doulton	Matt	DA17	1989	1999	125.00	175.00	250.00
b. Beswick (centenary)	Matt	2466/2536	1998	1998	150.00	200.00	300.00
c. Beswick	Matt	A2466/2536	1999	Current	125.00	N/A	365.00

Model No. 2467

LIPIZZANER WITH RIDER

SERIES: Connoisseur Horses

First Version - Hind legs attached to a circular base

Second Version - Tail and rear legs attached to oval base

Designer: Graham Tongue
Height: 10", 25.4 cm

FIRST VERSION: Hind legs attached to a circular base.

Colourway	Finish	Intro.	Disc.	U.K. £	U.S. $	Can. $
White	Gloss	1974	Unknown	450.00	625.00	950.00

SECOND VERSON: Tail and rear legs attached to an oval base.

Colourway	Finish	Intro.	Disc.	U.K. £	U.S. $	Can. $
White	Gloss	Unknown	1981	375.00	525.00	800.00

Model No. 2505

STEEPLECHASER

Designer: Graham Tongue
Height: 8 ¾", 22.2 cm

Colourway	Finish	Intro.	Disc.	U.K. £	U.S. $	Can. $
Dark brown	Gloss	1975	1981	375.00	525.00	800.00

Model No. 2510 / A2510

RED RUM

STYLE ONE: Large Size - 12"

SERIES: Connoisseur Horses

Designer: Graham Tongue
Height: 12", 30.5 cm

Colourway	Finish	Model	Intro.	Disc.	U.K. £	U.S. $	Can. $
Bay							
a. Beswick	Matt	2510	1975	1989	175.00	250.00	375.00
b. Royal Doulton	Matt	DA18	1989	1999	175.00	250.00	375.00
c. Beswick	Matt	A2510	1999	Current	175.00	N/A	765.00

Model No. 2511

RED RUM
BRIAN FLETCHER UP

SERIES: Connoisseur Horses

Designer: Graham Tongue
Height: 12 ¼", 31.1 cm

Colourway	Finish	Intro.	Disc.	U.K. £	U.S. $	Can. $
Bay	Matt	1975	1982	350.00	500.00	750.00

Model No. 2535

PSALM
ANN MOORE UP

SERIES: Connoisseur Horses

Designer: Graham Tongue
Height: 12 ¾", 32.4 cm

Colourway	Finish	Intro.	Disc.	U.K. £	U.S. $	Can. $
Brown	Matt	1975	1982	350.00	500.00	750.00

Model No. 2536

BLACK BEAUTY FOAL

Designer: Graham Tongue
Height: 3 ½", 8.9 cm

Colourway	Finish	Model	Intro.	Disc.	U.K. £	U.S. $	Can. $
Black							
a. Beswick	Matt	2536	1976	1989	35.00	50.00	75.00
b. Royal Doulton	Matt	DA66	1989	1999	35.00	50.00	75.00
c. Beswick	Matt	F2536	1999	Current	31.00	N/A	90.00
Brown	Matt	2536	1984	Unknown	35.00	50.00	75.00
Chocolate brown	Matt	2536	1984	Unknown	35.00	50.00	75.00
Palomino	Matt	2536	1984	Unknown	40.00	55.00	80.00
White	Matt	2536	1984	Unknown	35.00	50.00	75.00

Model No. 2540

PSALM

SERIES: Connoisseur Horses

Designer: Graham Tongue
Height: 11 ½", 29.2 cm

Colourway	Finish	Intro.	Disc.	U.K. £	U.S. $	Can. $
Brown	Matt	1975	1982	225.00	325.00	475.00

Model No. 2541A

WELSH MOUNTAIN STALLION "GREDINGTON SIMWNT"

This model of Gredington Simwnt was greatly adapted to produce "The Spirit of Whitfield."

SERIES: Connoisseur Horses

Designer: Graham Tongue
Height: 9", 22.9 cm

Colourway	Finish	Intro.	Disc.	U.K. £	U.S. $	Can. $
Light grey	Matt	1976	1989	250.00	375.00	575.00

Model No. 2548

WHITBREAD SHIRE HORSE

A small number of sample models of the Whitbread Shire Horse were made originally for sale as souvenirs from the Whitbread (Brewery) Shire Horse Farm, Kent, U.K., however they were never put into production.

Designer: Unknown
Height: 6", 15.2 cm

Colourway	Finish	Intro.	Disc.	U.K. £	U.S. $	Can. $
Grey	Gloss	1976	1976	400.00	575.00	850.00
Grey	Matt	1976	1976	400.00	575.00	850.00

Model No. 2558

GRUNDY

SERIES: Connoisseur Horses

Designer: Graham Tongue
Height: 11 ¼", 28.5 cm

Colourway	Finish	Model	Intro.	Disc.	U.K. £	U.S. $	Can. $
Chestnut							
a. Beswick	Matt	2558	1977	1989	150.00	225.00	350.00
b. Royal Doulton	Matt	DA20	1989	1997	175.00	250.00	375.00

Model No. 2562

LIFEGUARD

STYLE TWO: With sword

SERIES: Connoisseur Horses

Designer: Graham Tongue
Height: 14 ½", 36.8 cm

Colourway	Finish	Model	Intro.	Disc.	U.K. £	U.S. $	Can. $
Black							
a. Beswick	Gloss	2562	1977	1989	400.00	550.00	825.00
b. Royal Doulton	Gloss	DA22	1989	1996	400.00	550.00	825.00

Model No. 2578

SHIRE HORSE
(Large action shire)

Designer: Alan Maslankowski
Height: 8 ¼", 21.0 cm

Colourway	Finish	Model	Intro.	Disc.	U.K. £	U.S. $	Can. $
Brown	Gloss	2578	1980	1982	200.00	275.00	425.00
Brown							
a. Beswick	Matt	2578	1978	1989	175.00	250.00	375.00
b. Royal Doulton	Matt	DA62A	1989	1997	150.00	225.00	325.00
Grey	Gloss	2578	1978	1982	300.00	425.00	650.00
Grey	Matt	2578	1980	1983	275.00	400.00	600.00

SERIES: Harnessed Horses

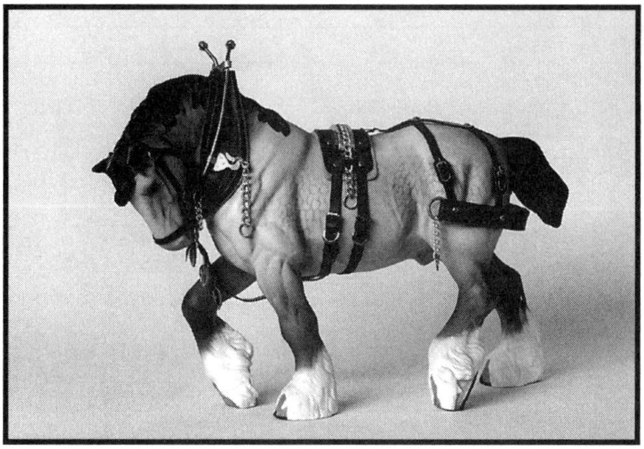

Colourway	Finish	Intro.	Disc.	U.K. £	U.S. $	Can. $
Brown	Matt	1978	1982	225.00	300.00	450.00
Grey	Matt	1978	1982	325.00	450.00	675.00

Model No. 2582

BLUES AND ROYALS

SERIES: Connoisseur Horses

Designer: Graham Tongue
Height: 14 ½", 36.8 cm

Colourway	Finish	Model	Intro.	Disc.	U.K. £	U.S. $	Can. $
Black							
a. Beswick	Matt	2582	1987	1989	425.00	600.00	900.00
b. Royal Doulton	Matt	DA25	1989	1996	425.00	600.00	900.00

Model No. 2605

MORGAN STALLION
" TARRYALL MAESTRO "

SERIES: Connoisseur Horses

Designer: Graham Tongue
Height: 11 ½", 29.2 cm

Colourway	Finish	Model	Intro.	Disc.	U.K. £	U.S. $	Can. $
Black							
a. Beswick	Matt	2605	1979	1989	200.00	300.00	450.00
b. Royal Doulton	Matt	DA28	1989	1996	200.00	300.00	450.00

Model No. 2608

THE MINSTREL

SERIES: Connoisseur Horses

Designer: Graham Tongue
Height: 13 ¼", 33.6 cm

Colourway	Finish	Model	Intro.	Disc.	U.K. £	U.S. $	Can. $
Chestnut							
a. Beswick	Matt	2608	1980	1989	175.00	250.00	375.00
b. Royal Doulton	Matt	DA31	1989	1997	175.00	250.00	375.00

Model No. 2671

MOONLIGHT

SERIES: Connoisseur Horses

Designer: Graham Tongue
Height: 11 ¼", 28.5 cm

Colourway	Finish	Model	Intro.	Disc.	U.K. £	U.S. $	Can. $
"Moonlight" - Grey							
a. Beswick	Matt	2671	1982	1989	150.00	200.00	300.00
b. Royal Doulton	Matt	DA35B	1989	1996	150.00	200.00	300.00
"Nightshade" - Black	Matt	—	1986	1989	175.00	250.00	375.00
"Sunburst" - Palomino							
a. Beswick	Matt	2671	1986	1989	175.00	250.00	375.00
b. Royal Doulton	Matt	DA36	1989	1995	175.00	250.00	375.00

Model No. 2674

TROY

SERIES: Connoisseur Horses

Designer: Graham Tongue
Height: 11 ¾", 29.8 cm

Colourway	Finish	Model	Intro.	Disc.	U.K. £	U.S. $	Can. $
Bay							
a. Beswick	Matt	2674	1981	1989	150.00	200.00	300.00
b. Royal Doulton	Matt	DA37	1989	1997	175.00	250.00	375.00

Model No. 2688

SPIRIT OF THE WIND

Designer: Graham Tongue
Height: 8", 20.3 cm

Colourway	Finish	Model	Intro.	Disc.	U.K. £	U.S. $	Can. $
Brown							
a. Beswick	Gloss	2688	1982	1989	75.00	100.00	150.00
b. Royal Doulton	Gloss	DA57A	1989	1996	75.00	100.00	150.00
Brown							
a. Beswick	Matt	2688	1982	1989	75.00	100.00	150.00
b. Royal Doulton	Matt	DA57A	1989	1996	75.00	100.00	150.00
Grey	Gloss	2688	1982	1989	95.00	135.00	200.00
Grey	Matt	2688	1982	1989	85.00	125.00	185.00
Palomino	Gloss	2688	1982	1989	90.00	130.00	195.00
Palomino	Matt	2688	1982	1989	80.00	120.00	175.00

SERIES: On Wooden Plinth

Colourway/Plinth	Finish	Model	Intro.	Disc.	U.K. £	U.S. $	Can. $
Black/Brown							
a. Beswick	Matt	2688	1986	1989	75.00	100.00	150.00
b. Royal Doulton	Matt	DA57B	1989	1990	75.00	100.00	150.00
Brown/Brown							
a. Beswick	Gloss	2688	1986	1989	75.00	100.00	150.00
b. Royal Doulton	Gloss	DA57B	1989	1999	75.00	100.00	150.00
c. Beswick	Gloss	H2688	1999	Current	72.00	N/A	150.00
Brown/Brown							
a. Beswick	Matt	2688	1986	1989	75.00	100.00	150.00
b. Royal Doulton	Matt	DA57B	1989	1999	75.00	100.00	150.00
c. Beswick	Matt	H2688	1999	Current	72.00	N/A	300.00
White/Black							
a. Beswick	Matt	2688	1982	1989	55.00	80.00	120.00
b. Royal Doulton	Matt	DA57B	1989	1999	55.00	80.00	120.00

Series: On Ceramic Plinth

Colourway	Finish	Intro.	Disc.	U.K. £	U.S. $	Can. $
Brown	Gloss	c.1987	c.1987	80.00	120.00	175.00

SERIES: Britannia Collection

Colourway	Finish	Intro.	Disc.	U.K. £	U.S. $	Can. $
Bronze	Gloss	1989	1993	70.00	100.00	150.00

Model No. 2689

SPIRIT OF FREEDOM

Model number 2689 was used together with model number 2353 to become the Spirit of Affection.

Designer: Graham Tongue
Height: 7", 17.8 cm

Colourway	Finish	Model	Intro.	Disc.	U.K. £	U.S. $	Can. $
Brown							
a. Beswick	Gloss	2689	1982	1989	60.00	90.00	135.00
b. Royal Doulton	Gloss	DA58A	1989	1997	60.00	90.00	135.00
Brown							
a. Beswick	Matt	2689	1982	1989	60.00	90.00	135.00
b. Royal Doulton	Matt	DA58A	1989	1997	60.00	90.00	135.00
Grey	Gloss	2689	1982	1989	95.00	135.00	200.00
Grey	Matt	2689	1982	1989	85.00	120.00	185.00
Palomino	Gloss	2689	1982	1989	90.00	125.00	190.00
Palomino	Matt	2689	1982	1989	80.00	115.00	175.00

SERIES: On Wooden Plinth

The black and brown versions were mounted on brown wooden plinths and the white version was issued on a black wooden plinth.

Colourway/Plinth	Finish	Model	Intro.	Disc.	U.K. £	U.S. $	Can. $
Black/brown							
a. Beswick	Matt	2689	1987	1989	75.00	100.00	150.00
b. Royal Doulton	Matt	DA58B	1989	1993	75.00	100.00	150.00
Brown/brown							
a. Beswick	Gloss	2689	1986	1989	75.00	100.00	150.00
b. Royal Doulton	Gloss	DA58B	1989	1999	75.00	100.00	150.00
c. Beswick	Gloss	A2689	1999	Current	72.00	N/A	150.00
Brown/brown							
a. Beswick	Matt	2689	1986	1989	75.00	100.00	150.00
b. Royal Doulton	Matt	DA58B	1989	1999	75.00	100.00	150.00
c. Beswick	Matt	H2689	1999	Current	72.00	N/A	300.00
White/black							
a. Beswick	Matt	2689	1982	1989	55.00	80.00	120.00
b. Royal Doulton	Matt	DA58B	1989	1999	55.00	80.00	120.00

SERIES: On Ceramic Plinth

Colourway	Finish	Model	Intro.	Disc.	U.K. £	U.S. $	Can. $
Brown	Gloss	2689	c.1987	c.1987	65.00	90.00	145.00

Model No. 2689/2536 — H2689/2536

SPIRIT OF AFFECTION

The Spirit of Affection is the Spirit of Freedom with the Black Beauty Foal. In all versions but one, the mare and the foal are the same colour. The brown, grey and palomino versions were mounted on a brown wooden plinth and the white version was mounted on a black wooden plinth.

SERIES: On Wooden Plinth

Designer: Graham Tongue
Height: 8", 20.3 cm

Colourway	Finish	Model	Intro.	Disc.	U.K. £	U.S. $	Can. $
Brown							
a. Beswick	Matt	2689/2536	1982	1989	100.00	150.00	225.00
b. Royal Doulton	Matt	DA64B	1989	1996	100.00	150.00	225.00
Grey mare, chocolate brown foal	Matt	2689/2536	1984	1989	125.00	175.00	275.00
Palomino	Matt	2689/2536	1984	1989	135.00	185.00	300.00
White							
a. Beswick	Matt	2689/2536	1982	1989	90.00	125.00	200.00
b. Royal Doulton	Matt	DA64B	1989	1999	90.00	125.00	200.00
c. Beswick	Matt	H2689/2536	1999	Current	88.00	N/A	N/A

Model No. 2703 / H2703

SPIRIT OF YOUTH

The Spirit of Youth is the same model as 2466 "Black Beauty."

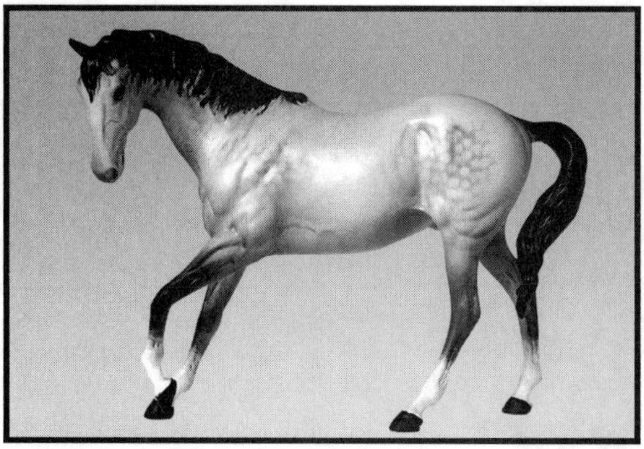

Designer: Graham Tongue
Height: 7", 17.8 cm

Colourway	Finish	Model	Intro.	Disc.	U.K. £	U.S. $	Can. $
Brown							
a. Beswick	Gloss	2703	1982	1989	60.00	90.00	135.00
b. Royal Doulton	Gloss	DA59A	1989	1996	60.00	90.00	135.00
Brown							
a. Beswick	Matt	2703	1982	1989	60.00	90.00	135.00
b. Royal Doulton	Matt	DA59A	1989	1996	60.00	90.00	135.00
Grey	Gloss	2703	1982	1989	95.00	135.00	200.00
Grey	Matt	2703	1982	1989	85.00	120.00	185.00
Palomino	Gloss	2703	1982	1989	90.00	135.00	200.00
Palomino	Matt	2703	1982	1989	80.00	120.00	175.00

SERIES: On Wooden Plinth

The black and brown models were issued on a brown wooden plinth and the white model was issued on a black wooden plinth.

Colourway/Plinth	Finish	Model	Intro.	Disc.	U.K. £	U.S. $	Can. $
Black/Brown							
a. Beswick	Matt	2703	1987	1989	75.00	100.00	150.00
b. Royal Doulton	Matt	DA59B	1989	1993	75.00	100.00	150.00
Brown/Brown							
a. Beswick	Gloss	2703	1982	1989	75.00	100.00	150.00
b. Royal Doulton	Gloss	DA59B	1989	1999	75.00	100.00	150.00
c. Beswick	Gloss	H2703	1999	Current	72.00	N/A	150.00
Brown/Brown							
a. Beswick	Matt	2703	1986	1989	75.00	100.00	150.00
b. Royal Doulton	Matt	DA59B	1989	1996	75.00	100.00	150.00
White/Black							
a. Beswick	Matt	2703	1982	1989	55.00	80.00	120.00
b. Royal Doulton	Matt	DA59B	1989	1995	55.00	80.00	120.00

SERIES: On Ceramic Plinth

Colourway	Finish	Model	Intro.	Disc.	U.K. £	U.S. $	Can. $
Brown	Gloss	2703	c.1987	c.1987	75.00	100.00	150.00

Model No. 2829

SPIRIT OF FIRE

Designer: Graham Tongue
Height: 8", 20.3 cm

Colourway	Finish	Model	Intro.	Disc.	U.K. £	U.S. $	Can. $
Brown							
a. Beswick	Gloss	2829	1984	1989	60.00	90.00	135.00
b. Royal Doulton	Gloss	DA60A	1989	1994	60.00	90.00	135.00
Brown							
a. Beswick	Matt	2829	1984	1989	60.00	90.00	135.00
b. Royal Doulton	Matt	DA60A	1989	1994	60.00	90.00	135.00
Grey	Gloss	2829	1984	1989	95.00	135.00	200.00
Grey	Matt	2829	1984	1989	85.00	120.00	175.00
Palomino	Gloss	2829	1984	1989	75.00	100.00	150.00
Palomino	Matt	2829	1984	1989	70.00	95.00	140.00

SERIES: On Wooden Plinth

The black and brown versions were issued on a brown wooden plinth and the white version was issued on a black wooden plinth.

Colourway/Plinth	Finish	Model	Intro.	Disc.	U.K. £	U.S. $	Can. $
Black/Brown							
a. Beswick	Matt	2829	1986	1989	60.00	90.00	135.00
b. Royal Doulton	Matt	DA60B	1989	1994	60.00	90.00	135.00
Brown/Brown							
a. Beswick	Matt	2829	1986	1989	75.00	100.00	150.00
b. Royal Doulton	Matt	DA60B	1989	1994	75.00	100.00	150.00
White/Black							
a. Beswick	Matt	2829	1984	1989	55.00	80.00	120.00
b. Royal Doulton	Matt	DA60B	1989	1993	55.00	80.00	120.00

SERIES: On Ceramic Plinth

Colourway	Finish	Model	Intro.	Disc.	U.K. £	U.S. $	Can. $
Brown	Gloss	2829	c.1987	c.1987	75.00	100.00	150.00

Model No. 2837 / F2837

SPRINGTIME

SERIES: Spirited Foals

Designer: Graham Tongue
Height: 4 ½", 11.9 cm

VARIATION No. 1 Free Standing

Colourway	Finish	Model	Intro.	Disc.	U.K. £	U.S. $	Can. $
Brown							
a. Beswick	Gloss	2837	1984	1989	30.00	45.00	65.00
b. Royal Doulton	Gloss	DA69A	1989	1999	30.00	45.00	65.00

VARIATION No. 2 On Wooden Plinth

Colourway/Plinth	Finish	Model	Intro.	Disc.	U.K. £	U.S. $	Can. $
Black/Brown	Matt	2837	1987	1989	30.00	45.00	65.00
Brown/Brown							
a. Beswick	Matt	2837	1986	1989	30.00	45.00	65.00
b. Royal Doulton	Matt	DA69B	1989	1999	30.00	45.00	65.00
White/Black							
a. Beswick	Matt	2837	1984	1989	30.00	45.00	65.00
b. Royal Doulton	Matt	DA69B	1989	1999	30.00	45.00	65.00
c. Beswick	Matt	F2837	1999	Current	31.00	N/A	90.00

Model No. 2839

YOUNG SPIRIT

Young Spirit was originally illustrated in a catalogue with his ears sticking out slightly. The model was changed to have the ears flat against the foals head, probably due to the potential problem of breakage in shipping. No date has been established for the mould change but it is probably either in the early stages of production, i.e. prototype or shortly after issue.

SERIES: Spirited Foals

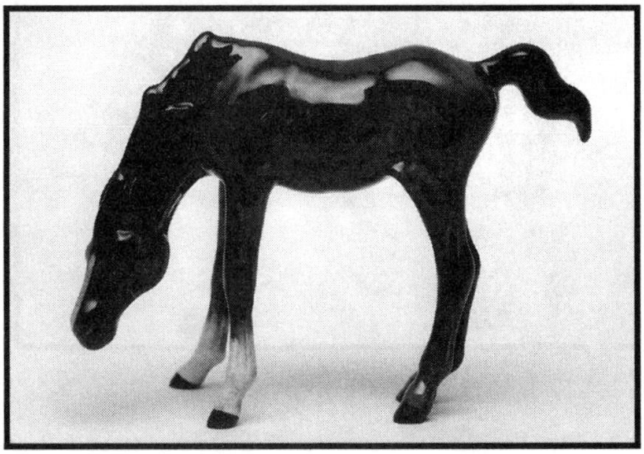

Designer: Graham Tongue
Height: 4 ½", 11.9 cm

VARIATION No. 1 Free Standing

Colourway	Finish	Model	Intro.	Disc.	U.K. £	U.S. $	Can. $
Brown							
a. Beswick	Gloss	2839	1984	1989	30.00	45.00	65.00
b. Royal Doulton	Gloss	DA70A	1989	1993	30.00	45.00	65.00

VARIATION No. 2 On Wooden Plinth

Colourway/Plinth	Finish	Model	Intro.	Disc.	U.K. £	U.S. $	Can. $
Black/Brown							
a. Beswick	Matt	2839	1987	1989	30.00	45.00	65.00
b. Royal Doulton	Matt	DA70B	1989	1996	30.00	45.00	65.00
Brown/Brown							
a. Beswick	Matt	2839	1986	1989	35.00	50.00	75.00
b. Royal Doulton	Matt	DA70B	1989	1995	35.00	50.00	75.00
White/Black							
a. Beswick	Matt	2839	1984	1989	30.00	45.00	65.00
b. Royal Doulton	Matt	DA70B	1989	1995	30.00	45.00	65.00

Model No. 2875

SUNLIGHT

SERIES: Spirited Foals

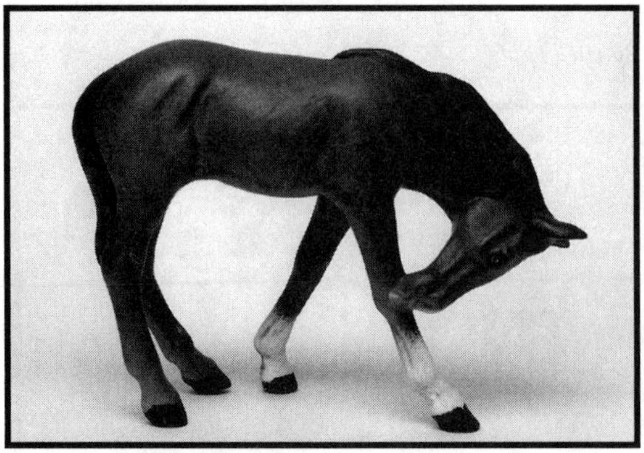

Designer: Graham Tongue
Height: 4 ½", 11.9 cm

VARIATION No. 1 Free Standing

Colourway	Finish	Model	Intro.	Disc.	U.K. £	U.S. $	Can. $
Brown							
a. Beswick	Gloss	2875	1987	1989	30.00	45.00	65.00
b. Royal Doulton	Gloss	DA71A	1989	1996	30.00	45.00	65.00

VARIATION No. 2 On Wooden Plinth

Colourway/Plinth	Finish	Model	Intro.	Disc.	U.K. £	U.S. $	Can. $
Black/Brown							
a. Beswick	Matt	2875	1987	1989	30.00	45.00	65.00
b. Royal Doulton	Matt	DA71B	1989	1996	30.00	45.00	65.00
Brown/Brown							
a. Beswick	Matt	2875	1987	1989	40.00	60.00	90.00
b. Royal Doulton	Matt	DA71B	1989	1996	40.00	60.00	90.00
White/Black							
a. Beswick	Matt	2875	1985	1989	25.00	35.00	55.00
b. Royal Doulton	Matt	DA71B	1989	1996	25.00	35.00	55.00

Model No. 2876

ADVENTURE

SERIES: Spirited Foals

Designer: Graham Tongue
Height: 4 ½", 11.9 cm

VARIATION No. 1 Free Standing

Colourway	Finish	Model	Intro.	Disc.	U.K. £	U.S. $	Can. $
Brown							
a. Beswick	Gloss	2876	1987	1989	30.00	45.00	65.00
b. Royal Doulton	Gloss	DA72A	1989	1997	30.00	45.00	65.00

VARIATION No. 2 On Wooden Plinth

Colourway/Plinth	Finish	Model	Intro.	Disc.	U.K. £	U.S. $	Can. $
Black/Brown	Matt	2876	1987	1989	35.00	50.00	75.00
Brown/Brown							
a. Beswick	Matt	2876	1987	1989	35.00	50.00	75.00
b. Royal Doulton	Matt	DA72B	1989	1997	35.00	50.00	75.00
White/Black							
a. Beswick	Matt	2876	1985	1989	30.00	45.00	65.00
b. Royal Doulton	Matt	DA72B	1989	1997	30.00	45.00	65.00

Model No. 2914

SPIRIT OF EARTH

Designer: Graham Tongue
Height: 7 ½", 19.1 cm

Colourway	Finish	Model	Intro.	Disc.	U.K. £	U.S. $	Can. $
Brown							
a. Beswick	Gloss	2914	1987	1989	75.00	110.00	165.00
b. Royal Doulton	Gloss	DA61A	1989	1993	75.00	110.00	165.00
Brown							
a. Beswick	Matt	2914	1987	1989	70.00	100.00	150.00
b. Royal Doulton	Matt	DA61A	1989	1993	70.00	100.00	150.00
Grey	Gloss	2914	1987	1989	125.00	175.00	250.00
Grey	Matt	2914	1987	1989	100.00	150.00	225.00

SERIES: On Wooden Plinth

The black and brown versions were issued on a brown wooden plinth and the white version was issued on a black wooden plinth.

Colourway/Plinth	Finish	Model	Intro.	Disc.	U.K. £	U.S. $	Can. $
Black/Brown							
a. Beswick	Matt	2914	1987	1989	75.00	110.00	165.00
b. Royal Doulton	Matt	DA61B	1989	1993	75.00	110.00	165.00
Brown/Brown							
a. Beswick	Matt	2914	1987	1989	85.00	120.00	175.00
b. Royal Doulton	Matt	DA61B	1989	1993	85.00	120.00	175.00
White/Black							
a. Beswick	Matt	2914	1986	1989	70.00	100.00	150.00
b. Royal Doulton	Matt	DA61B	1989	1993	70.00	100.00	150.00

SERIES: On Ceramic Plinth

Colourway/Plinth	Finish	Model	Intro.	Disc.	U.K. £	U.S. $	Can. $
Brown/Ceramic	Gloss	2914	c.1987	c.1987	100.00	150.00	225.00

SERIES: Britannia Collection

Colourway	Finish	Intro.	Disc.	U.K. £	U.S. $	Can. $
Brown	Gloss	1989	1993	100.00	150.00	225.00

Model No. 2916

SPIRIT OF PEACE

Designer: Graham Tongue
Height: 4 ¾", 12.1 cm

Colourway	Finish	Model	Intro.	Disc.	U.K. £	U.S. $	Can. $
Brown	Gloss	2916	1987	1989	65.00	95.00	145.00
Brown							
a. Beswick	Matt	2916	1987	1989	60.00	90.00	135.00
b. Royal Doulton	Matt	DA63A	1989	1997	60.00	90.00	135.00
Grey	Gloss	2916	1987	1989	100.00	150.00	225.00
Grey	Matt	2916	1987	1989	100.00	150.00	225.00
Palomino	Gloss	2916	1987	1989	80.00	115.00	165.00
Palomino	Matt	2916	1987	1989	80.00	115.00	165.00

SERIES: On Wooden Plinth

The black and brown versions were issued on a brown wooden plinth and the white version was issued on a black wooden plinth.

Colourway/Plinth	Finish	Model	Intro.	Disc.	U.K. £	U.S. $	Can. $
Black/Brown	Matt	2916	1987	1989	70.00	100.00	150.00
Brown/Brown							
a. Beswick	Matt	2916	1987	1989	80.00	115.00	165.00
b. Royal Doulton	Matt	DA63B	1989	1997	80.00	115.00	165.00
White/Black							
a. Beswick	Matt	2916	1986	1989	60.00	90.00	135.00
b. Royal Doulton	Matt	DA63B	1989	1997	60.00	90.00	135.00

SERIES: On Ceramic Plinth

Colourway	Finish	Model	Intro.	Disc.	U.K. £	U.S. $	Can. $
Brown	Gloss	2916	c.1987	c.1987	95.00	135.00	200.00

Model No. 2935

SPIRIT OF NATURE

Designer: Graham Tongue
Height: 5 ½", 14.0 cm

Colourway	Finish	Model	Intro.	Disc.	U.K. £	U.S. $	Can. $
Brown	Gloss	2935	1987	1989	60.00	90.00	135.00
Brown	Matt	2935	1987	1989	55.00	80.00	120.00
Grey	Gloss	2935	1987	1989	100.00	150.00	225.00
Grey	Matt	2935	1987	1989	100.00	150.00	225.00
Palomino	Gloss	2935	1987	1989	75.00	110.00	165.00
Palomino	Matt	2935	1987	1989	75.00	110.00	165.00

SERIES: On Wooden Plinth

The black and brown versions were mounted on brown wooden plinths and the white version was mounted on a black wooden plinth.

Colourway/Plinth	Finish	Model	Intro.	Disc.	U.K. £	U.S. $	Can. $
Black/Brown	Matt	2935	1987	1989	70.00	100.00	150.00
Brown/Brown							
a. Beswick	Matt	2935	1987	1989	75.00	110.00	165.00
b. Royal Doulton	Matt	DA73	1989	1996	75.00	110.00	165.00
White/Black	Matt	2935	1987	1989	60.00	90.00	135.00

SERIES: On Ceramic Plinth

Colourway	Finish	Model	Intro.	Disc.	U.K. £	U.S. $	Can. $
Brown	Gloss	2935	c.1987	c.1987	85.00	120.00	175.00

Model No. 3426 / A234

CANCARA – THE BLACK HORSE

Modelled from "Downland Cancara" graded Trakehner stallion famous for advertising Lloyds Bank. Backstamp - "1994 Special Beswick Centenary."

SERIES: CONNOISSEUR

Designer: Graham Tongue
Height: 16 ½", 41.9 cm

Colourway	Finish	Model	Intro.	Disc.	U.K. £	U.S. $	Can. $
Black							
a. Beswick	Matt	3426	1994	1994	300.00	425.00	650.00
b. Royal Doulton	Matt	DA234	1995	1999	300.00	425.00	650.00
b. Beswick	Matt	A234	1999	Current	310.00	N/A	N/A

Model No. 3464

TALLY HO

This model was made exclusively for the mail order company Grattans. The horse and rider, from the model "Rearing Huntsman," with three hounds are on a natural effect base (all gloss). This model stands on a wooden plinth which is topped with green baise and has a brass plaque on the front. Backstamp - "Beswick Ware Made in England Tally Ho! Beswick Centenary 1894-1994 © 1994 Royal Doulton."

Designer: Unknown
Height: 11" x 14", 27.9 x 35.5 cm

Colourway	Finish	Intro.	Disc.	U.K. £	U.S. $	Can. $
Brown	Gloss	1994	1994	350.00	500.00	750.00

Model No. A182

FIRST BORN

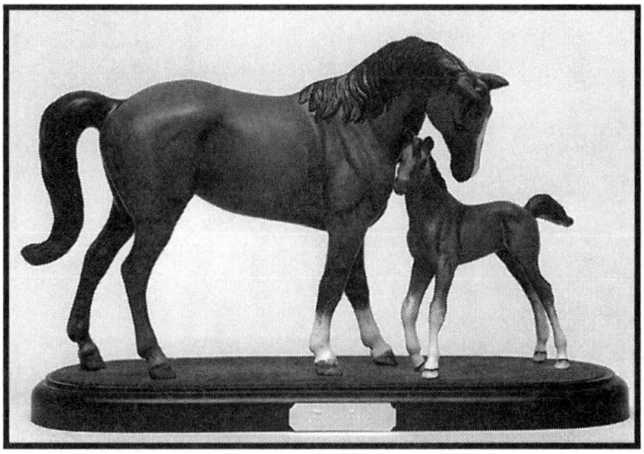

Designer: Amanda Hughes-Lubeck
Height: 7", 17.8 cm

Colourway	Finish	Model	Intro.	Disc.	U.K. £	U.S. $	Can. $
Chestnut mare and foal							
a. Royal Doulton	Matt	DA182	1992	1999	125.00	175.00	275.00
b. Beswick	Matt	A182	1999	Current	125.00	N/A	410.00

Model No. A183

SPIRIT OF THE WILD

Designer: Warren Platt
Height: 12", 30.5 cm

Colourway	Finish	Model	Intro.	Disc.	U.K. £	U.S. $	Can. $
Black							
a. Royal Doulton	Matt	DA183	1993	1999	95.00	140.00	210.00
b. Beswick	Matt	A183	1999	Current	88.00	N/A	N/A
Brown							
a. Royal Doulton	Matt	DA183	1993	1999	95.00	140.00	210.00
b. Beswick	Matt	A183	1999	Current	88.00	N/A	365.00
White							
a. Royal Doulton	Matt	DA183	1993	1999	90.00	130.00	200.00
b. Beswick	Matt	A183	1999	Current	72.00	N/A	300.00

Model No. A184

DESERT ORCHID

Designer: Warren Platt
Height: 7¾", 19.7 cm

Colourway	Finish	Model	Intro.	Disc.	U.K. £	U.S. $	Can. $
Light grey							
a. Royal Doulton	Matt	DA184	1994	1999	125.00	175.00	275.00
b. Beswick	Matt	A184	1999	Current	125.00	N/A	355.00

Model No. A193

MY FIRST HORSE

Designer: Amanda Hughes-Lubeck
Height: 8 ¼", 21.0 cm

Colourway	Finish	Model	Intro.	Disc.	U.K. £	U.S. $	Can. $
Chestnut							
a. Royal Doulton	Gloss	DA193B	1994	1999	60.00	90.00	150.00
b. Beswick	Gloss	A193	1999	Current	62.00	N/A	260.00

Model No. A226

RED RUM

STYLE TWO: Small size - 9"

Designer: Amanda Hughes-Lubeck
Height: 9", 22.9 cm

Colourway	Finish	Model	Intro.	Disc.	U.K. £	U.S. $	Can. $
Brown							
a. Royal Doulton	Matt	DA226	1995	1999	125.00	175.00	275.00
b. Beswick	Matt	A226	1999	Current	125.00	N/A	385.00

Model No. A244

NEW FOREST PONY

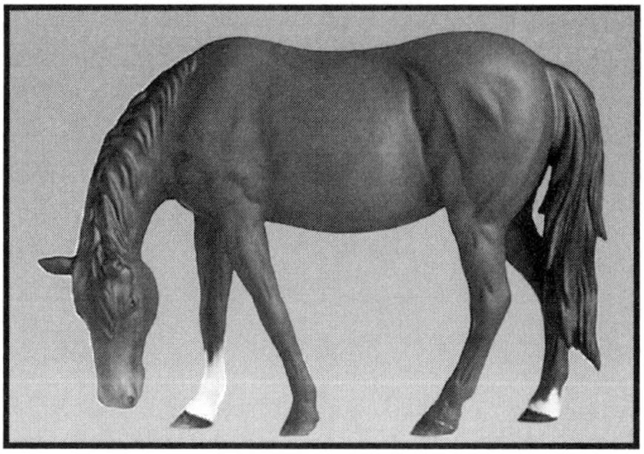

Designer: Shane Ridge
Height: 6", 15.0 cm

Colourway	Finish	Model	Intro.	Disc.	U.K. £	U.S. $	Can. $
Brown							
a. Royal Doulton	Matt	DA244	1997	1999	55.00	80.00	125.00
b. Beswick	Matt	A244	1999	Current	52.00	N/A	200.00

Model No. A247

WELSH MOUNTAIN PONY/ "CHAMPION WELSH MOUNTAIN PONY"

The Champion Welsh Mountain Pony was the 1999 Beswick Collectors Club "Special." A "Beswick" green rug with yellow binding has BCC99 on the corner, and a red rosette is on the bridle. The Champion Welsh Pony was issued in a limited edition of 580.

In 2000 the Welsh Pony was again chosen as the Collectors Club "Special." This verson, in white gloss, and issued in a limited edition of 505, has a green rug with yellow binding.

SERIES: Connoisseur

Welsh Mountain Pony

"Champion Welsh Mountain Pony"

Designer: Graham Tongue
Height: 8 ¼", 21.0 cm

Colourway	Finish	Model	Intro.	Disc.	U.K. £	U.S. $	Can. $
Black (BCC-1999)	Gloss	A247	1999	Ltd. Ed.	175.00	250.00	375.00
White (BCC-2000)	Gloss	A247	2000	Ltd. Ed.	175.00	250.00	375.00
White (General Issue)							
a. Royal Doulton	Gloss	DA247	1998	1999	125.00	175.00	275.00
b. Beswick	Gloss	A247	1999	Current	125.00	N/A	435.00

Model No. A250

LAMMTARRA

Designer: Warren Platt
Height: 7 ¾", 19.6 cm
Series: Connoisseur

Colourway	Finish	Model	Intro.	Disc.	U.K. £	U.S. $	Can. $
Chestnut							
a. Royal Doulton	Matt	DA250	1999	1999	125.00	175.00	250.00
b. Beswick	Matt	A250	1999	Current	125.00	N/A	N/A

Model No. A259

PALOMINO

Designer: Shane Ridge
Height: 6 ¾", 17.2 cm

Colourway	Finish	Model	Intro.	Disc.	U.K. £	U.S. $	Can. $
Palomino							
a. Royal Doulton	Gloss	DA259	1999	1999	70.00	100.00	150.00
b. Beswick	Gloss	A259	1999	Current	62.00	N/A	220.00

Model No. A260

HUNTER

Designer: Graham Tongue
Height: 8", 20.3 cm

Colourway	Finish	Model	Intro.	Disc.	U.K. £	U.S. $	Can. $
Grey							
a. Royal Doulton	Gloss	DA260	1999	1999	70.00	100.00	150.00
b. Beswick	Gloss	A260	1999	Current	67.00	N/A	N/A

Model No. A261

HACKNEY PONY

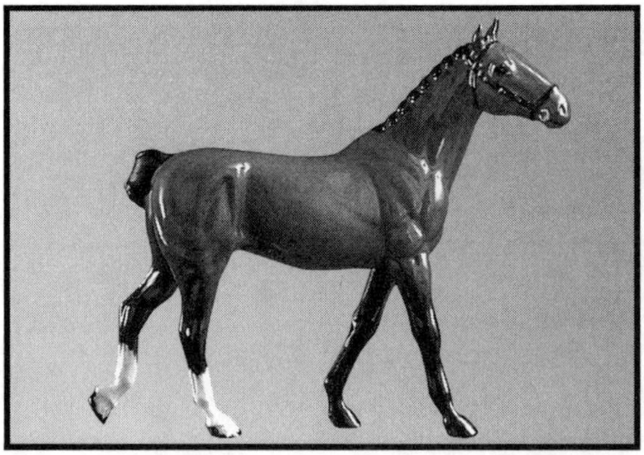

Designer: Martyn Alcock
Height: 6 ¾", 17.2 cm

Colourway	Finish	Model	Intro.	Disc.	U.K. £	U.S. $	Can. $
Bay							
a. Royal Doulton	Gloss	DA261	1999	1999	50.00	75.00	115.00
b. Beswick	Gloss	A261	1999	Current	49.00	N/A	180.00

Model No. A266

ONE MAN

Designer: Martyn Alcock
Height: 7 ½", 19.0 cm
Series: Connoisseur

Colourway	Finish	Intro.	Disc.	U.K. £	U.S. $	Can. $
Light dapple grey	Gloss	1999	Current	115.00	N/A	385.00

Model No. A270

WELSH COB STALLION

Designer: Robert Donaldson
Height: 7 ¼", 18.4 cm

Colourway	Finish	Intro.	Disc.	U.K. £	U.S. $	Can. $
Black	Matt	2000	Current	115.00	N/A	385.00

Note: See also "The Dartmoor Family" page 289.

Model No. A271

DRESSAGE STALLION

Modeller: Robert Donaldson
Height: 7 ½", 19.0 cm
Series: Connoisseur

Colourway	Finish	Intro.	Disc.	U.K. £	U.S. $	Can. $
Dark brown	Matt	2000	Current	115.00	N/A	385.00

Model No. A3990

ERISKAY PONY

Designer: Robert Donaldson
Height: 6", 15.24 cm
Series: Connoisseur

Colourway	Finish	Intro.	Disc.	U.K. £	U.S. $	Can. $
Light dapple grey	Matt	2000	Current	90.00	N/A	325.00

Note: Produced in association with the Rare Breeds Survival Trust.

Model No. A3998

CLYDESDALE

Designer: Robert Donaldson
Height: 8 ½", 21.5 cm
Series: Connoisseur

Colourway	Finish	Intro.	Disc.	U.K. £	U.S. $	Can. $
Bay	Matt	2000	Current	129.00	N/A	435.00

Note: Produced in association with the Rare Breeds Survival Trust.

Model No. A3999

CLEVELAND BAY

Designer: Robert Donaldson
Height: 8 ½", 21.5 cm
Series: Connoisseur

Colourway	Finish	Intro.	Disc.	U.K. £	U.S. $	Can. $
Bay	Matt	2000	Current	120.00	N/A	435.00

Note: Produced in association with the Rare Breeds Survival Trust.

Model No. A4000

SUFFOLK PUNCH

Designer: Robert Donaldson
Height: 8 ½", 21.5 cm
Series: Connoisseur

Colourway	Finish	Intro.	Disc.	U.K. £	U.S. $	Can. $
Chestnut	Matt	2000	Current	120.00	N/A	435.00

Note: Produced in association with the Rare Breeds Survival Trust.

Model No. H185

SHETLAND PONY / "HOLLYDELL DIXIE"

This Shetland Pony was the 1995 Beswick Collectors Circle "Special." It was decorated to represent Shetland Mare, Supreme Champion "Hollydell Dixie," and was issued in a limited edition of 553 in August 1995. Both the Beswick and BCC backstamps appear on this model.

Designer: Amanda Hughes-Lubeck
Height: 5 ¼", 13.3 cm

Colourway	Finish	Model	Intro.	Disc.	U.K. £	U.S. $	Can. $
Skewbald (BCC95)	Gloss	H185	1995	Ltd. Ed.	175.00	250.00	350.00
Dapple grey							
a. Royal Doulton	Gloss	DA185	1992	1999	50.00	70.00	100.00
b. Beswick	Gloss	H185	1999	Current	49.00	N/A	115.00

Model No. H4078

SPIRIT OF WISDOM

Designer: Shane Ridge
Height: 9 ½", 24.1 cm

Colourway	Finish	Intro.	Disc.	U.K. £	U.S. $	Can. $
Black	Matt	2001	Current	88.00	N/A	300.00
Brown	Matt	2001	Current	98.00	N/A	325.00
White	Matt	2001	Current	88.00	N/A	300.00

Model No. H4079

SPIRIT OF FLIGHT

Designer: Shane Ridge
Height: 9", 22.9 cm

Colourway	Finish	Intro.	Disc.	U.K. £	U.S. $	Can. $
Black	Matt	2001	Current	88.00	N/A	300.00
Brown	Matt	2001	Current	98.00	N/A	325.00
White	Matt	2001	Current	88.00	N/A	300.00

ANOTHER STAR

This model was commissioned for P.R. Middleweek and Co. from the John Beswick Studios and was issued in a special edition of 1,500.

Designer: Warren Platt
Height: 2 ½", 6.4 cm

Colourway	Finish	Intro.	Disc.	U.K. £	U.S. $	Can. $
Light Brown	Gloss	1998	Ltd. Ed.	40.00	55.00	80.00

Note: See also "The Dartmoor Family" page 289.

THE DARTMOOR FAMILY

Commissioned by P.R. Middleweek & Co. to commemorate the Millennium, this tableau is composed of *Warlord, Another Bunch* and *Another Star,* and was issued in 1999 in a limited edition of 150.

Modeller: Arthur Gredington, Graham Tongue, Warren Platt
Height: 7 ¼", 18.4 cm

Colourway	Finish	Intro.	Disc.	U.K. £	U.S. $	Can. $
Red bay (Warlord)	Gloss	1999	Ltd. Ed.	275.00	400.00	600.00
Red bay (Another Bunch)						
Light brown (Another Star)						

SPIRIT OF WHITFIELD

This model of "Kruger" was commissioned by the Chatterley Whitfield Mining Museum. Only four models exist.

Designer: Graham Tongue
Height: 9", 22.9 cm

Colourway	Finish	Intro.	Disc.	U.K. £	U.S. $	Can. $
Brown	Matt	1987	1987	Auction Sale 1994, £2,750.00		

WARLORD'S MARE
"ANOTHER BUNCH"

Another Bunch, issued in a special edition of 1,500, was the second in a series of specially commissioned models for P. R. Middleweek & Co. from The John Beswick Studios.

Designer: Graham Tongue
Height: 6", 15.1 cm

Colourway	Finish	Intro.	Disc.	U.K. £	U.S. $	Can. $
Bay/brown; red, white, blue sash	Gloss	1997	Spec. Ed.	65.00	100.00	150.00

Note: See also the Dartmoor Family page 289.

Wall Ornaments - Horses

INDEX BY MODEL NUMBER

Photograph not available at press time

Model No. 686
HORSE'S HEAD LOOKING LEFT THROUGH A HORSESHOE
First Version - Flat back

Designer: Mr. Owen
Height: 7 ¼" x 6", 18.4 x 15.0 cm
Colour: 1. Brown - gloss
2. Dark chestnut - gloss
Issued: 1938-1939
Varieties: 807

Colourway	U.K. £	U.S. $	Can. $
1. Brown	85.00	120.00	175.00
2. Dark chestnut	100.00	145.00	220.00

Photograph not available at press time

Model No. 687
HORSE'S HEAD LOOKING RIGHT THROUGH A HORSESHOE
First Version - Flat back

Designer: Mr. Owen
Height: 7 ¼" x 6", 18.4 x 15.0 cm
Colour: 1. Brown - gloss
2. Dark chestnut - gloss
Issued: 1939-1939
Varieties: 806

Colourway	U.K. £	U.S. $	Can. $
1. Brown	85.00	120.00	175.00
2. Dark chestnut	100.00	145.00	220.00

Model No. 806
HORSE'S HEAD LOOKING LEFT THROUGH A HORSESHOE
Second Version - Raised back

Designer: Mr. Owen
Height: 7 ¼" x 6", 18.4 x 15.0 cm
Colour: Brown - gloss
Issued: 1939-1968
Varieties: 687

Description	U.K. £	U.S. $	Can. $
Gloss	75.00	110.00	165.00

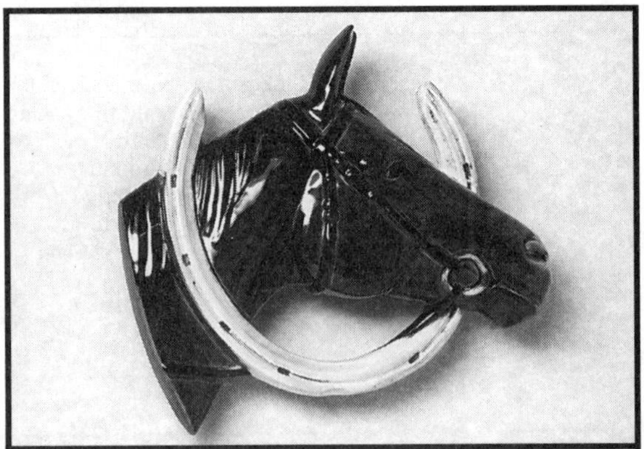

Model No. 807
HORSE'S HEAD LOOKING RIGHT THROUGH A HORSESHOE
Second Version - Raised back

Designer: Mr. Owen
Height: 7 ¼" x 6", 18.4 x 15.0 cm
Colour: Brown - gloss
Issued: 1938-1968
Varieties: 686

Description	U.K. £	U.S. $	Can. $
Gloss	75.00	110.00	165.00

Model No. 1382
HUNTER HEAD

Designer:	Arthur Gredington
Height:	4" x 4", 10.1 x 10.1 cm
Colour:	Brown - gloss
Issued:	1955-1969

Description	U.K. £	U.S. $	Can. $
Gloss	60.00	85.00	125.00

Model No. 1384
PALOMINO HEAD

Designer:	Arthur Gredington
Height:	4"x 4", 10.1 x 10.1 cm
Colour:	Palomino - gloss
Issued:	1955-1969

Description	U.K. £	U.S. $	Can. $
Gloss	75.00	110.00	165.00

Model No. 1385
ARAB HEAD

Designer:	Arthur Gredington
Height:	4" x 4", 10.1 x 10.1 cm
Colour:	Dark brown - gloss
Issued:	1955-1969

Description	U.K. £	U.S. $	Can. $
Gloss	70.00	100.00	150.00

Model No. 1505
HUNTSMAN

Designer:	Albert Hallam and James Hayward
Height:	8 ½", 21.6 cm
Colour:	1. Brown - gloss 2. Copper lustre
Issued:	1958-1962

Colourway	U.K. £	U.S. $	Can. $
1. Brown	175.00	250.00	375 .00
2. Copper lustre	125.00	175.00	250.00

Model No. 1513
"TAKING OFF"

Designer: Colin Melbourne
Height: 9", 22.9 cm
Colour: 1. Brown - gloss
2. Copper lustre
Issued: 1958-1962

Colourway	U.K. £	U.S. $	Can. $
1. Brown	185.00	275.00	425.00
2. Copper lustre	125.00	175.00	275.00

Model No. 1514
"LANDING"

Designer: Colin Melbourne
Height: 7 ¾", 19.7 cm
Colour: 1. Brown - gloss
2. Copper lustre
Issued: 1958-1962

Colourway	U.K. £	U.S. $	Can. $
1. Brown	185.00	275.00	425.00
2. Copper lustre	125.00	175.00	275.00

Model No. 1515
"GOING OVER"

Designer: Colin Melbourne
Height: 7 ½", 19.1 cm
Colour: 1. Brown - gloss
2. Copper lustre
Issued: 1958-1962

Colourway	U.K. £	U.S. $	Can. $
1. Brown	185.00	275.00	425.00
2. Copper lustre	125.00	175.00	275.00

Model No. 2699
TROY

Designer: Unknown
Height: 6", 15.0 cm
Colour: Brown - matt
Issued: 1984-1989
Series: Champions All

Description	U.K. £	U.S. $	Can. $
Matt	45.00	65.00	95.00

Model No. 2700
ARKLE

Designer:	Unknown
Height:	6″, 15.0 cm
Colour:	Bay - matt
Issued:	1984-1989
Series:	Champions All

Description	U.K. £	U.S. $	Can. $
Matt	50.00	75.00	125.00

Model No. 2701
THE MINSTREL

Designer:	Unknown
Height:	6″, 15.0 cm
Colour:	Chestnut - matt
Issued:	1984-1989
Series:	Champions All

Description	U.K. £	U.S. $	Can. $
Matt	50.00	75.00	125.00

Model No. 2702
RED RUM

Designer:	Unknown
Height:	6″, 15.0 cm
Colour:	Bay - matt
Issued:	1984-1989
Series:	Champions All

Description	U.K. £	U.S. $	Can. $
Matt	50.00	75.00	125.00

BESWICK
Connoisseur Range
COLLECTORS PIECES
HUNTER
RACEHORSE
HEREFORD BULL
THOROUGHBRED
ARAB
FRIESIAN BULL
BEAGLE
BASSETT HOUND
JOHN BESWICK LTD., Gold Street, Longton, Stoke-on-Trent, ST3 2JP, England
Telephone Stoke-on-Trent 33041
Cables Besware, Stoke-on-Trent
A MEMBER OF THE ROYAL DOULTON GROUP OF COMPANIES

Chapter Eight

WILD ANIMALS

The wild animals in this group have been produced by John Beswick for more than fifty years. Many are authentic and true to life in shape and colour, others are comical.

Beswick wild animals are very popular with collectors. They are less of a minefield for the inexperienced than some of the other series, as the animals are familiar and can be easily identified, since most carry the Beswick backstamp.

As you can see, Beswick produced these animals in a random order. It was not until the late 1930s that realism was created by the use of natural colours, instead of the very popular blue gloss used in earlier days. Around this time, the models were also refined to represent real animals.

The variety of animals is enormous and most animals are represented, ranging from the smallest mouse to the very large African elephant. The powerful bison, the gentle springbok and the elegant giraffe are just some of these superb pieces.

At the time of the introduction of the *Connoisseur Series* in 1967, most of the items were horses, and it was not until 1973 that three wild animals were absorbed into the series. These were the already existing versions of two elephants, numbers 998 and 1770, both free standing, and a puma on a rock, number 1702. As the name suggests, the *Connoisseur Series* comprises prestige models, and consequently were and are more expensive than the rest of the animals.

It is interesting to note that Arthur Gredington was the modeller responsible for the majority of the wild animals. Some collectors collect models from one particular designer or modeller, and these would make an excellent choice.

Many of the wild animals are avidly sought after. The search is a challenge, but well worth the effort if you can find your treasured piece.

MODELS TRANSFERRED TO
THE CHARLTON STANDARD CATALOGUE OF BESWICK COLLECTABLES

Model No.	Description	Model No.	Description
455	Rabbit Bookend	1336	Tortoise Girl With Bonnet
663	Elephant Toothbrush Holder	1337	Tortoise Boy With Cap
664	Fox Toothbrush Holder	1379	Bush Baby - With Mirror
665	Rabbit Toothbrush Holder	1380	Bush Baby - With Candlestick
1009	Squirrel - With Nut Cracker	1381	Bush Baby - With Book
1255	Monkey With Drum	2132	Rabbit With Baby
1256	Monkey With Tuba	SC1	Fly Fishing
1257	Monkey With Fiddle	SC2	Last Lion of Defense
1258	Monkey With Saxophone	SC3	It's a Knockout
1259	Monkey With Guitar	SC4	Sloping Off
1260	Monkey With Banjo	SC5	A Round with Foxy
1334	Tortoise Mother With Hat	SC6	Out For a Duck

INDEX BY MODEL NUMBER

Model No. 315
SQUIRREL - on pottery base

Designer: Miss Greaves
Height: 8 ¾″, 22.2 cm
Colour: See below
Issued: 1935-by 1954

Colourway	U.K. £	U.S. $	Can. $
1. Blue - gloss	135.00	200.00	300.00
2. Blue/brown - satin	100.00	150.00	225.00
3. Cream - satin matt	100.00	150.00	225.00
4. Natural - satin	135.00	200.00	300.00

Model No. 316
RABBIT - on pottery base

Designer: Miss Greaves
Height: 6 ¾″, 17.2 cm
Colour: See below
Issued: 1935-by 1954

Colourway	U.K. £	U.S. $	Can. $
1. Blue , gloss	135.00	200.00	300.00
2. Blue/brown, satin	100.00	150.00	225.00
3. Cream, satin matt	100.00	150.00	225.00
4. Natural, satin	135.00	200.00	300.00

Model No. 368
FROG - on pottery base

Designer: Miss Greaves
Height: 6 ¾″, 16.5 cm
Colour: See below
Issued: 1936-by 1954

Colourway	U.K. £	U.S. $	Can. $
1. Blue - gloss	135.00	200.00	300.00
2. Blue/brown - satin	100.00	150.00	225.00
3. Cream - satin matt	100.00	150.00	225.00
4. Gold		Rare	
5. Green - satin matt	100.00	150.00	225.00
6. Natural - satin	135.00	200.00	300.00

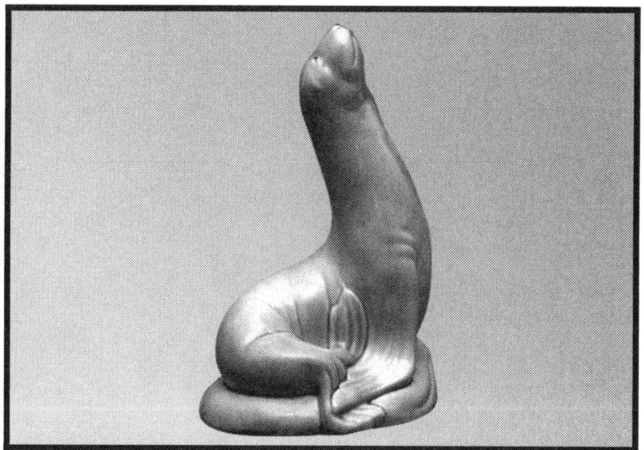

Model No. 383
SEAL - on pottery base

Designer: Mr. Owen
Height: 10″, 25.4 cm
Colour: See below
Issued: 1936-by 1954

Colourway	U.K. £	U.S. $	Can. $
1. Blue, gloss	135.00	200.00	300.00
2. Blue/brown, satin	100.00	150.00	225.00
3. Cream, satin matt	100.00	150.00	225.00
4. Natural, satin	135.00	200.00	300.00

Model No. 397
MONKEY - on pottery base

Designer: Mr. Owen
Height: 7", 17.8 cm
Colour: See below
Issued: 1936-by 1954

Colourway	U.K. £	U.S. $	Can. $
1. Blue, gloss	125.00	175.00	275.00
2. Blue/brown, satin	100.00	150.00	225.00
3. Cream, satin matt	100.00	150.00	225.00
4. Green, gloss	100.00	150.00	225.00
5. Natural, satin	125.00	175.00	275.00

Model No. 417
POLAR BEAR - on pottery base

Designer: Mr. Owen
Height: 7", 17.8 cm
Colour: See below
Issued: 1936-by 1954

Colourway	U.K. £	U.S. $	Can. $
1. Blue, gloss	135.00	200.00	300.00
2. Cream, satin matt	125.00	175.00	250.00
3. Green, gloss	125.00	175.00	250.00
4. Natural, satin	150.00	225.00	350.00

Model No. 568/569
CHARACTER ELEPHANT

Designer: Mr. Owen
Height: 1. Large - 9", 22.9 cm
2. Small - 4 ¾", 12.1 cm
Colour: See below
Issued: 1938-by 1954

Colourway	U.K. £	U.S. $	Can. $
1. Blue, gloss - large	375.00	525.00	800.00
2. Cream, satin - large	350.00	500.00	750.00
3. Blue, gloss - small	225.00	325.00	500.00
4. Cream, satin - small	200.00	275.00	425.00

Model No. 692
ELEPHANT WITH HOWDAH

Designer: Unknown
Height: 4 ¼", 10.8 cm
Colour: Blue - gloss
Issued: 1939-by 1954

Colourway	U.K. £	U.S. $	Can. $
Blue	150.00	225.00	350.00

Model No. 696
DEER ON ROCK

Designer: Arthur Gredington
Height: 8", 20.3 cm
Colour: See below
Issued: 1939-1954
Set: 721

Colourway	U.K. £	U.S. $	Can. $
1. Blue, gloss	85.00	125.00	200.00
2. Brown, gloss	75.00	100.00	150.00
3. Cream, satin	65.00	90.00	135.00
4. Flambé, gloss	200.00	275.00	400.00

Model No. 697
HIPPOPOTAMUS

Designer: Mr. Watkin
Height: 2 ¼", 5.7 cm
Colour: 1. Blue - gloss
2. Cream - satin matt
Issued: 1939-by 1954
Series: Fun Models

Colourway	U.K. £	U.S. $	Can. $
1. Blue	75.00	100.00	150.00
2. Cream	65.00	90.00	135.00

Model No. 698
GIRAFFE

Designer: Mr. Watkin
Height: 1. Large - 6", 15.0 cm
2. Small - 4", 10.1 cm
Colour: See below
Issued: 1939-by 1954
Series: Fun Models

Colourway	U.K. £	U.S. $	Can. $
1. Blue, gloss - large	125.00	175.00	275.00
2. Cream, satin - large	125.00	175.00	275.00
3. Blue, gloss - small	75.00	100.00	150.00
4. Cream, satin - small	75.00	100.00	150.00

Photograph not available.
Model No. 709 possibly
not put into production.

Model No. 709
BEAVER

Designer: Mr. Watkin
Height: Unknown
Colour: Unknown
Issued: 1939-Unknown

Description	U.K. £	U.S. $	Can. $
Beaver		Extremely Rare	

Note: Possibly not put into production.

Model No. 711
PANDA

Designer: Mr. Watkin
Height: 4 ½", 11.9 cm
Colour: See below
Issued: 1939-by 1954

Colourway	U.K. £	U.S. $	Can. $
1. Black/white, gloss	85.00	125.00	175.00
2. Blue, gloss	135.00	200.00	300.00
3. Cream, satin matt	85.00	125.00	175.00

Model No. 720
PANDA CUB

Designer: James Haywood
Height: 3 ¾", 9.5 cm
Colour: See below
Issued: 1939-by 1954

Colourway	U.K. £	U.S. $	Can. $
1. Black/white, gloss	95.00	135.00	200.00
2. Blue, gloss	75.00	100.00	150.00
3. Cream, satin matt	75.00	100.00	150.00

Model No. 721
DEER ON BASE

Designer: Arthur Gredington
Height: 4 ½", 11.9 cm
Colour: See below
Issued: 1939-by 1954
Set: 696

Colourway	U.K. £	U.S. $	Can. $
1. Blue, gloss	75.00	100.00	150.00
2. Brown, gloss	65.00	90.00	135.00
3. Green, matt	75.00	100.00	150.00
4. White, matt	75.00	100.00	150.00

Model No. 738
PANDA WITH BALL

Designer: Mr. Watkin
Height: 4 ½", 11.9 cm
Colour: See below
Issued: 1939-by 1954

Colourway	U.K. £	U.S. $	Can. $
1. Black/white, gloss	85.00	125.00	200.00
2. Blue, gloss	125.00	175.00	275.00
3. Cream, satin matt	85.00	125.00	200.00

Model No. 823
RABBIT - On haunches

Designer: Arthur Gredington
Height: 3", 7.6 cm
Colour: 1. Blue – gloss
2. Brown – gloss
Issued: 1. 1940-1954
2. 1940-1971
Set: 824, 825, 826

Colourway	U.K. £	U.S. $	Can. $
1. Blue, gloss	45.00	65.00	95.00
2. Brown, gloss	20.00	30.00	45.00

Model No. 824
RABBIT - Scratching ear

Designer: Arthur Gredington
Height: 2 ¼", 5.7 cm
Colour: 1. Blue – gloss
2. Brown – gloss
Issued: 1. 1940-1954
2. 1940-1971
Set: 823, 825, 826

Colourway	U.K. £	U.S. $	Can. $
1. Blue, gloss	40.00	55.00	80.00
2. Brown, gloss	15.00	20.00	30.00

Model No. 825
RABBIT - Crouching

Designer: Arthur Gredington
Height: 1 ½", 3.8 cm
Colour: 1. Blue – gloss
2. Brown – gloss
Issued: 1. 1940-1954
2. 1940-1971
Set: 823, 824, 826

Colourway	U.K. £	U.S. $	Can. $
1. Blue, gloss	30.00	45.00	65.00
2. Brown, gloss	15.00	20.00	30.00

Model No. 826
RABBIT - Seated

Designer: Arthur Gredington
Height: 2", 5.0 cm
Colour: 1. Blue – gloss
2. Brown – gloss
Issued: 1. 1940-1954
2. 1940-1971
Set: 823, 824, 825

Colourway	U.K. £	U.S. $	Can. $
1. Blue, gloss	30.00	45.00	65.00
2. Brown, gloss	15.00	20.00	30.00

Model No. 828
ELEPHANT

Designer: Mr. Owen
Colour: 1. Blue - gloss
2. Cream - satin matt
3. Pale grey - gloss
Issued: 1940-by 1954

Description	Colourway	Height	U.K. £	Price U.S. $	Can. $
Large	Blue	6", 15.0 cm	150.00	225.00	300.00
Large	Cream	6", 15.0 cm	125.00	175.00	250.00
Large	Pale grey	6", 15.0 cm	135.00	200.00	275.00
Medium	Blue	4 ½", 11.9 cm	125.00	175.00	250.00
Medium	Cream	4 ½", 11.9 cm	110.00	155.00	225.00
Medium	Pale grey	4 ½", 11.9 cm	115.00	165.00	235.00
Small	Blue	3", 7.6 cm	100.00	145.00	215.00
Small	Cream	3", 7.6 cm	70.00	100.00	150.00
Small	Pale grey	3", 7.6 cm	85.00	125.00	175.00

Model No. 830
LIZARD

Designer: Miss Joachim
Height: Unknown
Colour: Green - gloss
Issued: 1940-Unknown

Colourway	U.K. £	U.S. $	Can. $
Green		Extremely Rare	

Model No. 841
LEOPARD - Seated

Designer: Arthur Gredington
Height: 6 ¼", 15.9 cm
Colour: Tan brown, black spots - gloss
Issued: 1940-by 1954

Colourway	U.K. £	U.S. $	Can. $
Tan brown/black	600.00	850.00	1,250.00

Model No. 845A
ZEBRA
First Version - Tan with black stripes

Designer: Arthur Gredington
Height: 7 ¼", 18.4 cm
Colour: Tan with black stripes - gloss
Issued: 1940-Unknown

Colourway	U.K. £	U.S. $	Can. $
Tan/black	300.00	450.00	675.00

Model No. 845B
ZEBRA
Second Version - White with black stripes

Designer: Arthur Gredington
Height: 7 ¼", 18.4 cm
Colour: White with black stripes - gloss
Issued: Unknown-1969

Colourway	U.K. £	U.S. $	Can. $
White/black	100.00	150.00	225.00

Model No. 853
GIRAFFE - Small

Designer: Arthur Gredington
Height: 7 ¼″, 18.4 cm
Colour: See below
Issued: 1940-1975

Colourway	U.K. £	U.S. $	Can. $
1. Natural, gloss	85.00	125.00	175.00
2. Stone, satin finish	75.00	100.00	150.00
3. White, gloss	75.00	100.00	150.00

Model No. 954
STAG - Lying

Designer: Arthur Gredington
Height: 5 ½″, 14.0 cm
Colour: Light brown - gloss
Issued: 1941-1975

Colourway	U.K. £	U.S. $	Can. $
Light brown	50.00	70.00	100.00

Note: Earlier models appear with a red-brown colour.

Model No. 974
ELEPHANT - Trunk stretching - small

Designer: Arthur Gredington
Height: 4 ¾″, 12.1 cm
Colour: Grey - gloss or matt
Issued: 1. Gloss - 1943 -1996
2. Matt - 1985-1988

Description	U.K. £	U.S. $	Can. $
1. Gloss	30.00	45.00	65.00
2. Matt	35.00	50.00	75.00

Model No. 981
STAG - Standing

Designer: Arthur Gredington
Height: 8″, 20.3 cm
Colour: See below
Issued: 1a. Gloss - 1942-1997
1b. Matt - 1985-1988
2. Satin - 1989-1992
Series: 2. Britannia Collection

Colourways	U.K. £	U.S. $	Can. $
1a. Light brown, gloss	35.00	50.00	75.00
1b. Light brown, matt	35.00	50.00	75.00
2. Bronze, satin	40.00	55.00	80.00

Model No. 998
ELEPHANT - Trunk stretching - large

Designer: Arthur Gredington
Height: 10 ¼", 26.0 cm
Colour: Natural - gloss or satin matt
Issued: 1. Gloss - 1943-1975
2. Satin matt - 1970-1973
Series: Model in satin matt finish was transferred to Connoisseur Series in 1973.

Description	U.K. £	U.S. $	Can. $
1. Gloss	200.00	300.00	450.00
2. Satin matt	225.00	325.00	500.00

Model No. 999A
DOE

Designer: Arthur Gredington
Height: 6", 15.0 cm
Colour: 1. Light brown - gloss
2. Light and dark brown - matt
Issued: 1. Gloss - 1943-1997
2. Matt - 1985-1988

Description	U.K. £	U.S. $	Can. $
1. Gloss	30.00	40.00	55.00
2. Matt	25.00	35.00	50.00

Note: Earlier models appear with a red-brown colour.

Model No. 999B
DOE AND FAWN - on ceramic base

Designer: Arthur Gredington
Height: 7", 17.8 cm
Colour: Light brown - gloss
Issued: 1993-1996

Colourway	U.K. £	U.S. $	Can. $
Light brown	35.00	50.00	75.00

Note: Doe is no. 999, Fawn is no. 1000.

Model No. 1000A
FAWN
First Version - tail up

Designer: Arthur Gredington
Height: 3 ½", 8.9 cm
Colour: Light brown - gloss
Issued: 1943-1955

Colourway	U.K. £	U.S. $	Can. $
Light brown	75.00	100.00	150.00

Note: Earlier models appear with a red-brown colour.

Model No. 1000B
FAWN
Second Version - tail down

Designer: Arthur Gredington
Remodelled: Mr. Orwell
Height: 3 ½", 8.9 cm
Colour: Light brown - gloss or matt
Issued: 1. Gloss - 1955-1997
2. Matt - 1985-1988

Description	U.K. £	U.S. $	Can. $
1. Gloss	20.00	30.00	45.00
2. Matt	25.00	35.00	50.00

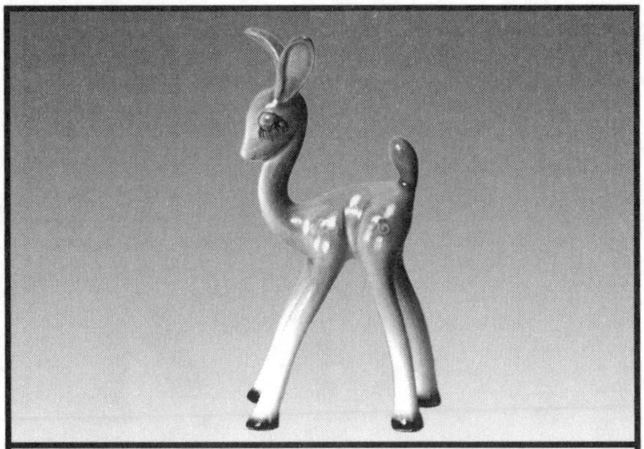

Model No. 1003
FAWNIE

Designer: Arthur Gredington
Height: 5 ¼", 13.3 cm
Colour: See below – gloss
Issued: 1944-1967
Series: Fun Models

Colourway	U.K. £	U.S. $	Can. $
1. Green	100.00	150.00	225.00
2. Grey-brown	150.00	200.00	300.00

Model No. 1005
KANGARINE

Designer: Arthur Gredington
Height: 5", 12.7 cm
Colour: 1. Blue with white markings - gloss
2. Brown - gloss
Issued: 1944-1966
Series: Fun Models

Colourway	U.K. £	U.S. $	Can. $
1. Blue	125.00	175.00	250.00
2. Brown	100.00	150.00	225.00

Model No. 1007
SQUIRREL - Standing

Designer: Arthur Gredington
Height: 2 ¼", 5.7 cm
Colour: Tan - gloss
Issued: 1944-c.1963
Set: 1008, 1009
Series: Fun Models

Colourway	U.K. £	U.S. $	Can. $
Tan	40.00	55.00	85.00

Note: Model 1009 has been transferred to *The Charlton Standard Catalogue of Beswick Collectables.*

Model No. 1008
SQUIRREL - Lying

Designer: Arthur Gredington
Height: 1 ¾", 4.5 cm
Colour: Tan - gloss
Issued: 1944-c.1963
Set: 1007, 1009
Series: Fun Models

Colourway	U.K. £	U.S. $	Can. $
Tan	40.00	55.00	85.00

Note: Model 1009 has been transferred to *The Charlton Standard Catalogue of Beswick Collectables.*

Model No. 1016A
FOX - Standing

Designer: Arthur Gredington
Height: 5 ½", 14.0 cm
Colour: Red-brown and white - gloss or matt
Issued: 1. Gloss - 1945-1997
2. Matt - 1985-1988
Varieties: 1016B

Description	U.K. £	U.S. $	Can. $
1. Gloss	20.00	30.00	45.00
2. Matt	30.00	45.00	70.00

Model No. 1016B
FOX - Standing - on ceramic base

Designer: Arthur Gredington
Height: 6 ¾", 17.2 cm
Colour: Red-brown and white - gloss
Issued: 1993-1996
Varieties: 1016A

Colourway	U.K. £	U.S. $	Can. $
Red-brown/white	30.00	45.00	65.00

Model No. 1017
FOX - Curled

Designer: Arthur Gredington
Height: 1 ¾", 3.2 cm
Colour: Red brown - gloss or matt
Issued: 1. Gloss - 1945 -1996
2. Matt - 1985-1988

Description	U.K. £	U.S. $	Can. $
1. Gloss	15.00	20.00	30.00
2. Matt	30.00	45.00	70.00

Model No. 1019
BISON

Designer: Arthur Gredington
Height: 5 ¾", 14.6 cm
Colour: Dark brown - gloss
Issued: 1945-1973

Colourway	U.K. £	U.S. $	Can. $
Dark brown	90.00	125.00	175.00

Model No. 1021
STOAT

Designer: Arthur Gredington
Height: 5 ½", 14.0 cm
Colour: 1. Tan (summer coat) - gloss
2. White (winter coat) - gloss
Issued: 1945-1963

Colourway	U.K. £	U.S. $	Can. $
1. Tan	175.00	250.00	375.00
2. White	150.00	225.00	350.00

Model No. 1024
HARE - Running

Designer: Arthur Gredington
Height: 5 ¼", 12.7 cm
Colour: Tan - gloss
Issued: 1945-1963

Colourway	U.K. £	U.S. $	Can. $
Tan	300.00	425.00	650.00

Model No. 1025
HARE - Seated

Designer: Arthur Gredington
Height: 7", 17.8 cm
Colour: Tan - gloss
Issued: 1945-1963

Colourway	U.K. £	U.S. $	Can. $
Tan	200.00	300.00	450.00

Model No. 1038
KOALA BEAR

Designer: Arthur Gredington
Height: 3 ½", 8.9 cm
Colour: Grey - gloss
Issued: 1945-1971
Set: 1039, 1040

Colourway	U.K. £	U.S. $	Can. $
Grey	35.00	50.00	75.00

Model No. 1039
KOALA BEAR - On branch

Designer: Arthur Gredington
Height: 2 ¼", 5.7 cm
Colour: Grey - gloss
Issued: 1945-1973
Set: 1038, 1040

Colourway	U.K. £	U.S. $	Can. $
Grey	25.00	35.00	50.00

Model No. 1040
KOALA BEAR

Designer: Arthur Gredington
Height: 2 ¼", 5.7 cm
Colour: Grey - gloss
Issued: 1945-1973
Set: 1038, 1039

Colourway	U.K. £	U.S. $	Can. $
Grey	25.00	35.00	50.00

Model No. 1043
CAMEL FOAL

Designer: Arthur Gredington
Height: 5", 12.7 cm
Colour: Light and dark brown - gloss
Issued: 1946-1971
Set: 1044

Colourway	U.K. £	U.S. $	Can. $
Brown	75.00	100.00	150.00

Model No. 1044
CAMEL

Designer: Arthur Gredington
Height: 7", 17.8 cm
Colour: Light and dark brown - gloss
Issued: 1946-1973
Set: 1043

Colourway	U.K. £	U.S. $	Can. $
Brown	125.00	175.00	250.00

Model No. 1048
SPRINGBOK

Designer: Arthur Gredington
Height: 7 ¼", 18.4 cm
Colour: Tan and white - gloss
Issued: 1946-1963

Colourway	U.K. £	U.S. $	Can. $
Tan/white	275.00	400.00	600.00

Model No. 1049
CHIMPANZEE WITH PIPE

Designer: Arthur Gredington
Height: 4 ¾", 12.1 cm
Colour: Brown - gloss
Issued: 1946-1969

Colourway	U.K. £	U.S. $	Can. $
Brown	100.00	150.00	225.00

Model No. 1082
LEOPARD

Designer: Arthur Gredington
Height: 4 ¾", 12.1 cm
Colour: 1. Golden brown with black markings - gloss
2. Black - satin
Issued: 1946-1975

Description	U.K. £	U.S. $	Can. $
1. Gloss	100.00	150.00	225.00
2. Satin	90.00	125.00	175.00

Model No. 1089
KOALA BEAR - With fruit

Designer: Miss Jones
Height: 3 ½", 8.9 cm
Colour: Grey - gloss
Issued: 1947-1971

Colourway	U.K. £	U.S. $	Can. $
Grey	35.00	50.00	75.00

Model No. 1160
KANGAROO

Designer: Arthur Gredington
Height: 5 ¾", 14.6 cm
Colour: Brown - gloss
Issued: 1949-1966

Colourway	U.K. £	U.S. $	Can. $
Brown	100.00	150.00	225.00

Model No. 1308
SKUNK

Designer: Arthur Gredington
Height: 2 ¾", 7.0 cm
Colour: Black and white - gloss
Issued: 1953-1963
Set: 1309, 1310

Colourway	U.K. £	U.S. $	Can. $
Black/white	45.00	65.00	95.00

Model No. 1309
SKUNK

Designer: Arthur Gredington
Height: 1 ½", 3.8 cm
Colour: Black and white - gloss
Issued: 1953-1963
Set: 1308, 1310

Colourway	U.K. £	U.S. $	Can. $
Black/white	45.00	65.00	95.00

Model No. 1310
SKUNK

Designer: Arthur Gredington
Height: 2", 5.0 cm
Colour: Black and white - gloss
Issued: 1953-1963
Set: 1307, 1309

Colourway	U.K. £	U.S. $	Can. $
Black/white	45.00	65.00	95.00

Model No. 1313
BEAR - Standing

Designer: Arthur Gredington
Height: 2 ½", 6.4 cm
Colour: Black or brown - gloss
Issued: 1953-1966
Set: 1314, 1315

Colourway	U.K. £	U.S. $	Can. $
1. Black	65.00	90.00	135.00
2. Brown	65.00	90.00	135.00

Model No. 1314
BEAR - On hind legs

Designer: Arthur Gredington
Height: 4 ½", 11.9 cm
Colour: Black or brown - gloss
Issued: 1953-1966
Set: 1313, 1315

Colourway	U.K. £	U.S. $	Can. $
1. Black	65.00	90.00	135.00
2. Brown	65.00	90.00	135.00

Model No. 1315
BEAR CUB - Seated

Designer: Arthur Gredington
Height: 2 ¼", 5.7 cm
Colour: Black or brown - gloss
Issued: 1953-1966
Set: 1313, 1314

Colourway	U.K. £	U.S. $	Can. $
1. Black	45.00	65.00	95.00
2. Brown	45.00	65.00	95.00

Model No. 1440
FOX - Standing

Designer: Arthur Gredington
Height: 2 ½", 6.4 cm
Colour: Red-brown and white - gloss or matt
Issued: 1. Gloss - 1956-1997
2. Matt - 1985-1988

Description	U.K. £	U.S. $	Can. $
1. Gloss	10.00	15.00	20.00
2. Matt	15.00	20.00	30.00

Model No. 1486
TIGRESS

Designer: Colin Melbourne
Height: 4 ¼", 10.8 cm
Colour: Tan with black stripes and markings - gloss
Issued: 1957-1975

Colourway	U.K. £	U.S. $	Can. $
Tan/black	100.00	150.00	225.00

Model No. 1506
LION - Facing right

Designer: Colin Melbourne
Height: 5 ¼", 13.3 cm
Colour: Golden brown - gloss
Issued: 1957-1967
Set: 1507, 1508

Colourway	U.K. £	U.S. $	Can. $
Golden brown	75.00	125.00	175.00

Model No. 1507
LIONESS - Facing left

Designer: Colin Melbourne
Height: 4 ¾", 12.1 cm
Colour: See below
Issued: 1957-1967
Set: 1506, 1508

Colourway	U.K. £	U.S. $	Can. $
1. Black satin - matt	50.00	75.00	125.00
2. Golden brown - gloss	75.00	100.00	150.00

Note: The black satin matt colourway was probably considered a panther.

Model No. 1508
LION CUB - Facing right

Designer:	Colin Melbourne
Height:	4", 10.1 cm
Colour:	See below
Issued:	1957-1967
Set:	1506, 1507

Colourway	U.K. £	U.S. $	Can. $
1. Black satin - matt	150.00	200.00	300.00
2. Golden brown - gloss	50.00	75.00	125.00

Note: The black satin matt colourway was probably considered a panther.

Model No. 1532
HIPPOPOTAMUS

Designer:	Colin Melbourne
Height:	3 ½", 8.9 cm
Colour:	Dark grey with pink underneath - gloss
Issued:	1958-1966

Colourway	U.K. £	U.S. $	Can. $
Dark grey	175.00	250.00	375.00

Model No. 1533
POLAR BEAR

Designer:	Arthur Gredington
Height:	4 ¾", 12.1 cm
Colour:	White - gloss
Issued:	1958-1966

Colourway	U.K. £	U.S. $	Can. $
White	150.00	225.00	325.00

Model No. 1534
SEAL

Designer:	Arthur Gredington
Length:	5 ¾", 14.6 cm
Colour:	Grey - gloss
Issued:	1958-1966

Colourway	U.K. £	U.S. $	Can. $
Grey	125.00	175.00	275.00

Model No. 1551
CHAMOIS

Designer: Pal Zalmen
Height: 4″, 10.1 cm
Colour: Fawn or grey - gloss
Issued: 1958-1971
Series: Fun Models

Colourway	U.K. £	U.S. $	Can. $
1. Fawn	60.00	85.00	125.00
2. Grey	60.00	85.00	125.00

Model No. 1597
GIRAFFE

Designer: J. Lawson
Height: 4 ¼″, 10.8 cm
Colour: Tan with dark patches - gloss
Issued: 1959-1971
Series: Fun Models

Colourway	U.K. £	U.S. $	Can. $
Tan	60.00	85.00	125.00

Model No. 1615A
BABYCHAM
First Version - Large eyes

Designer: Albert Hallam
Height: 4″, 10.1 cm
Colour: Yellow - gloss
Issued: 1960-1975
Series: Fun Models

Description	U.K. £	U.S. $	Can. $
Large eyes	60.00	85.00	125.00

Model 1615B
BABYCHAM
Second Version - Small eyes, name on ribbon

Designer: Albert Hallam
Height: 4", 10.1 cm
Colour: Yellow - gloss
Issued: Unknown
Series: Fun Models

Description	U.K. £	U.S. $	Can. $
Small eyes	60.00	85.00	125.00

Model No. 1631
GIRAFFE - Large

Designer: J. Lawson
Height: 12", 30.5 cm
Colour: Light brown with dark brown patches - gloss
Issued: 1959-1975

Colourway	U.K. £	U.S. $	Can. $
Brown	175.00	250.00	375.00

Note: Pattern and colour varies.

Model No. 1678
MOUSE

Designer: Albert Hallam
Height: 2 ½", 6.4 cm
Colour: Grey - gloss
Issued: 1960-1997

Colourway	U.K. £	U.S. $	Can. $
Grey	20.00	30.00	45.00

Model No. 1688
REINDEER

Designer: J. Lawson
Height: 3 ¾", 9.5 cm
Colour: 1. Fawn - gloss
2. Grey - gloss
Issued: 1960-1971
Series: Fun Models

Colourway	U.K. £	U.S. $	Can. $
1. Fawn	60.00	85.00	125.00
2. Grey	60.00	85.00	125.00

Model No. 1702
PUMA ON ROCK
Style One

Designer: Arthur Gredington
Height: 8 ½", 21.6 cm
Colour: 1. Black - gloss
2. Tawny - gloss or matt
Issued: 1. Black
a. Gloss - 1960-1973
Reissued: b. Gloss - 1979-1983
Issued: 2. Tawny
a. Gloss - 1960-1975
b. Matt - 1970-1973
c. Satin matt - 1973-1989
Reissued: d. Gloss - 1979-1983
Series: 2c. Connoisseur Series

Colourway	U.K. £	U.S. $	Can. $
1. Black			
a. Gloss	150.00	200.00	300.00
b. Reissued	150.00	200.00	300.00
2. Tawny			
a. Gloss	150.00	200.00	300.00
b. Matt	125.00	175.00	275.00
c. Satin matt	125.00	175.00	275.00
d. Reissued, gloss	125.00	175.00	275.00

Model No. 1720
ELEPHANT AND TIGER

Designer: Arthur Gredington
Height: 12", 30.5 cm
Colour: Grey, tan with black stripes - gloss
Issued: 1960-1975

Description	U.K. £	U.S. $	Can. $
Gloss	650.00	900.00	1,350.00

Note: The elephant is the same model as used in 1770.

Model No. 1733
COMICAL FOX

Designer: Harry Sales
Height: 3 ¼", 8.3 cm
Colour: Red-brown and white - gloss
Issued: 1961-1968
Series: Fun Models

Description	U.K. £	U.S. $	Can. $
Gloss	60.00	90.00	135.00

Model No. 1748
FOX - Seated

Designer: Arthur Gredington
Height: 3", 7.6 cm
Colour: Red-brown and white - gloss or matt
Issued: 1. Gloss - 1961-1997
2. Matt - 1985-1988

Description	U.K. £	U.S. $	Can. $
1. Gloss	10.00	15.00	20.00
2. Matt	15.00	20.00	30.00

Model No. 1770
ELEPHANT - Trunk in salute

Designer: Arthur Gredington
Height: 12", 30.5 cm
Colour: Grey - gloss or satin matt
Issued: 1. Gloss - 1961-1975
2. Satin matt - 1970-1973

Description	U.K. £	U.S. $	Can. $
1. Gloss	250.00	350.00	525.00
2. Satin matt	275.00	400.00	600.00

Note: Satin matt transferred to Connoiseur Series in 1973. Elephant same model as used in 1720.

Model No. 1815
PANDA CUB

Designer: Albert Hallam
Height: 2 ¼", 5.7 cm
Colour: Black and white - gloss or matt
Issued: 1. Gloss - 1962-1997
2. Matt - 1985-1988

Description	U.K. £	U.S. $	Can. $
1. Gloss	15.00	20.00	30.00
2. Matt	15.00	20.00	30.00

Model No. 1823
PUMA ON ROCK
Style Two

Designer: Arthur Gredington
Height: 6", 15.0 cm
Colour: 1. Black - gloss
2. Tawny - gloss
Issued: 1. Black - 1962-1973
2. Tawny - 1962-1975

Colourway	U.K. £	U.S. $	Can. $
1. Black	100.00	150.00	225.00
2. Tawny	125.00	200.00	300.00

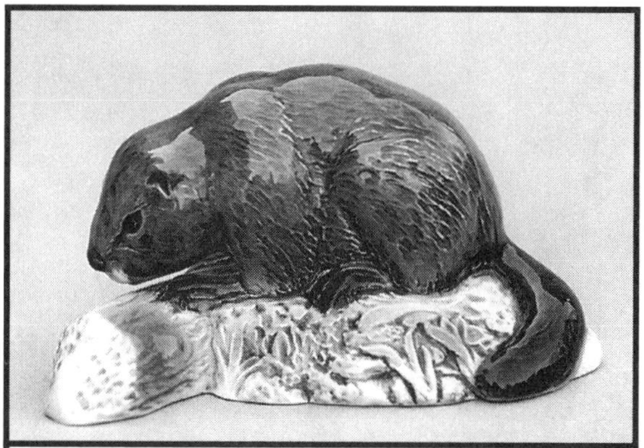

Model No. 1943
BEAVER ON LOG - Facing left

Designer: Albert Hallam
Height: 2 ½", 6.4 cm
Colour: Tan - gloss
Issued: 1964-1967

Colourway	U.K. £	U.S. $	Can. $
Tan	175.00	250.00	375.00

Model No. 2089
LION - Facing left

Designer: Graham Tongue
Height: 5 ½", 14.0 cm
Colour: Golden brown - gloss
Issued: 1967-1984

Colourway	U.K. £	U.S. $	Can. $
Golden brown	60.00	85.00	125.00

Model No. 2090
MOOSE

Designer: Arthur Gredington
Height: 6 ¼", 15.9 cm
Colour: Dark brown - gloss or satin matt
Issued: 1967-1973

Description	U.K. £	U.S. $	Can. $
1. Gloss	650.00	900.00	1,350.00
2. Satin matt	650.00	900.00	1,350.00

Model No. 2096
TIGER

Designer: Graham Tongue
Height: 7 ½", 19.1 cm
Colour: Tan with black stripes - gloss or matt
Issued: 1. Gloss - 1967-1990
2. Matt - 1985-1988

Description	U.K. £	U.S. $	Can. $
1. Gloss	85.00	125.00	200.00
2. Matt	75.00	100.00	150.00

Note: Example known in black satin matt - very rare.

Model No. 2097
LIONESS - Facing right

Designer: Graham Tongue
Height: 5 ¾", 14.6 cm
Colour: Golden brown - gloss
Issued: 1967-1984

Colourway	U.K. £	U.S. $	Can. $
Golden brown	60.00	85.00	125.00

Model No. 2098
LION CUB - Facing left

Designer: Graham Tongue
Height: 4", 10.1 cm
Colour: Golden brown - gloss
Issued: 1967-1984

Colourway	U.K. £	U.S. $	Can. $
Golden brown	35.00	50.00	75.00

Model No. 2131
RABBIT

Designer: Albert Hallam, Graham Tongue
Height: 3", 7.6 cm
Colour: Light brown and white - gloss
Issued: 1967-1973
Series: Fun Models

Colourway	U.K. £	U.S. $	Can. $
Brown/white	75.00	110.00	165.00

Model No. 2194
RACOON ON LOG

Designer: Albert Hallam
Height: 4 ¼", 10.8 cm
Colour: Dark grey - gloss
Issued: 1968-1972

Colourway	U.K. £	U.S. $	Can. $
Dark grey	175.00	250.00	375.00

Model No. 2195
BEAVER ON LOG - Facing right

Designer:	Albert Hallam
Height:	4 ½", 11.9 cm
Colour:	Brown - gloss
Issued:	1968-c.1973

Colourway	U.K. £	U.S. $	Can. $
Brown	175.00	250.00	375.00

Model No. 2237
BABYCHAM WALL PLAQUE

Designer:	Graham Tongue
Height:	3" x 6 ¼", 7.6 x 15.9 cm (Concave)
Colour:	Unknown - gloss
Issued:	c.1970-c.1975
Series:	Wall Plaques

Description	U.K. £	U.S. $	Can. $
Gloss	100.00	150.00	225.00

Model No. 2253
HEDGEHOG

Designer:	Harry Sales
Height:	3 ½" 8.9 cm
Colour:	1. Blue - gloss 2. Brown - gloss
Issued:	1969-1971
Series:	Moda Range

Colourway	U.K. £	U.S. $	Can. $
1. Blue	135.00	200.00	300.00
2. Brown	135.00	200.00	300.00

Photograph not available.
Model No. 2302 possibly
not put into production.

Model No. 2302
MOUSE

Designer:	Albert Hallam
Height:	1 ¾", 8.9 cm
Colour:	Unknown
Issued:	1969-Unknown

Description	U.K. £	U.S. $	Can. $
Mouse	Possibly not put into production.		

Model No. 2312
KANGAROO

Designer:	Albert Hallam
Height:	5", 12.7 cm
Colour:	Light and dark brown - gloss
Issued:	1970-1973

Description	U.K. £	U.S. $	Can. $
Gloss	125.00	175.00	275.00

Model No. 2348
FOX

Designer:	Graham Tongue
Height:	12 ½", 31.7 cm
Colour:	Red-brown and white - gloss
Issued:	1970-1984
Series:	Fireside Model

Description	U.K. £	U.S. $	Can. $
Gloss	250.00	350.00	525.00

Model No. 2554A
LION ON ROCK

Designer:	Graham Tongue
Height:	8 ¼", 21.0 cm
Colour:	Golden brown - satin matt
Issued:	1975-1984
Varieties:	2554B (standing)
Series:	Connoisseur

Description	U.K. £	U.S. $	Can. $
Satin matt	175.00	250.00	375.00

Model No. 2554B
LION - Standing

Designer:	Graham Tongue
Height:	6 ¾", 17.2 cm
Colour:	Golden brown - gloss
Modelled:	1975
Issued:	1987-1995

Description	U.K. £	U.S. $	Can. $
Gloss	100.00	150.00	225.00

Model No. 2613
PANDA "CHI CHI"
First Version - With bamboo shoot

Designer:	Unknown
Height:	3 ¾", 9.5 cm
Colour:	Black and white - gloss
Issued:	1978-c.1980
Varieties:	2944

Description	U.K. £	U.S. $	Can. $
Gloss	250.00	350.00	525.00

Note: This model was produced for the British Museum, backstamp reads BM (NH).

Model No. 2629
STAG

Designer:	Graham Tongue
Height:	13 ½", 34.3 cm
Colour:	1. Golden brown - satin matt 2. Bronze with black shading - satin
Issued:	See below
Series:	2. Connoisseur

Colourway	U.K. £	U.S. $	Can. $
Golden brown			
1a. Beswick, 1978-1989	200.00	300.00	450.00
1b. Doulton, 1989-1996	200.00	300.00	450.00
2. Bronze/black shading	200.00	300.00	450.00

Model No. 2686
OTTER

Designer:	David Lyttleton
Height:	2 ¼", 5.7 cm
Colour:	Grey - matt
Issued:	1985-1985

Description	U.K. £	U.S. $	Can. $
Matt	40.00	60.00	90.00

Note: Part of a trial run in 1985 but never put into general production.

Model No. 2687
BADGER

Designer:	David Lyttleton
Height:	3", 7.6 cm
Colour:	Black - matt
Issued:	1985-1985

Description	U.K. £	U.S. $	Can. $
Matt	40.00	60.00	90.00

Note: Part of a trial run in 1985 but never put into general production.

Model No. 2693
SEAL

Designer: Graham Tongue
Height: 3 ½", 8.9 cm
Colour: Grey - matt
Issued: 1985-1985

Description	U.K. £	U.S. $	Can. $
Matt	40.00	60.00	90.00

Note: Part of a trial run in 1985 but never put into general production.

Model No. 2725
CHEETAH ON ROCK

Designer: Graham Tongue
Height: 6 ½", 16.5 cm
Colour: Pale brown with dark spots - satin finish
Issued: 1981-1989
Series: Connoisseur

Description	U.K. £	U.S. $	Can. $
Satin finish	125.00	175.00	275.00

Note: Transferred to R.D. backstamp as *The Watering Hole* (DA 39), 08/89, with model modifications.

Model No. 2944
PANDA "CHI CHI"
Second Version - Without bamboo shoot

Designer: Unknown
Height: 3 ¾", 9.5 cm
Colour: Black and white - matt
Issued: 1985-1985
Varieties: 2613

Description	U.K. £	U.S. $	Can. $
Matt	125.00	175.00	275.00

Note: Part of a trial run in 1985 but did not go into general production.

Model No. 3009
CHEETAH - Standing

Designer: Graham Tongue
Height: 5", 12.7 cm
Colour: Golden brown with dark spots - gloss
Issued: 1986-1995

Description	U.K. £	U.S. $	Can. $
Gloss	75.00	100.00	150.00

Model No. 3392
BADGER CUB

Designer:	Amanda Hughes-Lubeck
Height:	2″, 5.0 cm
Colour:	Black and white - gloss
Issued:	1992-1997
Set:	3393, 3394

Description	U.K. £	U.S. $	Can. $
Gloss	20.00	30.00	45.00

Model No. 3393
BADGER - Male

Designer:	Amanda Hughes-Lubeck
Height:	2″, 5.0 cm
Colour:	Black and white - gloss
Issued:	1992-1997
Set:	3392, 3394

Description	U.K. £	U.S. $	Can. $
Gloss	20.00	30.00	45.00

Model No. 3394
BADGER - Female

Designer:	Amanda Hughes-Lubeck
Height:	2″, 5.0 cm
Colour:	Black and white - gloss
Issued:	1992 -1997
Set:	3392, 3393

Description	U.K. £	U.S. $	Can. $
Gloss	20.00	30.00	45.00

Model No. 3397
HARVEST MOUSE

Designer:	Martyn Alcock
Height:	2 ¼″, 5.7 cm
Colour:	Brown - gloss
Issued:	1992-1997

Description	U.K. £	U.S. $	Can. $
Gloss	20.00	30.00	45.00

Model No. 3399
WOODMOUSE

Designer: Martyn Alcock
Height: 3 ¼", 8.3 cm
Colour: Brown - gloss
Issued: 1992-1997

Description	U.K. £	U.S. $	Can. $
Gloss	20.00	30.00	45.00

Model No. 3568
MEERKAT - Seated

Designer: Martyn Alcock
Height: 3", 7.6 cm
Colour: Grey and brown - gloss
Issued: 1996 in a limited edition of 1,250

Description	U.K. £	U.S. $	Can. $
Gloss	35.00	50.00	75.00

Model No. 3571
MEERKAT - Standing

Designer: Martyn Alcock
Height: 3 ½", 8.9 cm
Colour: Grey and brown - gloss
Issued: 1996 in a limited edition of 1,250

Description	U.K. £	U.S. $	Can. $
Gloss	35.00	50.00	75.00

WILD ANIMAL WALL PLAQUES

INDEX BY MODEL NUMBER

Model No. 2933
LION'S HEAD

Designer: Graham Tongue
Height: 6", 15.0 cm
Colour: Golden brown - matt
Issued: 1985-1989

Description	U.K. £	U.S. $	Can. $
Matt	50.00	70.00	100.00

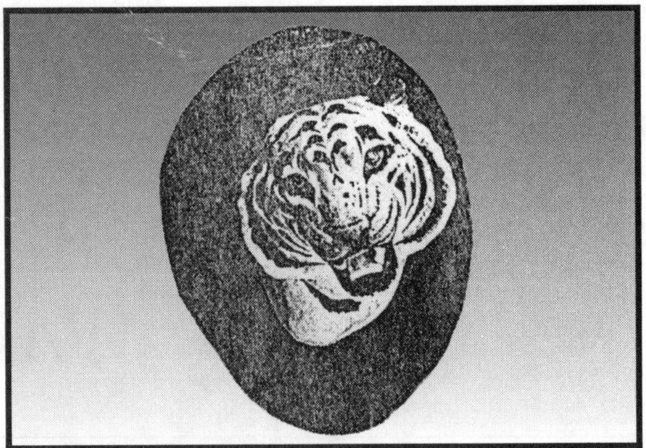

Model No. 2934
TIGER'S HEAD

Designer: Arthur Gredington
Height: 6", 15.0 cm
Colour: Tan - matt
Issued: 1985-1989

Description	U.K. £	U.S. $	Can. $
Matt	50.00	70.00	100.00

Model No. 2936
STAG'S HEAD

Designer: Graham Tongue
Height: 6", 15.0 cm
Colour: Light brown - matt
Issued: 1985-1989

Description	U.K. £	U.S. $	Can. $
Matt	50.00	70.00	100.00

Chapter Nine

THE CM SERIES

This unique series of models, all created by Colin Melbourne, evokes great emotion amongst collectors; it is either loved or hated there are no half measures here. The models were called "contemporary" when they were in production during the late 1950s. They reflected the mood of the time, both in style and in decoration. None of the decorations are realistic, and all are stylized, some to a greater extent than others.

The decoration for the models in this section fall into two categories:

Series 1. Issued 1956-1962

This series is sub-divided in three groups:

1. Colour combinations—charcoal grey/red/white gloss
2. Spotted colour combinations—yellow/shaded charcoal/black
3. Solid colours—grey/brown/green blue/white

Series 2. Issued 1962-1966

This was called the chalk design. The background colour was white and the decorations in geometric shapes or floral designs appeared in a variety of colourways.

INDEX BY MODEL NUMBER

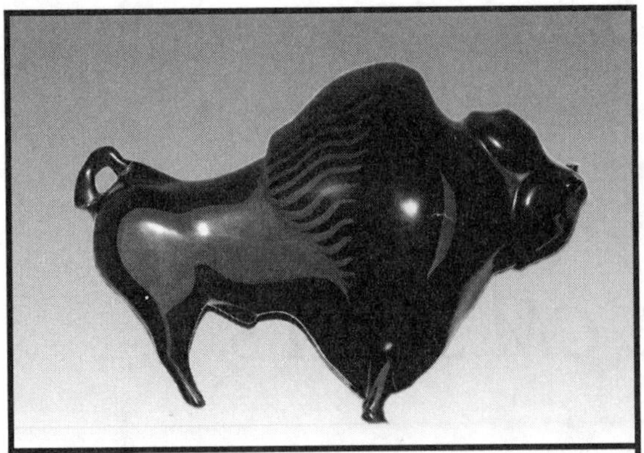

Model No. 1409
BISON - Large

Designer: Colin Melbourne
Length: 7 ½" x 10 ½", 19.1 x 26.7 cm
Colour: For colour combinations and varieties see page 331
Issued: 1956-by 1963

Description	U.K. £	U.S. $	Can. $
Series 1	145.00	225.00	325.00
Series 2	185.00	275.00	400.00

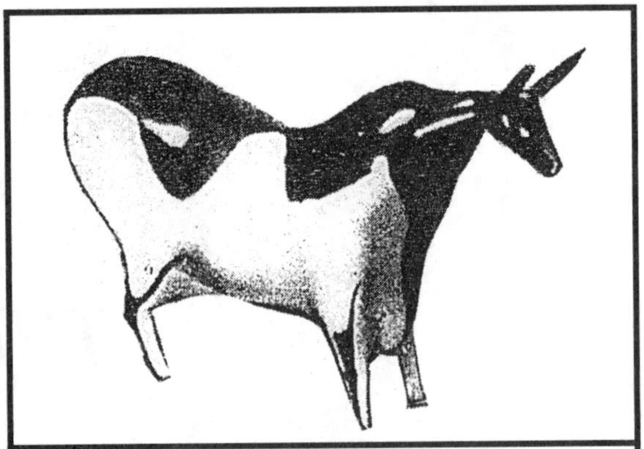

Model No. 1410
COW

Designer: Colin Melbourne
Height: 5", 12.7 cm
Colour: For colour combinations and varieties see page 331
Issued: 1956-by 1963

Description	U.K. £	U.S. $	Can. $
Series 1	145.00	225.00	325.00

Model No. 1411
HORSE

Designer: Colin Melbourne
Height: 8 ½", 21.6 cm
Colour: For colour combinations and varieties see page 331
Issued: 1956-by 1966

Description	U.K. £	U.S. $	Can. $
Series 1	145.00	225.00	325.00
Series 2	225.00	325.00	500.00

Model No. 1412
CAT - Large

Designer: Colin Melbourne
Height: 9 ½", 24.0 cm
Colour: For colour combinations and varieties see page 331
Issued: 1956-by 1966

Description	U.K. £	U.S. $	Can. $
Series 1	165.00	250.00	350.00
Series 2	185.00	275.00	400.00

Model No. 1413
DOVE

Designer: Colin Melbourne
Height: 9", 22.9 cm
Colour: For colour combinations and varieties see page 331
Issued: 1956-by 1965

Description	U.K. £	U.S. $	Can. $
Series 1	125.00	185.00	275.00
Series 2	145.00	225.00	325.00

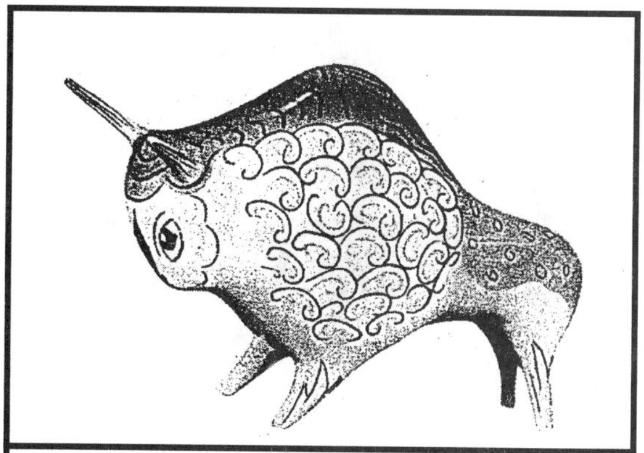

Model No. 1414
BISON - Medium

Designer: Colin Melbourne
Length: 5 ½" x 8 ¾", 14.0 x 22.2 cm
Colour: For colour combinations and varieties see page 331
Issued: 1956-by 1966

Description	U.K. £	U.S. $	Can. $
Series 1	145.00	225.00	325.00
Series 2	165.00	250.00	350.00

Model No. 1415
BIRD

Designer: Colin Melbourne
Height: 3", 7.6 cm
Colour: For colour combinations and varieties see page 331
Issued: 1956-by 1965

Description	U.K. £	U.S. $	Can. $
Series 1	125.00	185.00	275.00
Series 2	145.00	225.00	325.00

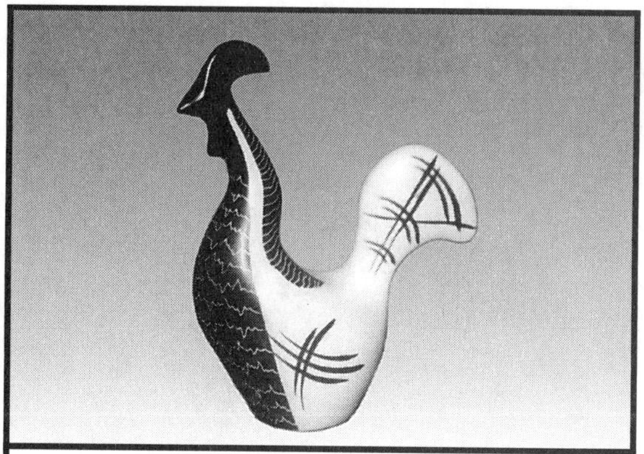

Model No. 1416
COCK - Small

Designer: Colin Melbourne
Height: 5", 12.7 cm
Colour: For colour combinations and varieties see page 331
Issued: 1956-by 1965

Description	U.K. £	U.S. $	Can. $
Series 1	145.00	225.00	325.00
Series 2	185.00	275.00	400.00

Model No. 1417
CAT

Designer: Colin Melbourne
Height: 5 ½", 14.0 cm
Colour: For colour combinations and varieties see page 331
Issued: 1956-by 1966

Description	U.K. £	U.S. $	Can. $
Series 1	80.00	125.00	175.00
Series 2	165.00	250.00	350.00

Model No. 1418
FOX - Small

Designer: Colin Melbourne
Length: 2" x 8", 5.0 x 20.3 cm
Colour: For colour combinations and varieties see page 331
Issued: 1956-by 1966

Description	U.K. £	U.S. $	Can. $
Series 1	100.00	145.00	200.00
Series 2	145.00	225.00	325.00

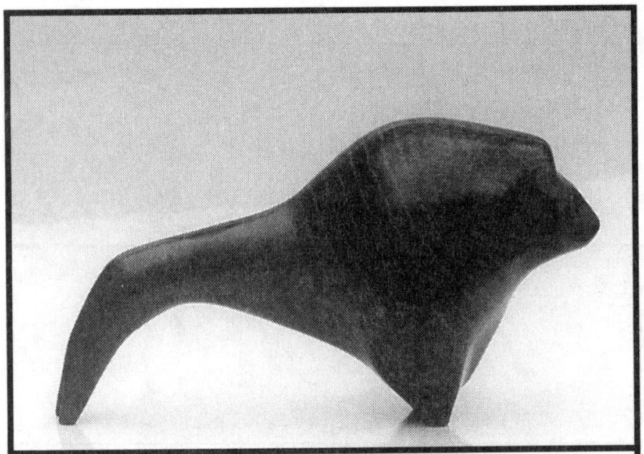

Model No. 1419
LION

Designer: Colin Melbourne
Height: 4 ¾", 12.1 cm
Colour: For colour combinations and varieties see page 331
Issued: 1956-by 1963

Description	U.K. £	U.S. $	Can. $
Series 1	145.00	225.00	325.00

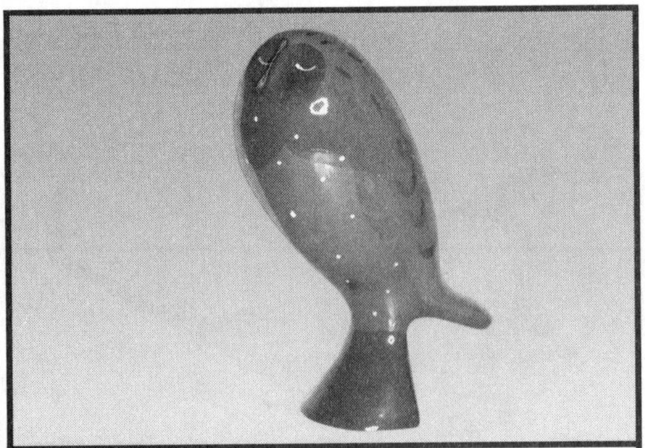

Model No. 1420
OWL - Small

Designer: Colin Melbourne
Height: 4 ¾", 12.1 cm
Colour: For colour combinations and varieties see page 331
Issued: 1956-by 1965

Description	U.K. £	U.S. $	Can. $
Series 1	125.00	185.00	275.00
Series 2	145.00	225.00	325.00

Model No. 1462
OWL - Large

Designer: Colin Melbourne
Height: 8 ¼", 21.0 cm
Colour: For colour combinations and varieties see page 331
Issued: 1956-by 1965

Description	U.K. £	U.S. $	Can. $
Series 1	145.00	225.00	325.00
Series 2	165.00	250.00	350.00

Model No. 1463
BULLDOG

Designer: Colin Melbourne
Height: Unknown
Colour: For colour combinations and varieties see page 331
Issued: 1956-1970

Description	U.K. £	U.S. $	Can. $
Series 1	125.00	185.00	275.00

Model No. 1465
ZEBRA

Designer: Colin Melbourne
Height: 6", 15.0 cm
Colour: For colour combinations and varieties see page 331
Issued: 1956-by 1966

Description	U.K. £	U.S. $	Can. $
Series 1	185.00	275.00	400.00
Series 2	225.00	325.00	500.00

Model No. 1467
COCK - Large

Designer: Colin Melbourne
Height: 11 ¾", 29.8 cm
Colour: For colour combinations and varieties see page 331
Issued: 1956-by 1963

Description	U.K. £	U.S. $	Can. $
Series 1	185.00	275.00	400.00
Series 2	235.00	350.00	525.00

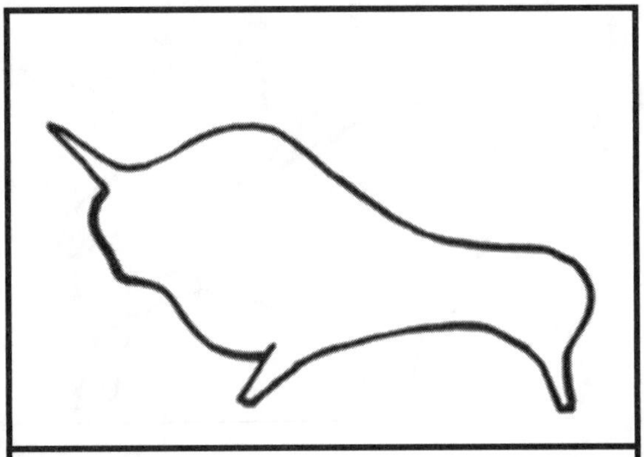

Model No. 1468
BISON - Small

Designer: Colin Melbourne
Height: Unknown
Colour: For colour combinations and varieties see page 331
Issued: 1956-by 1966

Description	U.K. £	U.S. $	Can. $
Series 1	145.00	225.00	325.00
Series 2	185.00	275.00	400.00

Model No. 1469
DACHSHUND

Designer: Colin Melbourne
Length: 7", 17.8 cm
Colour: For colour combinations and varieties see page 331
Issued: 1957-1970

Description	U.K. £	U.S. $	Can. $
Series 1	100.00	145.00	200.00
Series 2	145.00	225.00	325.00

Model No. 1470
CLOWN ON HORSE - Small

Designer: Colin Melbourne
Height: 5 ¾", 14.6 cm
Colour: For colour combinations and varieties see page 331
Issued: 1957-by 1966

Description	U.K. £	U.S. $	Can. $
Series 1	165.00	250.00	350.00
Series 2	225.00	325.00	500.00

Model No. 1471
GOOSE

Designer: Colin Melbourne
Height: 3 ½", 8.9 cm
Colour: For colour combinations and varieties see page 331
Issued: 1957-by 1962

Description	U.K. £	U.S. $	Can. $
Series 1	125.00	175.00	250.00

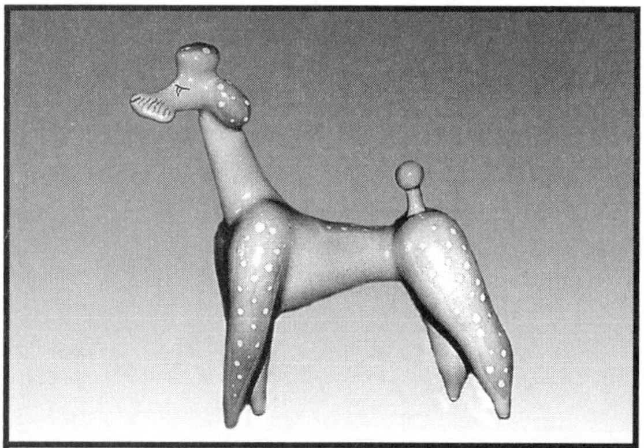

Model No. 1472
POODLE

Designer: Colin Melbourne
Height: 5 ¾", 14.6 cm
Colour: For colour combinations and varieties see page 331
Issued: 1957-1962

Description	U.K. £	U.S. $	Can. $
Series 1	165.00	250.00	350.00

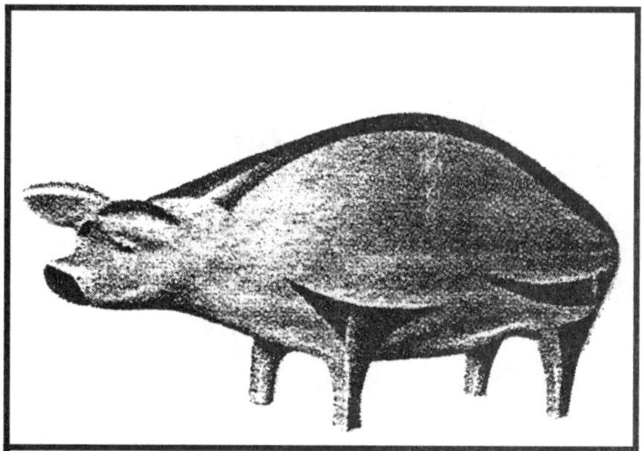

Model No. 1473
PIG

Designer: Colin Melbourne
Length: 2 ½" x 6", 6.4 x 15.0 cm
Colour: For colour combinations and varieties see page 331
Issued: 1957-by 1965

Description	U.K. £	U.S. $	Can. $
Series 1	125.00	175.00	250.00
Series 2	145.00	225.00	325.00

Model No. 1474
CAT

Designer: Colin Melbourne
Height: 5 ¼", 13.3 cm
Colour: For colour combinations and varieties see page 331
Issued: 1957-by 1966

Description	U.K. £	U.S. $	Can. $
Series 1	145.00	225.00	325.00
Series 2	165.00	250.00	350.00

Model No. 1475
FOX - Large

Designer: Colin Melbourne
Length: 10 ½", 26.7 cm
Colour: For colour combinations and varieties see page 331
Issued: 1957-by 1966

Description	U.K. £	U.S. $	Can. $
Series 1	145.00	225.00	325.00
Series 2	165.00	250.00	350.00

Model No. 1476
CLOWN ON HORSE - Large

Designer: Colin Melbourne
Height: 8 ½", 21.6 cm
Colour: For colour combinations and varieties see page 331
Issued: 1957-by 1966

Description	U.K. £	U.S. $	Can. $
Series 1	265.00	400.00	600.00
Series 2	325.00	475.00	700.00

Model No. 1481
REINDEER

Designer: Colin Melbourne
Height: 5 ½", 14.0 cm
Colour: For colour combinations and varieties see page 331
Issued: 1957-by 1966

Description	U.K. £	U.S. $	Can. $
Series 1	165.00	250.00	350.00
Series 2	185.00	275.00	400.00

Model No. 1482
PEACOCK

Designer: Colin Melbourne
Height: 3 ½", 8.9 cm
Colour: For colour combinations and varieties see page 331
Issued: 1957-by 1965

Description	U.K. £	U.S. $	Can. $
Series 1	145.00	225.00	325.00
Series 2	165.00	250.00	350.00

Chapter Ten

LITTLE LIKEABLES

INDEX BY MODEL NUMBER

LL1
FAMILY GATHERING™
(Hen and Two Chicks)

Designer: Diane Griffiths
Height: 4 ½", 11.9 cm
Colour: White hen and chicks with yellow beaks and gold comb on hen - gloss
Issued: 1985 - 1987

Description	U.K. £	U.S. $	Can. $
Gloss	50.00	75.00	125.00

LL2
WATCHING THE WORLD GO BY™
(Frog)

Designer: Robert Tabbenor
Height: 3 ¾", 9.5 cm
Colour: White frog, black and green eyes - gloss
Issued: 1985-1987

Description	U.K. £	U.S. $	Can. $
Gloss	50.00	75.00	125.00

LL3
HIDE AND SEEK™
(Pig and Two Piglets)

Designer: Robert Tabbenor
Height: 3 ¼", 8.3 cm
Colour: White pigs with pink noses, ears and tails - gloss
Issued: 1985-1987

Description	U.K. £	U.S. $	Can. $
Gloss	50.00	75.00	125.00

LL4
MY PONY™
(Pony)

Designer: Diane Griffiths
Height: 7 ¼", 18.4 cm
Colour: White pony with blue highlights in mane and tail - gloss
Issued: 1985-1987

Description	U.K. £	U.S. $	Can. $
Gloss	50.00	75.00	125.00

LL5
ON TOP OF THE WORLD™
(Elephant)

Designer: Diane Griffiths
Height: 3 ¾", 9.5 cm
Colour: White elephant with black eyes and gold nails - gloss
Issued: 1985-1987

Description	U.K. £	U.S. $	Can. $
Gloss	50.00	75.00	125.00

LL6
TREAT ME GENTLY™
(Fawn)

Designer: Diane Griffiths
Height: 4 ½", 11.9 cm
Colour: White fawn with black and brown eyes, black nose and gold hoof - gloss
Issued: 1985-1987

Description	U.K. £	U.S. $	Can. $
Gloss	50.00	75.00	125.00

LL7
OUT AT LAST™
(Duckling)

Designer: Robert Tabbenor
Height: 3 ¼", 8.3 cm
Colour: White duck with black and brown eyes and gold beak - gloss
Issued: 1985-1987

Description	U.K. £	U.S. $	Can. $
Gloss	50.00	75.00	125.00

LL8
CATS CHORUS™
(Cats)

Designer: Robert Tabbenor
Height: 4 ¾", 12.1 cm
Colour: Two white cats with black and green eyes, black nose, pink ears and mouth - gloss
Issued: 1985-1987

Description	U.K. £	U.S. $	Can. $
Gloss	50.00	75.00	125.00

Chapter Eleven

STUDIO SCULPTURES

The series of Studio Sculptures made a very brief appearance, most for a maximum of two years, and some for only six months, between 1984 and 1985. When the collection was launched, Harry Sales, Beswick's Design Manager, explained "The new bonded ceramic body gives us endless opportunities to capture every minute detail of the subject and bring the sculptures to life."

The models in this new medium formed four groups, of which two are relevant to this book. These are: the "Countryside Series" which consists of fourteen models and includes birds, a squirrel, dogs, and rabbits, and the "Young Friends Series" which contained four different models, two of which are in two colourways, of pet cats and dogs. None of the models were "free standing" for the model incorporated a base, and some had an additional wooden plinth.

The Studio Sculptures were completely different in style and detail because of the different medium used. They were also different in price! In 1985 their prices ranged from £13.95 to £59.00 and they were considerably more than models in earthenware. For example the Studio Sculpture Wren "Early Bird" retailed at £15.95 whilst the Beswick Wren (993) was £4.95 quite a difference. Therefore it was not too surprising to find that overall the series was not the expected commercial success and so it was not listed in the 1986 price list.

INDEX BY MODEL NUMBER

For other figurines in the Studio Sculpture Series see *The Charlton Standard Catalogue of Royal Doulton Beswick Storybook Figurines.*

Beatrix Potter Series- SS1, SS2, SS3, SS4, SS11, SS26, SS27
Thelwell Series - SS7, SS12; SS23-25 not allocated.

SS5
PUPPY LOVE (Two puppies)

Designer: Unknown
Height: 4 ½", 11.9 cm
Colour: 1. One brown/white, one black/white - satin matt
2. One black/white, one white with black patches - satin matt
Issued: 1984-1986
Series: Young Friends

Colourway	U.K. £	U.S. $	Can. $
1. Brown/black	40.00	55.00	80.00
2. Black/white	40.00	55.00	80.00

SS6
I SPY
(Two kittens)

Designer: Unknown
Height: 4 ½", 11.9 cm
Colour: 1. Two white cats - satin matt
2. One tabby, one ginger - satin matt
Issued: 1984-1986
Series: Young Friends

Colourway	U.K. £	U.S. $	Can. $
1. White	40.00	55.00	80.00
2. Tabby/ginger	40.00	55.00	80.00

SS8
CONTENTMENT
(Dutch Rabbits)

Designer: Unknown
Length: 4 ¾", 12.1 cm
Colour: 1. Brown and white - satin matt
2. Black and white - satin matt
Issued: 1984-1986
Series: Countryside

Colourway	U.K. £	U.S. $	Can. $
1. Brown/white	30.00	45.00	65.00
2. Black/white	30.00	45.00	65.00

SS9
BRIGHT EYES
(Dutch Rabbit)

Designer: Unknown
Length: 4 ½", 11.9 cm
Colour: 1. Brown and white - satin matt
2. Black and white - satin matt
Issued: 1984-1986
Series: Countryside

Colourway	U.K. £	U.S. $	Can. $
1. Brown/white	30.00	45.00	65.00
2. Black/white	30.00	45.00	65.00

SS10
MIND HOW YOU GO
(Goose and goslings)

Designer: Unknown
Length: 5 ¼", 13.3 cm
Colour: White goose and yellow goslings - satin matt
Issued: 1984-1986
Series: Countryside

Description	U.K. £	U.S. $	Can. $
Satin matt	60.00	85.00	125.00

SS13
HAPPY LANDINGS
(Swan on wooden base)

Designer: Unknown
Height: 5", 12.7 cm
Colour: White - satin matt
Issued: 1984-1986
Series: Countryside

Description	U.K. £	U.S. $	Can. $
Satin matt	60.00	85.00	125.00

SS14
THE CHASE
(Dogs on wooden base)

Designer: Unknown
Height: 4", 10.1 cm
Colour: Shaded brown and white - satin matt
Issued: 1984-1986
Series: Countryside

Description	U.K. £	U.S. $	Can. $
Satin matt	60.00	85.00	125.00

SS15
HIDE AND SEEK
(Dogs on wooden base)

Designer: Unknown
Height: 4 ½", 11.9 cm
Colour: Shaded brown - satin matt
Issued: 1984-1986
Series: Countryside

Description	U.K. £	U.S. $	Can. $
Satin matt	60.00	85.00	125.00

SS16
MENU FOR TODAY
(Spaniel puppy with kitten)

Designer: Unknown
Height: 3 ½", 8.9 cm
Colour: 1. Brown puppy, white kitten - satin matt
2. Brown puppy, tabby kitten - satin matt
Issued: 1984-1986
Series: Young Friends

Colourway	U.K. £	U.S. $	Can. $
1. Brown/white	45.00	65.00	100.00
2. Brown/tabby	45.00	65.00	100.00

SS17
SHARING
(German Shepherd puppy with kitten)

Designer: Unknown
Height: 3 ½", 8.9 cm
Colour: Black and brown dog, white kitten - satin matt
Issued: 1984-1986
Series: Young Friends

Description	U.K. £	U.S. $	Can. $
Satin matt	50.00	70.00	100.00

SS18
PLANNING AHEAD
(Squirrel)

Designer: Unknown
Height: 3", 7.6 cm
Colour: Red - satin matt
Issued: 1984-1986
Series: Countryside

Description	U.K. £	U.S. $	Can. $
Satin matt	35.00	50.00	75.00

SS19
EARLY BIRD
(Wren)

Designer: Unknown
Height: 2 ½", 6.4 cm
Colour: Dark and light brown - satin matt
Issued: 1984-1986
Series: Countryside

Description	U.K. £	U.S. $	Can. $
Satin matt	35.00	50.00	75.00

Photograph not available at press time

SS20
GOLDEN RETRIEVER - on wooden base

Designer: Unknown
Height: 5", 12.7 cm
Colour: Golden brown - satin matt
Issued: 1984-1986
Series: Countryside

Description	U.K. £	U.S. $	Can. $
Satin matt	50.00	70.00	100.00

Photograph not available at press time

SS21
POINTER - on wooden base

Designer: Unknown
Height: 5", 12.7 cm
Colour: White and brown - satin matt
Issued: 1984-1986
Series: Countryside

Description	U.K. £	U.S. $	Can. $
Satin matt	50.00	70.00	100.00

Photograph not available at press time

SS22
ENGLISH SETTER - on wooden base

Designer: Unknown
Height: 5", 12.7 cm
Colour: White and liver - satin matt
Issued: 1984-1986
Series: Countryside

Description	U.K. £	U.S. $	Can. $
Satin matt	50.00	70.00	100.00

SS28
ROBIN

Designer: Unknown
Height: 3", 7.6 cm
Colour: Brown and red - satin matt
Issued: 1985-1986
Series: Countryside

Description	U.K. £	U.S. $	Can. $
Satin matt	35.00	50.00	70.00

SS29
BLUE TIT

Designer: Unknown
Height: 2 ½", 6.4 cm
Colour: Yellow, green and white - satin matt
Issued: 1985-1986
Series: Countryside

Description	U.K. £	U.S. $	Can. $
Satin matt	35.00	50.00	70.00

SS30
CHAFFINCH

Designer: Unknown
Height: 2 ¼", 5.7 cm
Colour: Brown, ochre, grey, black - satin matt
Issued: 1985-1986
Series: Countryside

Description	U.K. £	U.S. $	Can. $
Satin matt	35.00	50.00	70.00

Chapter Twelve
WHISKY FLASKS

INDEX BY MODEL NUMBER

Model No. 2051
LOCH NESS MONSTER (NESSIE)

Designer: Albert Hallam
Height: 3", 7.6 cm
Colour: Grey-green - gloss
Issued: 1965-1986

Description	U.K. £	U.S. $	Can. $
1. Head stopper	25.00	35.00	50.00
2. Base stopper	25.00	35.00	50.00

Model No. 2104
EAGLE

Designer: Graham Tongue
Height: 4", 10.1 cm
Colour: Brown - gloss
Issued: 1967-1986

Description	U.K. £	U.S. $	Can. $
Gloss	15.00	20.00	30.00

Model No. 2281A
EAGLE
First Version — Fixed Head

Designer: Graham Tongue
Height: 10 3/8", 27.3 cm
Colour: Light and dark brown - gloss
Issued: 1969 - Unknown

Description	U.K. £	U.S. $	Can. $
Fixed Head	85.00	125.00	175.00

Note: Model no. 2281A was first issued with a fixed head. See opposite for movable head varieties.

Model No. 2281B
EAGLE
Second Version — Moveable Head
a. Without lugs at neck
b. With small lugs at neck

Designer: Graham Tongue
Height: 10 3/8", 27.3 cm
Colour: Light and dark brown - gloss
Issued: Unkown - 1980

Description	U.K. £	U.S. $	Can. $
1. Without lugs	85.00	125.00	175.00
2. With small lugs	85.00	125.00	175.00

Model No. 2350
HAGGIS BIRD

Designer: James Haywood
Remodelled: Albert Hallam
Height: 2 ½", 6.4 cm
Colour: Brown - gloss
Issued: 1971-1986

Description	U.K. £	U.S. $	Can. $
Gloss	15.00	20.00	30.00

Model No. 2561
GROUSE

Designer: David Lyttleton
Height: 9", 22.9 cm
Colour: Brown and red - gloss
Issued: 1976-1984

Description	U.K. £	U.S. $	Can. $
Gloss	65.00	100.00	150.00

Note: Model no. 2561 was remodelled with a removable head stopper.

Model No. 2583
OSPREY

Designer: David Lyttleton
Height: 7 ¾", 19.7 cm
Colour: Browns and white - gloss
Issued: 1977-1986

Description:	U.K. £	U.S. $	Can. $
Gloss	50.00	70.00	100.00

Model No. 2636
SQUIRREL

Designer: David Lyttleton
Height: 3 ½", 8.9 cm
Colour: Red-brown - gloss
Issued: 1978-1986

Description	U.K. £	U.S. $	Can. $
Gloss	15.00	20.00	30.00

Model No. 2639
KESTREL

Designer: Graham Tongue
Height: 6 ½", 16.5 cm
Colour: Dark grey and white - gloss
Issued: 1979-1986

Description	U.K. £	U.S. $	Can. $
Gloss	50.00	70.00	100.00

Model No. 2640
BUZZARD

Designer: Graham Tongue
Height: 6 ½", 16.5 cm
Colour: Dark brown and grey - gloss
Issued: 1979-1986

Description	U.K. £	U.S. $	Can. $
Gloss	65.00	90.00	135.00

Model No. 2641
MERLIN

Designer: Graham Tongue
Height: 6 ½", 16.5 cm
Colour: Dark grey and white - gloss
Issued: 1979-1986

Description	U.K. £	U.S. $	Can. $
Gloss	65.00	90.00	135.00

Model No. 2642
PEREGRINE FALCON

Designer: Graham Tongue
Height: 6 ½", 16.5 cm
Colour: Dark grey and white - gloss
Issued: 1979-1986

Description	U.K. £	U.S. $	Can. $
Gloss	65.00	90.00	135.00

Model No. 2678
EAGLE
Third Version — Moveable Head, Large Lugs

Designer: Graham Tongue
Height: 10 ½", 26.7 cm
Colour: Light and dark brown - gloss
Issued: 1980- 1987

Description	U.K. £	U.S. $	Can. $
Large lugs	65.00	90.00	135.00

Note: The head locking mechanism on this model has large lugs on a wider, full-bodied bird.

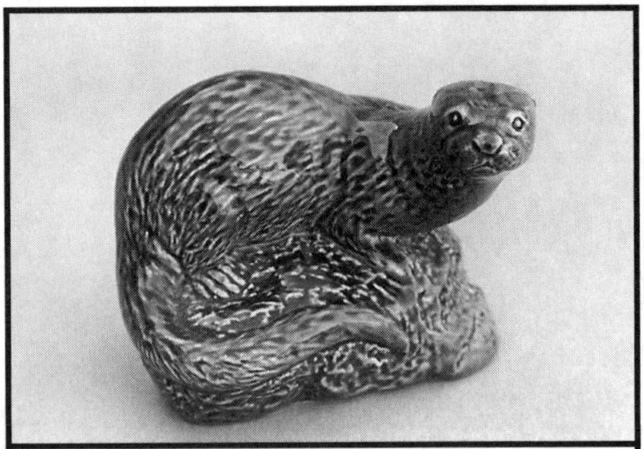

Model No. 2686
OTTER

Designer: David Lyttleton
Height: 2 ¼", 5.7 cm
Colour: Grey and brown - gloss
Issued: 1981-1986

Description	U.K. £	U.S. $	Can. $
Gloss	15.00	20.00	30.00

Model No. 2687
BADGER

Designer: David Lyttleton
Height: 3", 7.6 cm
Colour: Black and white - gloss
Issued: 1981-1986

Description	U.K. £	U.S. $	Can. $
Gloss	15.00	20.00	30.00

Model No. 2693
SEAL

Designer: Graham Tongue
Height: 3 ½", 8.9 cm
Colour: Grey - gloss
Issued: 1980-1986

Description	U.K. £	U.S. $	Can. $
Gloss	15.00	20.00	30.00

Model No. 2781
TAWNY OWL

Designer: Graham Tongue
Height: 6 ¼", 15.9 cm
Colour: Brown - gloss
Issued: 1982-1987

Description	U.K. £	U.S. $	Can. $
Gloss	65.00	90.00	135.00

Model No. 2798
GROUSE

Designer: David Lyttleton
Height: 9 ½", 24.0 cm
Colour: Brown and red - matt
Issued: 1982-1987

Description	U.K. £	U.S. $	Can. $
Matt	65.00	90.00	135.00

Model No. 2809
BARN OWL

Designer: Graham Tongue
Height: 6 ¾", 17.2 cm
Colour: Tan-brown and white - gloss
Issued: 1983-1987

Description	U.K. £	U.S . $	Can. $
Gloss	65.00	90.00	135.00

Model No. 2825
SHORT-EARED OWL

Designer: Graham Tongue
Height: 6 ¾", 17.2 cm
Colour: Dark and light brown - gloss
Issued: 1983-1987

Description	U.K. £	U.S. $	Can. $
Gloss	65.00	90.00	135.00

Model No. 2826
SNOWY OWL

Designer: Graham Tongue
Height: 1. 6 ½", 16.5 cm
2. 5 ¾", 14.6 cm
Colour: White - gloss
Issued: 1983-1987

Description	U.K. £	U.S . $	Can. $
1. Large	65.00	90.00	135.00
2. Small	50.00	70.00	100.00

Model No. 2281B Second Version Narrow Body	Model No. 2678 Third Version Wide Body	Model No. 2281B Second Version Small lugs at neck	Model No. 2678 Third Version Large lugs at neck

Chapter Thirteen
COMMISSIONED MODELS

During the early 1990s Beswick used some of its current freestanding models and now attached them to either a ceramic or wooden base.

Various companies, including British Coal, one of the major home shopping networks and a direct mail corporation, seem to be the largest commissioners of these items.

Little is known about these models, for they are not listed in the Beswick product line.

INDEX BY MODEL NUMBER

Model No. 818
"HORSES GREAT AND SMALL" - on ceramic base

Designer: Arthur Gredington
Height: 10", 25.4 cm
Colour: Dark brown and white - gloss
Issued: Unknown

Description	U.K. £	U.S. $	Can. $
Gloss	110.00	150.00	225.00

Model No. 967
COCKER SPANIEL "HORSESHOE PRIMULA"

Designer: Arthur Gredington
Height: 6 ¾", 17.1 cm
Colour: Golden brown - gloss
Issued: Unknown

Description	U.K. £	U.S. $	Can. $
Gloss	85.00	125.00	175.00

Model No. 1436/1460
"SHARING" - on ceramic base

Designer: Arthur Gredington and Colin Melbourne
Height: 4 ¾", 12.1 cm
Colour: Grey cat, brown dog - gloss
Issued: Unknown

Description	U.K. £	U.S. $	Can. $
Gloss	75.00	100.00	150.00

Model No. 1558/1678
"WATCH IT" - on ceramic base

Designer: Albert Hallam and Pal Zalmen
Height: 8 ¾", 22.2 cm
Colour: Chocolate point cat, grey mouse - gloss
Issued: Unknown

Description	U.K. £	U.S. $	Can. $
Gloss	75.00	100.00	150.00

Model No. 1867
"PERSIAN CAT" - on brass plate

Designer: Albert Hallam
Height: 9 ½", 24.0 cm
Colour: Ginger - gloss
Issued: Unknown

Description	U.K. £	U.S. $	Can. $
Gloss	90.00	135.00	200.00

Model No. 1886/3093
"PLAYTIME" - on ceramic base

Designer: Albert Hallam
Height: 5", 12.7 cm
Colour: White kitten with pink or lemon ball of wool - gloss
Issued: Unknown

Description	U.K. £	U.S. $	Can. $
Gloss	55.00	80.00	125.00

Model No. 2221
ST. BERNARD "CORNA GARTH STROLLER"
- on ceramic base

Designer:	Albert Hallam
Height:	6 ¾", 17.1 cm
Colour:	Dark brown, tan and white - gloss
Issued:	Unknown

Description	U.K. £	U.S. $	Can. $
Gloss	100.00	150.00	225.00

Model No. 2590/1436
"GOOD FRIENDS" - on ceramic base

Designer:	Colin Melbourne
Height:	6", 15.2 cm
Colour:	White and tan dog, ginger kitten - gloss
Issued:	Unknown

Description	U.K. £	U.S. $	Can. $
Gloss	75.00	100.00	150.00

Model No. 4677
SOLID FRIENDSHIP - on wooden plinth

Designer:	Albert Hallam and Warren Platt
Height:	5 ½", 14.0 cm
Colour:	White mouse, black and white cat, and white dog with brown patches - gloss
Issued:	1993

Description	U.K. £	U.S. $	Can. $
Gloss	85.00	125.00	175.00

Note: This model was a special commission for British Coal.

Chapter Fourteen
MISCELLANEOUS

INDEX BY MODEL NUMBER

Model No. 2093
OLD STAFFORDSHIRE LION

Designer: Graham Tongue
Height: 5 ¾", 14.6 cm
Colour: Grey, cream, green - gloss
Issued: 1967-1971

Description	U.K. £	U.S. $	Can. $
Gloss	300.00	425.00	650.00

Model No. 2094
OLD STAFFORDSHIRE UNICORN

Designer: Graham Tongue
Height: 6", 15.0 cm
Colour: Grey, cream, green - gloss
Issued: 1967-1971

Description	U.K. £	U.S. $	Can. $
Gloss	300.00	425.00	650.00

Model No. 2137
T'ANG HORSE - Small

Designer: Graham Tongue
Height: 8", 20.3 cm
Colour: Green/bronze - gloss
Issued: 1967-1972

Description	U.K. £	U.S. $	Can. $
Gloss	300.00	450.00	650.00

Model No. 2182
HERALDIC UNICORN ON BASE

Designer: Graham Tongue
Height: 8 ½", 21.6 cm
Colour. Unknown
Issued: 1968 - Unknown

Description	U.K. £	U.S. $	Can. $
Gloss	Extremely Rare		

Note: Model 2182 may not have been put into production.

Model No. 2205
T'ANG HORSE- Large

Designer: Graham Tongue
Height: 13", 33.0 cm
Colour: Green/bronze - gloss
Issued: 1968-1972

Description	U.K. £	U.S. $	Can. $
Gloss	375.00	525.00	800.00

Model No. 2222
LION (CAERNARVON 1969)

Designer: Mrs. Elliot
Height: 4", 10.1 cm
Colour: Cream, red lettering - matt
Issued: 1968-1969
Series: Pair with 2223

Description	U.K.£	U.S.$	Can.$
Matt	Only known example in the Beswick Museum		

Note: Issued to commemorate the investiture of Prince of Wales, Caernarvon, 1969.

Model No. 2223
UNICORN (PRINCE OF WALES)

Designer: Mrs. Elliott
Height: 4", 10.1 cm
Colour. Cream, red lettering - matt
Issued: 1968-1969
Series: Pair with 2222

Description	U.K. £	U.S. $	Can. $
Matt	Only known example in the Beswick Museum		

Note: Issued to commemorate the Investiture of the Prince of Wales, Caernarvon, 1969.

Model No. 2514
"WHITE HORSE WHISKY"

Designer: Alan Maslankowski
Height: 6 ¾", 17.2 cm
Colour: White - gloss
Issued: 1974
Series: Advertising

Description	U.K. £	U.S. $	Can. $
Gloss	500.00	700.00	1,100.00

Model No. 3021 **UNICORN**

Designer: Graham Tongue
Height: 9″, 2.9 cm
Series: Britannia Collection

Colourway	Finish	Intro.	Disc.	U.K. £	U.S. $	Can. $
1. Cream	Matt	1989	Unknown	225.00	325.00	475.00
2. Brown	Gloss	1989	1992	125.00	175.00	250.00

INDEX OF MODEL NUMBERS

ALPHABETICAL INDEX